Teacher Guide

Grade 4

Printed in the U.S.A.

ISBN 978-0-358-39110-4

6 7 8 9 10 2331 29 28 27 26 25 24 23 22

4500844257

r9.21

Program Authors

Michael A. DiSpezio

Global Educator
North Falmouth, Massachusetts

Michael DiSpezio has authored many HMH instructional programs for Science and Mathematics. He has also authored numerous trade books and multimedia programs on various topics and hosted dozens of studio and location broadcasts for various organizations in the U.S. and worldwide. Most recently, he has been working with educators to provide strategies for implementing the Next Generation Science Standards—particularly the Science and Engineering Practices and Crosscutting Concepts—and for using Evidence Notebooks. To all his projects, he brings his extensive background in science, his expertise in classroom teaching at the elementary, middle, and high school levels, and his deep experience in producing interactive and engaging instructional materials.

Marjorie Frank

Science Writer and Content-Area Reading Specialist
Brooklyn, New York

An educator and linguist by training, a writer and poet by nature, Marjorie Frank has authored and designed a generation of instructional materials in all subject areas, including past HMH Science programs. Her other credits include authoring science issues of an award-winning children's magazine, writing game-based digital assessments, developing blended learning materials for young children, and serving as instructional designer and coauthor of pioneering school-to-work software. In addition, she has served on the adjunct faculty of Hunter, Manhattan, and Brooklyn Colleges, teaching courses in science methods, literacy, and writing. For *HMH Into Science*, she has guided the development of our K–2 strands and our approach to making connections between NGSS and Common Core ELA/literacy standards.

Michael R. Heithaus, PhD

Dean, College of Arts, Sciences & Education
Professor, Department of Biological Sciences
Florida International University
Miami, Florida

Mike Heithaus joined the FIU Biology Department in 2003 and has served as Director of the Marine Sciences Program and as Executive Director of the School of Environment, Arts, and Society, which brings together the natural and social sciences and humanities to develop solutions to today's environmental challenges. He now serves as Dean of the College of Arts, Sciences & Education. His research focuses on predator-prey interactions and the ecological importance of large marine species. He has helped guide the development of Life Science content in *HMH Into Science* with a focus on strategies for teaching challenging content as well as the science and engineering practices of analyzing data and using computational thinking.

Peter McLaren

Executive Director of Next Gen Education, LLC
Providence, Rhode Island

Peter McLaren is Executive Director of Next Gen Education, LLC, consulting with schools implementing the Next Generation Science Standards. His previous roles in science education policy include: Director of State and District Support for Science at Achieve, Science and Technology Specialist at the Rhode Island Department of Education, and President of the Council of State Science Supervisors. He served on the writing committees for the Next Generation Science Standards, the National Academy of Engineering's *Guiding Implementation of K–12 Engineering Education*, and the National Academy of Science's *Developing Assessments for the Next Generation Science Standards*. McLaren helped guide the development of the three-dimensional formative assessments in *HMH Into Science*.

Bernadine Okoro

Social Emotional Learning Consultant
STEM Learning Advocate & Consultant
Washington, DC

Bernadine Okoro is a chemical engineer by training and a playwright, novelist, director, and actress by nature. Okoro went from working with patents and biotechnology to teaching in K–12 classrooms. A 12-year science educator and Albert Einstein Distinguished Fellow, Okoro was one of the original authors of the Next Generation Science Standards. As a member of the Diversity and Equity Team, her focus on alternative education and community schools and on integrating social emotional learning and brain-based learning into NGSS is the vehicle she uses as a pathway to support underserved groups from elementary school to adult education. An article and book reviewer for NSTA and other educational publishing companies, Okoro currently works as a STEM Learning Advocate & Consultant.

Cary I. Sneider, PhD

Associate Research Professor
Portland State University
Portland, Oregon

While studying astrophysics at Harvard, Cary Sneider volunteered to teach in an Upward Bound program and discovered his real calling as a science teacher. After teaching middle and high school science in Maine, California, Costa Rica, and Micronesia, he settled for nearly three decades at Lawrence Hall of Science in Berkeley, California, where he developed skills in curriculum development and teacher education. Over his career, Sneider directed more than 20 federal, state, and foundation grant projects and was a writing team leader for the Next Generation Science Standards. He has been instrumental in ensuring *HMH Into Science* meets the high expectations of the NGSS and provides an effective three-dimensional learning experience for all students.

Program Advisors

Paul D. Asimow, PhD
Eleanor and John R. McMillan Professor of Geology and Geochemistry
California Institute of Technology
Pasadena, California

Eileen Cashman, PhD
Professor of Environmental Resources Engineering
Humboldt State University
Arcata, California

Mark B. Moldwin, PhD
Professor of Climate and Space Sciences and Engineering
University of Michigan
Ann Arbor, Michigan

Kelly Y. Neiles, PhD
Associate Professor of Chemistry
St. Mary's College of Maryland
St. Mary's City, Maryland

Sten Odenwald, PhD
Astronomer
NASA Goddard Spaceflight Center
Greenbelt, Maryland

Bruce W. Schafer
Director of K–12 STEM Collaborations, retired
Oregon University System
Portland, Oregon

Barry A. Van Deman
President and CEO
Museum of Life and Science
Durham, North Carolina

Kim Withers, PhD
Assistant Professor
Texas A&M University-Corpus Christi
Corpus Christi, Texas

Educator Advisory Board Members

Julie Ahern
2nd Grade Teacher
Andrew Cooke Magnet School
Waukegan, Illinois

Kecia Allen-Rodgers
Science Lab Teacher
Idlewild Elementary School
Memphis, Tennessee

Amy Berke
Classroom Teacher
South Park Elementary School
Rapid City, South Dakota

Kelly Brotz
2nd Grade Teacher
Cooper Elementary School
Sheboygan, Wisconsin

Marsha Campbell
1st Grade Teacher
Murray Elementary School
Hobbs, New Mexico

Deborah Falaise
4th Grade Teacher
Benjamin Banneker Academy
East Orange, New Jersey

Noelle Foito
5th Grade Teacher
Madison School
Bridgeport, Connecticut

Theresa Gailliout
Classroom Teacher
James R. Ludlow Elementary School
Philadelphia, Pennsylvania

Robert Gray
Classroom Teacher
Essex Elementary School
Baltimore, Maryland

Bonnie Lock
Classroom Teacher
La Center Elementary School
La Center, Washington

Kara Miller
3rd Grade Teacher
Ridgeview Elementary School
Beckley, West Virginia

Dena Morosin
Classroom Teacher
Shasta Elementary School
Klamath Falls, Oregon

Joanna O'Brien
3rd Grade Teacher
Palmyra Elementary School
Palmyra, Missouri

Julie Padavic
Classroom Teacher
Lindsay Elementary School
Springfield, Illinois

Nora Rowe
Classroom Head Teacher
Peoria Traditional School
Peoria, Arizona

April Thompson
Classroom Teacher
Roll Hill School
Cincinnati, Ohio

Terri Trebilcock
Classroom Teacher
Fairmount Elementary School
Golden, Colorado

Classroom Reviewers

Julie Ahern
Andrew Cooke Magnet School
Waukegan, Illinois

Amy Berke
South Park Elementary School
Rapid City, South Dakota

Pamela Bluestein
Sycamore Canyon School
Newbury Park, California

Kelly Brotz
Cooper Elementary School
Sheboygan, Wisconsin

Andrea Brown
HLPUSD Science and STEAM TOSA, Retired
Hacienda Heights, California

Marsha Campbell
Murray Elementary School
Hobbs, New Mexico

Leslie C. Antosy-Flores
Star View Elementary School
Midway City, California

Theresa Gailliout
James R. Ludlow Elementary School
Philadelphia, Pennsylvania

Emily Giles
Assistant Principal
White's Tower Elementary School
Independence, Kentucky

Robert Gray
Essex Elementary School
Baltimore, Maryland

Stephanie Greene
Science Department Chair
Sun Valley Magnet School
Sun Valley, California

Roya Hosseini
Junction Avenue K–8 School
Livermore, California

Rana Mujtaba Khan
Will Rogers High School
Van Nuys, California

George Kwong
Schafer Park Elementary School
Hayward, California

Kristin Kyde
Templeton Middle School
Sussex, Wisconsin

Marie LaCross
Sulphur Springs United School District
Santa Clarita, California

Bonnie Lock
La Center Elementary School
La Center, Washington

Imelda Madrid
Assistant Principal
Montague Charter Academy for the Arts and Sciences
Pacoima, California

Susana Martinez O'Brien
Diocese of San Diego
San Diego, California

Kara Miller
Ridgeview Elementary School
Beckley, West Virginia

Mercy D. Momary
Local District Northwest
Los Angeles, California

Dena Morosin
Shasta Elementary School
Klamath Falls, Oregon

Craig Moss
Mt. Gleason Middle School
Sunland, California

Joanna O'Brien
Palmyra Elementary School
Palmyra, Missouri

Wendy Savaske
Education Consultant
Wisconsin Department of Public Instruction

Isabel Souto
Schafer Park Elementary
Hayward, California

Michelle Sullivan
Balboa Elementary School
San Diego, California

April Thompson
Roll Hill School
Cincinnati, Ohio

Tina Topoleski
District Science Supervisor
Jackson School District
Jackson, New Jersey

Terri Trebilcock
Fairmount Elementary School
Golden, Colorado

Emily R.C.G. Williams
South Pasadena Middle School
South Pasadena, California

Notes:

For the Teacher

Unit 1 Engineering and Technology 2

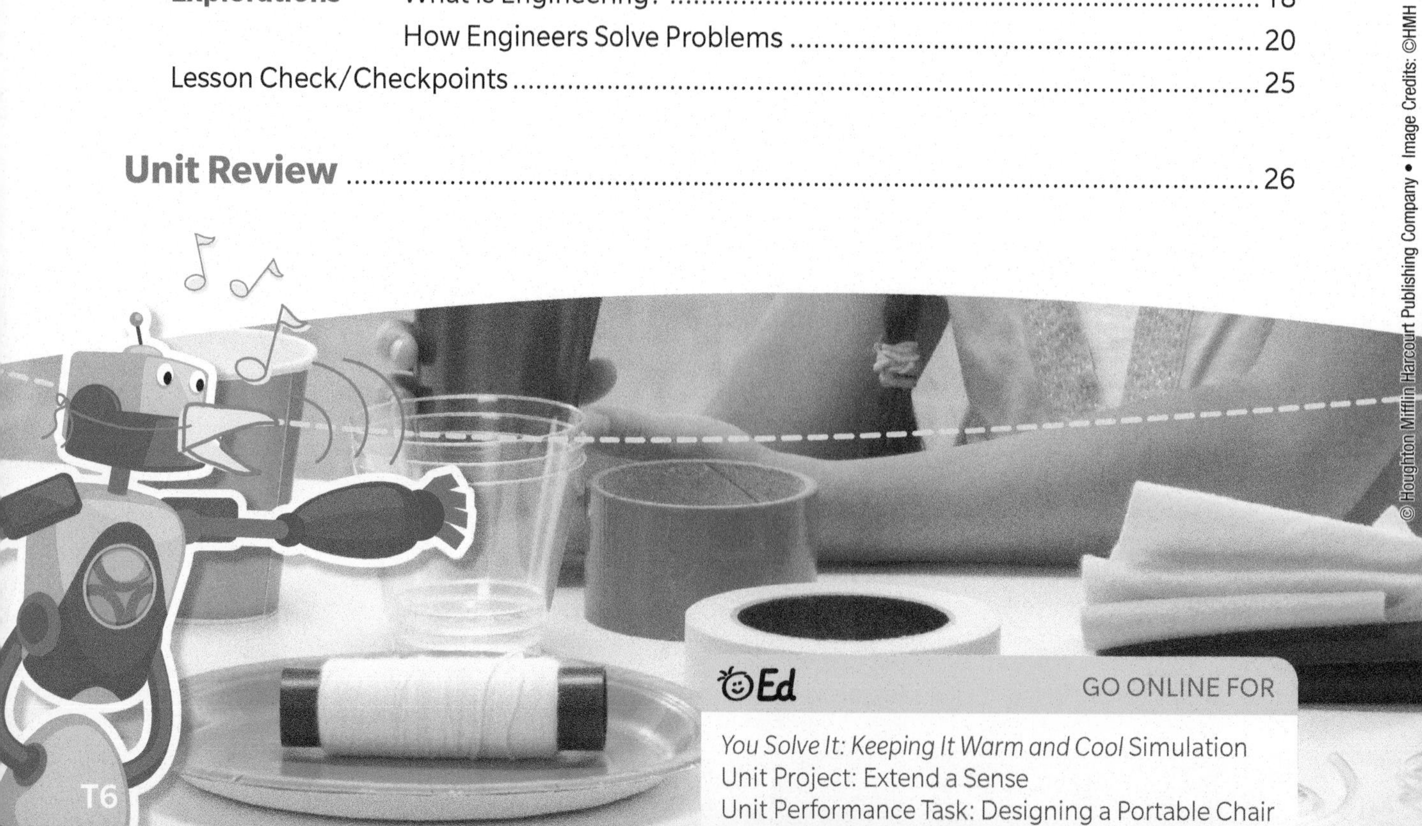

Ed GO ONLINE FOR

You Solve It: Keeping It Warm and Cool Simulation
Unit Project: Extend a Sense
Unit Performance Task: Designing a Portable Chair

Unit 2 Plant and Animal Structure and Function

Ed GO ONLINE FOR

You Solve It: Break It Down Simulation
Unit Project: Plant and Animal Partnerships
Unit Performance Task: Communication of the Wild

Unit 3 Energy and Communication

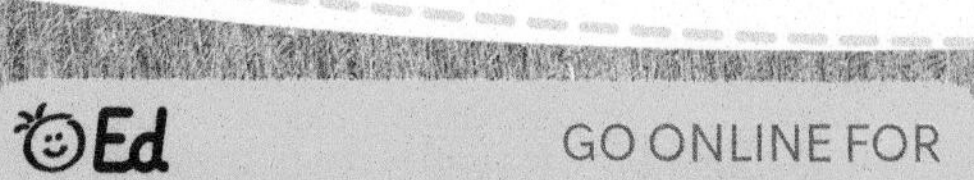

You Solve It: Crash Course Simulation
Unit Project: Wave Patterns
Unit Performance Task: Colliding Objects

Unit 4 Shaping Landforms

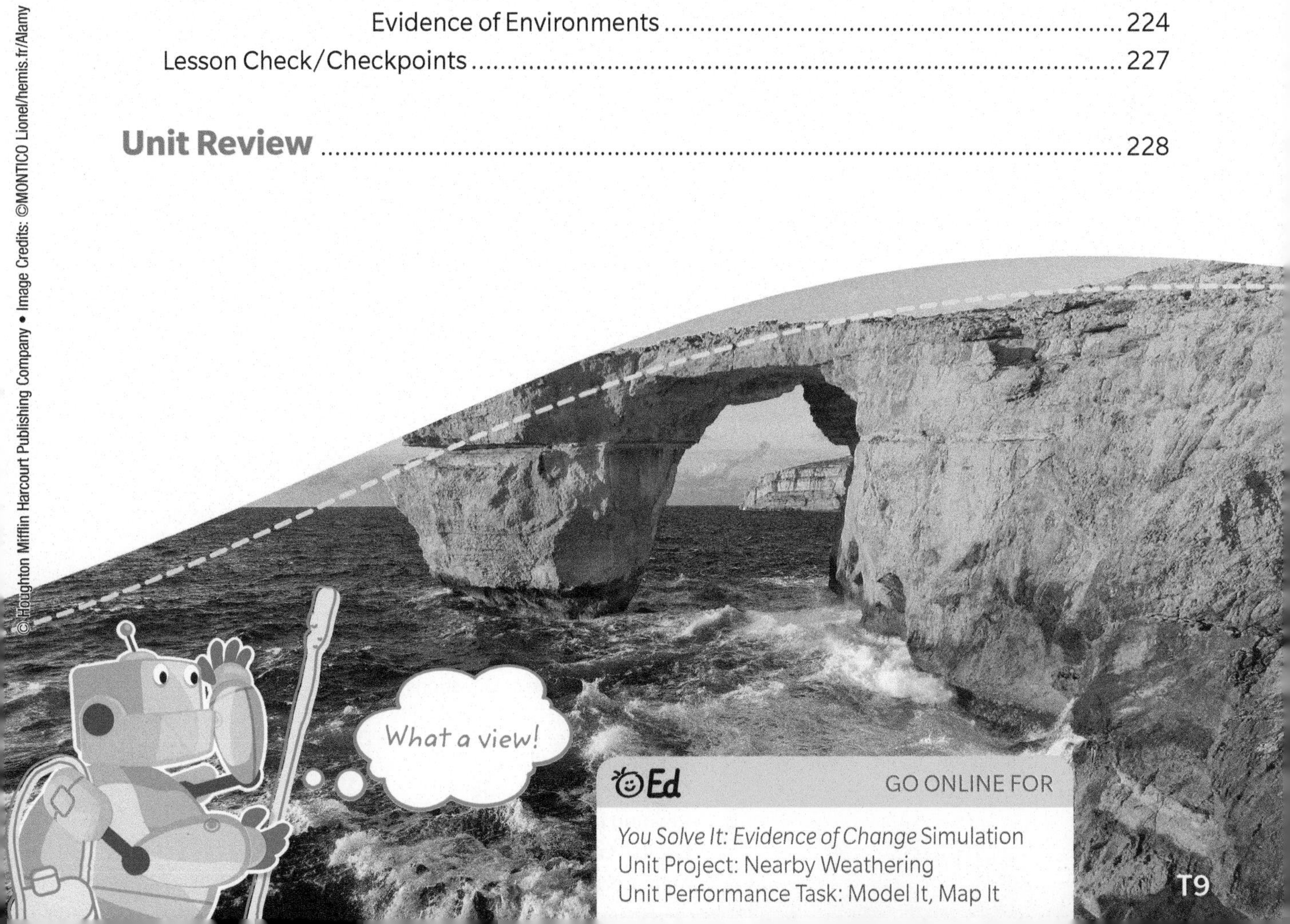

Ed GO ONLINE FOR

You Solve It: Evidence of Change Simulation
Unit Project: Nearby Weathering
Unit Performance Task: Model It, Map It

Unit 5 Earth's Features and Resources

GO ONLINE FOR

You Solve It: Developing Renewable Energy Guidelines Simulation
Unit Project: Natural Resources Report Card
Unit Performance Task: Withstanding Water

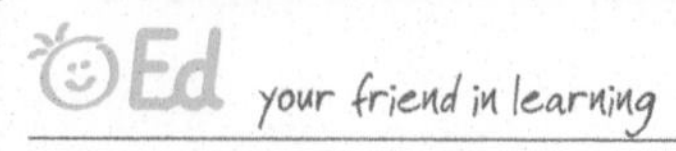

GO ONLINE FOR

Professional Development
- The Next Generation Science Standards: A Reason to Cheer
- Evidence Notebooks
- Aligning English Language Arts and Science
- NGSS and College and Career Readiness
- The Question of Questions
- Ensuring Educational Equity for Students
- Support for English Language Development
- SEL Foundations

Calendar Pacing Guide
Reading in the Science Content Area
English Language Arts Correlations
Math Correlations

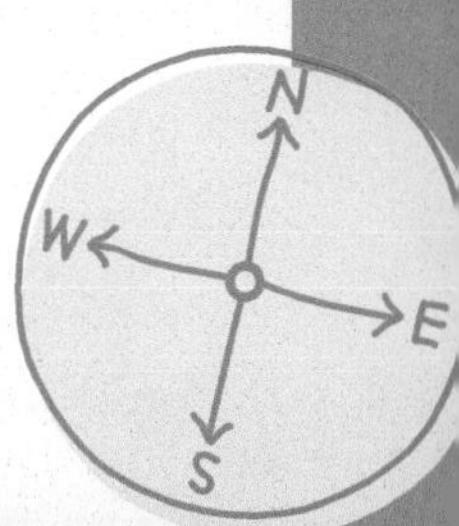

Instructional Model

PRINT

Student Activity Guide

- Introduces the Anchoring Phenomenon
- Includes Hands-On Investigations for exploring investigative phenomena

FUNomenal Readers

- Leveled by reading levels
- Model investigative sensemaking

Teacher Guide

- Provides strategies for
  - Introducing phenomena
  - Guiding Student Explorations
  - Supporting student sensemaking through 3D learning
  - Assessing students
- Provides point-of-use strategies for
  - Incorporating readers into an ELA lesson
  - Incorporating Social Emotional Learning (SEL) strategies
  - Leveling strategies

ONLINE

Go online to access components that include

Student Ebook: Provides additional in-depth materials and explorations for early finishers/motivated students

Teacher Ebook: Provides additional teaching information and strategies that help focus on 3D learning

ASSESSMENT

- Scaffolds toward higher-level thinking
- Provides formative and summative options to help you identify how your students are progressing toward mastering Performance Expectations
- Helps determine if students are making sense of phenomena
- Provides modified options for students that struggle with reading

Student Sensemaking Journey

The student journey is a five-step process centered around a phenomenon.

1
Students experience a phenomenon requiring explanation. (a sense of wonder)

2
Students wonder, talk, share and try to explain using what they already know.

3
Students ask questions about the phenomenon and their explanations.

4
Students conduct activities, read, talk to experts, gather information from the Internet, and analyze all that they discover.

5
Students revisit phenomenon to revise or augment their explanations supported by their previous understandings and by the new evidence they have gathered.

ANCHORING PHENOMENON

Your Teacher Journey—What Happens in a Lesson

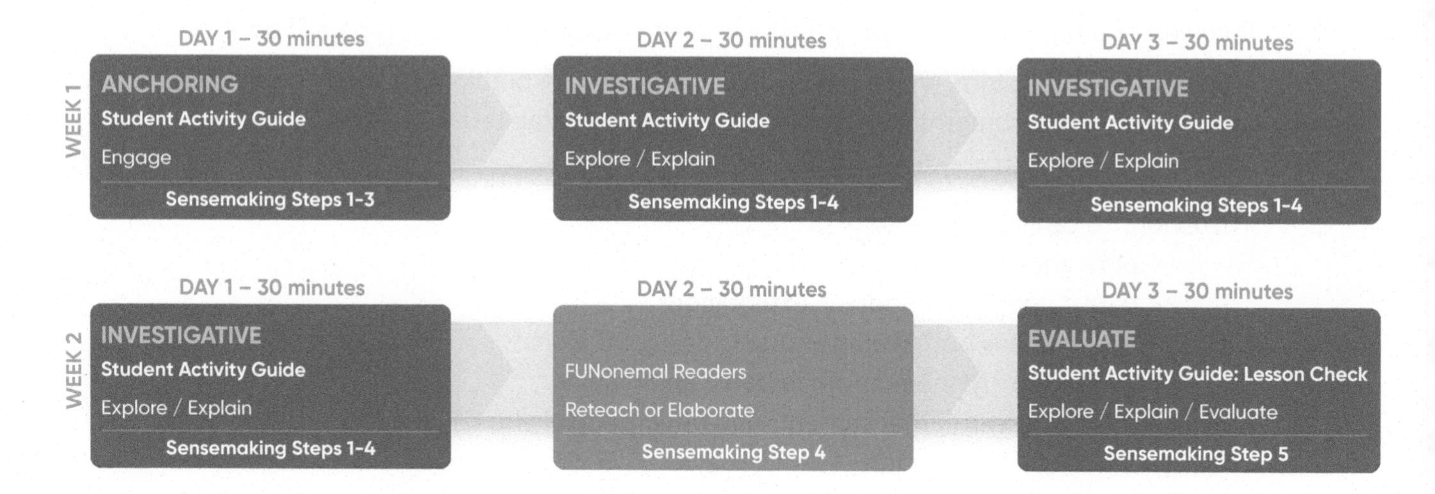

Your Teaching Journey and the Student Sensemaking Journey are tightly interlinked.

Week 1/Day 1: Introduce Anchoring Phenomenon (*Reinforces Steps 1–3 of Student Sensemaking Journey*).

- Students discuss and begin exploration.
- Students offer initial explanations.
- Students begin to ask questions that should be recorded.

Week 1/Day 2–3, Week 2: Have students explore the Anchoring Phenomenon through Investigative Phenomena (*Step 4 of Student Sensemaking Journey*).

- Students conduct the investigations in the Student Activity Guide.
- They relate their discoveries back to the Anchoring Phenomenon to show how what they have discovered relates to part of the explanation of the Anchoring Phenomenon.

Week 2 /Day 2: Use the FUNomenal Readers and the Online Student Edition to continue Exploration and do the Elaborate part of the lesson cycle (*Step 4 of Student Sensemaking Journey*).

- FUNomenal Readers allow students to explore the same Performance Expectations using the same or alternative phenomenon.

Week 2/Day 3: Administer Formative Assessment (*Step 5 of Student Sensemaking Journey*) using the Can You Explain It? in Lesson Check.

- Formative Assessment continues the explore/explain and allows you to enter the evaluate phase.
- Students return to the Anchoring Phenomenon with what they have learned as they have explored.
- Student explanations should be richer, more elaborate, and more connected to a claims, evidence, reasoning model of understanding and argument.
- If student sensemaking is still in need of formation, reteach using the Online Student Edition or by revisiting the FUNomenal Reader.

Claims, Evidence, Reasoning (CER) for Sensemaking

Making sense of phenomena requires a bookended approach of initial explanation followed by a revised understanding after a series of explorations. CER is part of both.

A student makes a **claim**, which can be an explanation or a prediction based on evidence. Ideally, the claim is something that should be subject to a fair test.

The evidence can include

- prior knowledge
- data gathered in hands-on explorations
- observations both within and outside explorations
- information gathered from research and reading
- discussion with other students and other people who could be sources of information

In reasoning,

- students evaluate the quality of the evidence
- students relate the evidence to the explanation by explaining how that piece of evidence supports the explanation

But it doesn't stop here: students continue to discuss and critique explanations offered using the same claim-evidence-reasoning chain until they come to a conclusion that provides a "best-fit" explanation for the phenomenon that incorporates all of the available, valid evidence.

Your role in this? Be ready with questions such as, "What is your evidence for that conclusion?" "How does the evidence support your claim?" "What evidence do you have?" You guide the sensemaking by constantly returning students to the central ideas of CER.

Download *Think Like a Scientist* posters for your classroom.

Getting students comfortable thinking like scientists is no small feat, but it's the best way to teach science.

Search HMH Think Like a Scientist

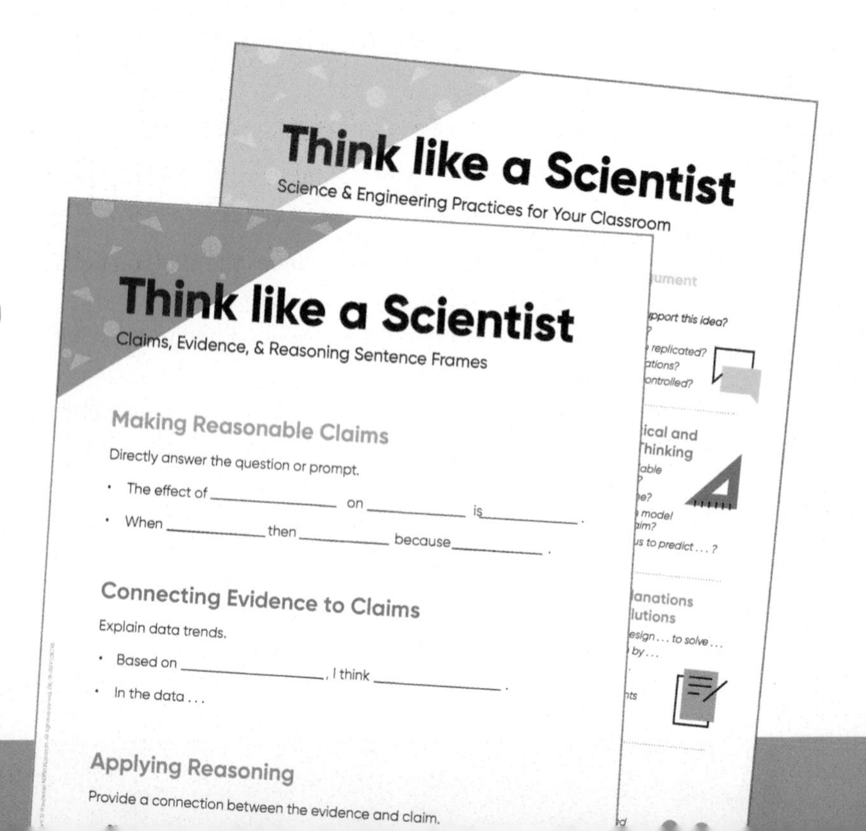

Social Emotional Learning at HMH

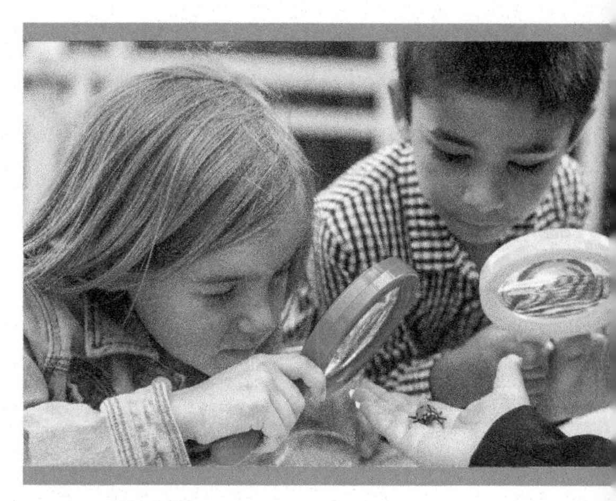

We believe that learning is an intellectual, social, and emotional process for the whole child. Learning has highs and lows, victories and setbacks—each of which causes emotions that drive and affect how students learn and view themselves. Learning goes beyond acquiring facts and expanding knowledge and becomes a personal story of curiosity, perseverance, and growth.

We believe that schools—and those who collaborate with them—have a responsibility to empower learners and educators by providing opportunities in safe environments that allow every child to be engaged and supported in the interwoven cognitive, behavioral, social, and emotional facets of learning.

We commit to empowering ALL students to author their own learning story.

Research suggests integrating Social Emotional Learning (SEL) directly into the core curriculum every day is the most effective practice. Our activities provide daily opportunities to practice SEL skills within real-world contexts in an encouraging and safe environment. We offer teacher support in the form of teacher blogs, courses focused on SEL competencies, and supplemental supports aligned with practical ways to integrate SEL skills into your curriculum.

Benefits:

- Improved quality of instruction and teacher-student interactions
- Improved student performance
- Ease of social adjustments for students

HMH SEL activities foster mastery of competencies and transfer of skills because students are consistently practicing over time. We invite you to find relevancy in your classroom communities through HMH learning products, and we are here to support your SEL endeavors.

HMH Into Science™ Pacing Guide

Common Pacing Guide Model—Applicable to All Units

HMH Into Science is designed with the time constraints of the K–5 science classroom in mind. The chart below identifies recommended choices for learning experiences within units and lessons. You can also customize your own pacing to meet your classroom needs.

- **Core Path** The Core path is recommended as it covers all of the Next Generation Science Standards. At Grade 4, this will require about 120 days of 30-minute instructional segments.
- **Extended Path** If you have additional time, the Extended path provides additional opportunities to explore and reinforce the science content.
- **Short on Time Path** If you have less time than the Core path assumes, the Short on Time path highlights key pieces to focus on. However, this may not cover all of the standards thoroughly.
- **Blended Path** If you are short on time, we recommend using the Blended path. In the Blended path, you use available science instruction time plus 30 minutes of English Language Arts instruction time to explore the FUNomenal Readers in order to more thoroughly cover all of the standards.

Section	Short on Time	Core	Extended	Blended
Lessons 1–4				
Engage Can You Explain It?	✓	✓	✓	✓
Explorations 1–2 Hands-On Activity	✓	✓	✓	✓
Explorations 3–5		✓	✓	
Elaborate FUNomenal Reader			✓	ELA
Elaborate Take It Further (digital-only)			✓	
Evaluate Can You Explain It?	✓	✓	✓	✓
Evaluate Checkpoints		✓	✓	
Unit				
You Solve It (digital-only)			✓	
Unit Project (digital-only)			✓	
Unit Performance Task (digital-only)			✓	
Unit Review		✓	✓	
Unit Test (Assessment Guide)	✓	✓	✓	✓

Specific pacing information for learning experiences are found at point-of-use throughout your Teacher Guide. Those point-of-use timings are summarized in the chart below.

1 Instructional Day = 30 minutes

Section	Short on Time	Core	Extended	Blended
Unit 1 Engineering and Technology	**5 days**	**10 days**	**19.5 days**	**6 days**
Lesson 1 Engineering Design	4 days	8 days	10.5 days	5 days
Unit 1 Resources	1 day	2 days	9 days	1 day
Unit 2 Plant and Animal Structure and Function	**16 days**	**28 days**	**42.5 days**	**19 days**
Lesson 1 Plant Parts and How They Function	5 days	8 days	10.5 days	6 days
Lesson 2 Animal Parts and How they Function	5 days	9 days	11.5 days	6 days
Lesson 3 How Senses Work	5 days	9 days	11.5 days	6 days
Unit 2 Resources	1 day	2 days	9 days	1 day
Unit 3 Energy and Communication	**19 days**	**30 days**	**46 days**	**23 days**
Lesson 1 Energy Transfer and Transformation	5 days	8 days	10.5 days	6 days
Lesson 2 Collisions	4 days	6 days	9 days	5 days
Lesson 3 Waves	4 days	7 days	9.5 days	5 days
Lesson 4 Information Transfer	5 days	7 days	10 days	6 days
Unit 3 Resources	1 day	2 days	7 days	1 day
Unit 4 Shaping Landforms	**15 days**	**23 days**	**37.5 days**	**18 days**
Lesson 1 Factors That Shape Earth's Surface	4 days	6 days	8.5 days	5 days
Lesson 2 Fast and Slow Changes	5 days	7 days	9.5 days	6 days
Lesson 3 Rock Layers Record Landform Changes	5 days	8 days	10.5 days	6 days
Unit 4 Resources	1 day	2 days	9 days	1 day
Unit 5 Earth's Features and Resources	**17 days**	**29 days**	**45 days**	**20 days**
Lesson 1 Patterns on Earth	4 days	6 days	9 days	5 days
Lesson 2 Reducing the Impacts of Natural Hazards	5 days	9 days	12 days	6 days
Lesson 3 Resources	7 days	12 days	14.5 days	8 days
Unit 5 Resources	1 day	2 days	9.5 days	1 day

Grade 4 Unit Correlations and K–8 Program Storyline

This chart shows the Unit-level Grade 4 correlations and how the Next Generation Science Standards and the three-dimensions of learning build across the grades. Detailed correlations are also available at the Lesson level. This chart also shows the completely coherent program storyline that grows in sophistication across K–8.

Grades K–2 Storyline	Grades 3–5 Storyline
	Gr 4 Unit 1 Engineering and Technology
K-2-ETS1-1 Ask questions, make observations, and gather information about a situation people want to change to define a simple problem that can be solved through the development of a new or improved object or tool.	Gr 3 **3-5-ESS3-1** Make a claim about the merit of a design solution that reduces the impacts of a weather-related hazard.* Gr 4 **3-5-ETS1-1** Define a simple design problem reflecting a need or a want that includes specified criteria for success and constraints on materials, time, or cost.
K-2-ETS1-2 Develop a simple sketch, drawing, or physical model to illustrate how the shape of an object helps it function as needed to solve a given problem. **K-2-ETS1-3** Analyze data from tests of two objects designed to solve the same problem to compare the strengths and weaknesses of how each performs.	Gr 4 **3-5-ETS1-2** Generate and compare multiple possible solutions to a problem based on how well each is likely to meet the criteria and constraints of the problem.
K-2-ETS1-2 Develop a simple sketch, drawing, or physical model to illustrate how the shape of an object helps it function as needed to solve a given problem. **K-2-ETS1-3** Analyze data from tests of two objects designed to solve the same problem to compare the strengths and weaknesses of how each performs.	Gr 4 **3-5-ETS1-3** Plan and carry out fair tests in which variables are controlled and failure points are considered to identify aspects of a model or prototype that can be improved.
	Gr 4 Unit 2 Plant and Animal Structures
K-LS1-1 Use observations to describe patterns of what plants and animals (including humans) need to survive. **1-LS1-1** Use materials to design a solution to a human problem by mimicking how plants and/or animals use their external parts to help them survive, grow, and meet their needs.	Gr 3 **3-LS1-1** Develop models to describe that organisms have unique and diverse life cycles but all have in common birth, growth, reproduction, and death. Gr 4 **4-LS1-1** Construct an argument that plants and animals have internal and external structures that function to support survival, growth, behavior, and reproduction. Gr 5 **5-LS1-1** Support an argument that plants get the materials they need for growth chiefly from air and water.
	Gr 4 **4-LS1-2** Use a model to describe that animals receive different types of information through their senses, process the information in their brain, and respond to the information in different ways.

Performance Expectations

Grades 6–8 Storyline

MS-ETS1-1 Define the criteria and constraints of a design problem with sufficient precision to ensure a successful solution, taking into account relevant scientific principles and potential impacts on people and the natural environment that may limit possible solutions.

MS-ETS1-2 Evaluate competing design solutions using a systematic process to determine how well they meet the criteria and constraints of the problem.

MS-ETS1-3 Analyze data from tests to determine similarities and differences among several design solutions to identify the best characteristics of each that can be combined into a new solution to better meet the criteria for success.

MS-ETS1-4 Develop a model to generate data for iterative testing and modification of a proposed object, tool, or process such that an optimal design can be achieved.

MS-LS1-1 Conduct an investigation to provide evidence that living things are made of cells; either one cell or many different numbers and types of cells.

MS-LS1-2 Develop and use a model to describe the function of a cell as a whole and ways parts of cells contribute to the function.

MS-LS1-3 Use argument supported by evidence for how the body is a system of interacting subsystems composed of groups of cells.

MS-LS1-4 Use argument based on empirical evidence and scientific reasoning to support an explanation for how characteristic animal behaviors and specialized plant structures affect the probability of successful reproduction of animals and plants respectively.

MS-LS1-4 Use argument based on empirical evidence and scientific reasoning to support an explanation for how characteristic animal behaviors and specialized plant structures affect the probability of successful reproduction of animals and plants respectively.

MS-LS1-8 Gather and synthesize information that sensory receptors respond to stimuli by sending messages to the brain for immediate behavior or storage as memories.

Notes:

Grade 4 Unit Correlations and K–8 Program Storyline

Grades K–2 Storyline	Grades 3–5 Storyline
	Gr 4 Unit 2 Plant and Animal Structures *cont.*
1-PS4-2 Make observations to construct an evidence-based account that objects in darkness can be seen only when illuminated. **1-PS4-3** Plan and conduct investigations to determine the effect of placing objects made with different materials in the path of a beam of light.	Gr 3 **3-PS2-2** Make observations and/or measurements of an object's motion to provide evidence that a pattern can be used to predict future motion. Gr 4 **4-PS4-2** Develop a model to describe that light reflecting from objects and entering the eye allows objects to be seen.
	Gr 4 Unit 3 Energy and Communication
	Gr 3 **3-PS2-2** Make observations and/or measurements of an object's motion to provide evidence that a pattern can be used to predict future motion. Gr 4 **4-PS3-1** Use evidence to construct an explanation relating the speed of an object to the energy of that object.
K-PS3-1 Make observations to determine the effect of sunlight on Earth's surface. **K-PS3-2** Use tools and materials to design and build a structure that will reduce the warming effect of sunlight on an area.*	Gr 4 **4-PS3-2** Make observations to provide evidence that energy can be transferred from place to place by sound, light, heat, and electric currents. Gr 5 **5-PS3-1** Use models to describe that energy in animals' food (used for body repair, growth, motion, and to maintain body warmth) was once energy from the sun.
	Gr 4 **4-PS3-3** Ask questions and predict outcomes about the changes in energy that occur when objects collide.
	Gr 4 **4-PS3-4** Apply scientific ideas to design, test, and refine a device that converts energy from one form to another.
1-PS4-1 Plan and conduct investigations to provide evidence that vibrating materials can make sound and that sound can make materials vibrate.	Gr 4 **4-PS4-1** Develop a model of waves to describe patterns in terms of amplitude and wavelength and that waves can cause objects to move.
1-PS4-4 Use tools and materials to design and build a device that uses light or sound to solve the problem of communicating over a distance.	Gr 4 **4-PS4-3** Generate and compare multiple solutions that use patterns to transfer information.
K-2-ETS1-1 Ask questions, make observations, and gather information about a situation people want to change to define a simple problem that can be solved through the development of a new or improved object or tool.	Gr 4 **3-5-ETS1-1** Define a simple design problem reflecting a need or a want that includes specified criteria for success and constraints on materials, time, or cost.
K-2-ETS1-2 Develop a simple sketch, drawing, or physical model to illustrate how the shape of an object helps it function as needed to solve a given problem. **K-2-ETS1-3** Analyze data from tests of two objects designed to solve the same problem to compare the strengths and weaknesses of how each perform.	Gr 4 **3-5-ETS1-2** Generate and compare multiple possible solutions to a problem based on how well each is likely to meet the criteria and constraints of the problem.

Performance Expectations

Grades 6–8 Storyline

MS-PS4-2 Develop and use a model to describe that waves are reflected, absorbed, or transmitted through various materials.

MS-PS3-1 Construct and interpret graphical displays of data to describe the relationships of kinetic energy to the mass of an object and to the speed of an object.

MS-PS3-4 Plan an investigation to determine the relationships among the energy transferred, the type of matter, the mass, and the change in the average kinetic energy of the particles as measured by the temperature of the sample.

MS-PS2-1 Apply Newton's Third Law to design a solution to a problem involving the motion of two colliding objects.

MS-PS3-3 Apply scientific principles to design, construct, and test a device that either minimizes or maximizes thermal energy transfer.*

MS-PS3-5 Construct, use, and present arguments to support the claim that when the kinetic energy of an object changes, energy is transferred to or from the object.

MS-PS4-1 Use mathematical representations to describe a simple model for waves that includes how the amplitude of a wave is related to the energy in a wave.

MS-PS4-3 Integrate qualitative scientific and technical information to support the claim that digitized signals are a more reliable way to encode and transmit information than analog signals.

MS-ETS1-1 Define the criteria and constraints of a design problem with sufficient precision to ensure a successful solution, taking into account relevant scientific principles and potential impacts on people and the natural environment that may limit possible solutions.

MS-ETS1-2 Evaluate competing design solutions using a systematic process to determine how well they meet the criteria and constraints of the problem.

Notes:

Grade 4 Unit Correlations and K–8 Program Storyline

Grades K–2 Storyline	Grades 3–5 Storyline
	Gr 4 Unit 4 Shaping Landforms
2-ESS1-1 Use information from several sources to provide evidence that Earth events can occur quickly or slowly.	Gr 4 **4-ESS1-1** Identify evidence from patterns in rock formations and fossils in rock layers to support an explanation for changes in a landscape over time.
2-ESS2-1 Compare multiple solutions designed to slow or prevent wind or water from changing the shape of the land.*	Gr 4 **4-ESS2-1** Make observations and/or measurements to provide evidence of the effects of weathering or the rate of erosion by water, ice, wind, or vegetation. Gr 5 **5-ESS2-1** Develop a model using an example to describe ways the geosphere, biosphere, hydrosphere, and/or atmosphere interact.
	Gr 4 Unit 5 Earth's Features and Resources
2-ESS2-2 Develop a model to represent the shapes and kinds of land and bodies of water in an area. **2-ESS2-3** Obtain information to identify where water is found on Earth and that it can be solid or liquid.	Gr 4 **4-ESS2-2** Analyze and interpret data from maps to describe patterns of Earth's features. Gr 5 **5-ESS2-2** Describe and graph the amounts and percentages of water and fresh water in various reservoirs to provide evidence about the distribution of water on Earth.
K-ESS3-1 Use a model to represent the relationship between the needs of different plants or animals (including humans) and the places they live. **K-ESS3-3** Communicate solutions that will reduce the impact of humans on the land, water, air, and/or other living things in the local environment.	Gr 4 **4-ESS3-1** Obtain and combine information to describe that energy and fuels are derived from natural resources and their uses affect the environment. Gr 5 **5-ESS3-1** Obtain and combine information about ways individual communities use science ideas to protect the Earth's resources and environment.
K-ESS3-2 Ask questions to obtain information about the purpose of weather forecasting to prepare for, and respond to, severe weather. **K-ESS3-3** Communicate solutions that will reduce the impact of humans on the land, water, air, and/or other living things in the local environment.	Gr 3 **3-ESS3-1** Make a claim about the merit of a design solution that reduces the impacts of a weather-related hazard. Gr 4 **4-ESS3-2** Generate and compare multiple solutions to reduce the impacts of natural Earth processes on humans. Gr 5 **5-ESS3-1** Obtain and combine information about ways individual communities use science ideas to protect the Earth's resources and environment.
	Gr 4 **4-PS3-4** Apply scientific ideas to design, test, and refine a device that converts energy from one form to another.
K-2-ETS1-2 Develop a simple sketch, drawing, or physical model to illustrate how the shape of an object helps it function as needed to solve a given problem. **K-2-ETS1-3** Analyze data from tests of two objects designed to solve the same problem to compare the strengths and weaknesses of how each performs.	Gr 4 **3-5-ETS1-2** Generate and compare multiple possible solutions to a problem based on how well each is likely to meet the criteria and constraints of the problem.

Performance Expectations

Grades 6–8 Storyline

MS-ESS2-2 Construct an explanation based on evidence for how geoscience processes have changed Earth's surface at varying time and spatial scales.

MS-ESS1-4 Construct a scientific explanation based on evidence from rock strata for how the geologic time scale is used to organize Earth's 4.6-billion-year-old history.

MS-ESS2-1 Develop a model to describe the cycling of Earth's materials and the flow of energy that drives this process.

MS-ESS2-2 Construct an explanation based on evidence for how geoscience processes have changed Earth's surface at varying time and spatial scales.

MS-ESS2-3 Analyze and interpret data on the distribution of fossils and rocks, continental shapes, and seafloor structures to provide evidence of the past plate motions.

MS-ESS3-1 Construct a scientific explanation based on evidence for how the uneven distributions of Earth's mineral, energy, and groundwater resources are the result of past and current geoscience processes.

MS-ESS3-4 Construct an argument supported by evidence for how increases in human population and per-capita consumption of natural resources impact Earth's systems.

MS-ESS3-2 Analyze and interpret data on natural hazards to forecast future catastrophic events and inform the development of technologies to mitigate their effects.

MS-ESS3-3 Apply scientific principles to design a method for monitoring and minimizing a human impact on the environment.*

MS-PS3-3 Apply scientific principles to design, construct, and test a device that either minimizes or maximizes thermal energy transfer.*

MS-ETS1-2 Evaluate competing design solutions using a systematic process to determine how well they meet the criteria and constraints of the problem.

Notes:

Grade 4 Unit Correlations and K–8 Program Storyline

Grades K–2 Storyline	Grades 3–5 Storyline
	Gr 4 Unit 1 Engineering and Technology
Asking Questions and Defining Problems (define a problem that can be solved with a tool or object)	**Asking Questions and Defining Problems** (define a problem that includes criteria and constraints)
Planning and Carrying Out Investigations (plan and conduct an investigation with peers; plan and conduct an investigation collaboratively to produce data; make observations or measurements to collect data for comparisons)	**Planning and Carrying Out Investigations** (plan and conduct an investigation collaboratively to produce data)
Constructing Explanations and Designing Solutions (generate or compare multiple solutions to a problem)	**Constructing Explanations and Designing Solution** (generate or compare multiple solutions to a problem based on criteria and constraints)
	Gr 4 Unit 2 Plant and Animal Structure
Developing and Using Models (develop a model to represent amounts, relationships, scales, or patterns; develop a simple model based on evidence)	**Developing and Using Models** (use a model to test relationships or interactions in a system)
Engaging in Argument from Evidence (support a claim with evidence)	**Engaging in Argument from Evidence** (support an argument with evidence, data, model)
Analyzing and Interpreting Data (develop a model to represent amounts, relationships, scales, or patterns; develop a simple model based on evidence)	**Analyzing and Interpreting Data** (analyze and interpret data to make sense of phenomena)
	Gr 4 Unit 3 Energy and Communication
Asking Questions and Defining Problems (ask questions about the world)	**Asking Questions and Defining Problems** (ask questions and predict outcomes based on patterns)
Planning and Carrying Out Investigations (plan and conduct an investigation in collaboration with peers; plan and conduct an investigation collaboratively to produce data; make observations or measurements to collect data for comparisons)	**Planning and Carrying Out Investigations** (make observations or measurements to produce data to explain a phenomenon)
Constructing Explanations and Designing Solutions (construct an evidence-based account for natural phenomena; design and build a device that solves a problem)	**Constructing Explanations and Designing Solutions** (use evidence to construct or support an explanation or design a solution; apply scientific ideas to solve design problems)
Developing and Using Models (develop a model to represent amounts, relationships, scales, or patterns; develop a simple model based on evidence)	**Developing and Using Models** (use a model to test relationships or interactions in a system)
Scientific Knowledge is Based on Empirical Evidence (scientists look for patterns when making observations)	**Scientific Knowledge is Based on Empirical Evidence** (science findings are based on recognizing patterns)

Science and Engineering Practices

Grades 6–8 Storyline

Asking Questions and Defining Problems (define a problem that includes criteria and constraints including scientific knowledge)

Planning and Carrying Out Investigations (collect data about the performance of an object, tool, process, system; conduct an investigation or revise the experimental design; plan an investigation individually and collaboratively; identify independent and dependent variables)

Constructing Explanations and Designing Solutions (design, construct, and test the design of an object, tool, process, or system; construct or implement a solution that meets specific criteria and constraints)

Developing and Using Models (develop or use a model to generate data to test ideas)

Engaging in Argument from Evidence (support an oral or written argument with empirical evidence and scientific reasoning)

Analyzing and Interpreting Data (analyze and interpret data to provide evidence for phenomena; construct, analyze, and interpret data or data sets to identify relationships)

Asking Questions and Defining Problems (ask questions to clarify arguments; ask questions that can be investigated and frame a hypothesis)

Planning and Carrying Out Investigations (collect data about the performance of an object, tool, process, system; conduct an investigation or revise the experimental design; plan an investigation individually and collaboratively; identify independent and dependent variables)

Constructing Explanations and Designing Solutions (construct an explanation that predicts or describes phenomena; construct an explanation based on valid/reliable evidence and assumption that theories and laws operate today as they did in the past and will in the future; construct, revise, or use an explanation for real-world phenomena)

Scientific Knowledge is Based on Empirical Evidence (science is based on logical and conceptual connections between evidence and explanations)

Notes:

Grade 4 Unit Correlations and K–8 Program Storyline

Grades K–2 Storyline	Grades 3–5 Storyline
	Gr 4 Unit 4 Shaping Landforms
Planning and Carrying Out Investigations (plan and conduct an investigation with peers; plan and conduct an investigation collaboratively to produce data; make observations or measurements to collect data for comparisons)	**Planning and Carrying Out Investigations** (make observations or measurements to produce data to explain a phenomenon)
Constructing Explanations and Designing Solutions (construct an evidence-based account for natural phenomena)	**Constructing Explanations and Designing Solutions** (identify evidence that supports particular points in an explanation)
	Gr 4 Unit 5 Earth's Features and Resources
Constructing Explanations and Designing Solutions (generate or compare multiple solutions to a problem)	**Constructing Explanations and Designing Solutions** (generate or compare multiple solutions to a problem based on criteria and constraints)
Obtaining, Evaluating, and Communicating Information (read texts and use media to obtain information; obtain information from text and media to answer a question or support a claim; communicate information or design ideas/solutions orally or in writing)	**Obtaining, Evaluating, and Communicating Information** (obtain and combine information from books and media to explain phenomena or solutions)
Analyzing and Interpreting Data (analyze data to determine if an object or tool works as intended)	**Analyzing and Interpreting Data** (analyze and interpret data to make sense of phenomena)
Asking Questions and Defining Problems (ask questions about the world)	**Asking Questions and Defining Problems** (ask questions and predict outcomes based on patterns)

Science and Engineering Practices

Grades 6–8 Storyline

Planning and Carrying Out Investigations (collect data to answer questions or design solutions; conduct an investigation or revise the experimental design; plan an investigation individually and collaboratively; identify independent and dependent variables)

Constructing Explanations and Designing Solutions (construct an explanation based on valid/reliable evidence and assumption that theories and laws operate today as they did in the past and will in the future; construct, revise, or use an explanation for real-world phenomena; design, construct, and test the design of an object, tool, process, or system)

Constructing Explanations and Designing Solutions (design, construct, and test the design of an object, tool, process, or system; construct or implement a solution that meets specific criteria and constraints)

Obtaining, Evaluating, and Communicating Information (integrate text, media, and visual displays to clarify claims and findings; gather, read, synthesize information from multiple sources and assess credibility, accuracy, bias)

Analyzing and Interpreting Data (analyze and interpret data to provide evidence for phenomena; construct, analyze, and interpret data or data sets to identify relationships)

Asking Questions and Defining Problems (ask questions to clarify arguments; ask questions that can be investigated and frame a hypothesis)

Notes:

Grade 4 Unit Correlations and K–8 Program Storyline

Grades K–2 Storyline	Grades 3–5 Storyline
	Gr 4 Unit 1 Engineering and Technology
DCI.K-2-ETS1.A: Defining and Delimiting Engineering Problems (asking questions, making observations, and gathering information help in thinking about problems to be solved)	Gr 4 **DCI.3-5-ETS1.A: Defining and Delimiting Engineering Problems** (solutions can be compared by how well they meet criteria and take constraints into account)
DCI.K-2-ETS1.B: Developing Possible Solutions (designs can be conveyed through sketches, drawings, and physical models)	Gr 4 **DCI.3-5-ETS1.B: Developing Possible Solutions** (carry out research before designing a solution; communicate with others about your solution; test the solution)
DCI.K-2-ETS1.C: Optimizing the Design Solution (there is always more than one possible solution; compare and test designs)	Gr 4 **DCI.3-5-ETS1.C: Optimizing the Design Solution** (test different solutions to determine which best solves the problem)
	Gr 4 Unit 2 Plant and Animal Structure
DCI.K-LS1.C: Organization for Matter and Energy Flow in Organisms (animals need food in order to live and grow; plants need water and light) **DCI.1-LS1.A: Structure and Function** (all organisms have external body parts that help them survive and grow)	Gr 3 **DCI.3-LS3.B: Variation of Traits** (organisms vary according to their inherited information; the environment can affect traits) Gr 4 **DCI.4-LS1.A: Structure and Function** (plants and animals have structures that help them survive and reproduce)
DCI.1-LS1.D: Information Processing (animals have body parts that capture different kinds of information from the environment)	Gr 4 **DCI.4-LS1.D: Information Processing** (animals have senses that help them acquire information about their environment and react to it)
DCI.1-PS4.B: Electromagnetic Radiation (objects can be seen if they reflect light or give off light; materials can be transparent, translucent, or opaque)	Gr 4 **DCI.4-PS4.B: Electromagnet Radiation** (an object can be seen when light reflected from its surface enters the eyes)
	Gr 4 Unit 3 Energy and Communication
DCI.K-PS2.B: Types of Interactions (when objects touch or collide, they push on one another and can change motion) **DCI.K-PS3.B: Conservation of Energy and Energy Transfer** (sunlight warms Earth's surface)	Gr 4 **DCI.4-PS3.A: Definitions of Energy** (energy can be moved from place to place; faster objects have greater energy)

Disciplinary Core Ideas

Grades 6–8 Storyline

DCI.MS-ETS1.A: Defining and Delimiting Engineering Problems (the more a design task's criteria and constraints are defined, the more likely it is that the solution will be successful)

DCI.MS-ETS1.B: Developing Possible Solutions (evaluate solutions with respect to criteria and constraints; use models to test solutions and then modify a solution based on test results)

DCI.MS-ETS1.C: Optimizing the Design Solution (iterative process of testing and modifying based on test results leads to an optimal solution)

DCI.MS-LS1.A: Structure and Function (all living things are made up of cells; multicellular organisms have multiple interacting body systems)

DCI.MS-LS1.D: Information Processing (senses allow organisms to respond to the environment)

DCI.MS-PS4.B: Electromagnetic Radiation (light is a wave that travels in straight lines; it is not a matter wave; objects can reflect, absorb, or transmit light)

DCI.MS-PS3.A: Definitions of Energy (heat refers to energy transferred due to temperature difference; temperature is one measure of an object's energy; objects may have kinetic and/or potential energy)

Notes:

Grade 4 Unit Correlations and K–8 Program Storyline

Grades K–2 Storyline	Grades 3–5 Storyline
	Gr 4 Unit 3 Energy and Communication *cont.*
DCI.K-PS3.B: Conservation of Energy and Energy Transfer (sunlight warms Earth's surface)	Gr 4 **DCI.4-PS3.B: Conservation of Energy and Energy Transfer** (energy is present whenever there are moving objects, sound, light, or heat and can be transferred from one object or place to another)
DCI.K-PS2.B: Types of Interactions (when objects touch or collide, they push on one another and can change motion)	Gr 3 **DCI.3-PS2.A: Forces and Motion:** (every force has a strength and direction; patterns of motion can be used to predict future motion) Gr 3 **DCI.3-PS2.B: Types of Interactions** (objects in contact exert forces on each other; electromagnetic forces do not require contact) Gr 4 **DCI.4-PS3.C: Relationship Between Energy and Forces** (when objects collide, the contact forces transfer energy and change the objects' motions)
	Gr 4 **DCI.4-PS3.D: Energy in Chemical Processes and Everyday Life** (stored energy can be converted into a form for practical use Gr 5 **DCI.5-PS3.D: Energy in Chemical Processes and Everyday Life** (energy released from food was once energy from the sun) Gr 5 **DCI.5-LS1.C: Organization for Matter and Energy Flow in Organisms** (plants acquire material for growth chiefly from air and water; animals get these materials from food)
DCI.K-2-ETS1.A: Defining and Delimiting Engineering Problems (asking questions, making observations, and gathering information help in thinking about problems to be solved) **DCI.K-2-ETS1.B: Developing Possible Solutions** (designs can be conveyed through sketches, drawings, and physical models)	Gr 3 **DCI.3-5-ETS1.C: Optimizing the Design Solution** (test different solutions to determine which best solves the problem) Gr 4 **DCI.3-5-ETS1.B: Developing Possible Solutions** (carry out research before designing a solution; communicate with others about your solution; test the solution)
DCI.K-2-ETS1.C: Optimizing the Design Solution (there is always more than one possible solution; compare and test designs)	Gr 3 **DCI.3-5-ETS1.C: Optimizing the Design Solution** (test different solutions to determine which best solves the problem) Gr 4 **DCI.3-5-ETS1.C: Optimizing the Design Solution** (test different solutions to determine which best solves the problem)

Grades 6–8 Storyline

DCI.MS-PS3.B: Conservation of Energy and Energy Transfer (when motion changes, so does energy; energy is transferred from hotter regions to colder; energy required for temperature change depends on the nature and size of matter and its environment)

DCI.MS-PS4.B: Electromagnetic Radiation (light is a wave that travels in straight lines; it is not a matter wave; objects can reflect, absorb, or transmit light)

DCI.MS-PS2.A: Forces and Motion (motion of an object is a result of all forces acting on it, and is described within a frame of reference; for pairs of objects the force exerted by each object on the other is of equal strength)

DCI.MS-PS2.B: Types of Interactions (non-contact forces can be explained by fields that extend through space)

DCI.MS-PS3.C: Relationship Between Energy and Forces (when objects interact each exerts a force on the other that can cause energy to be transferred)

DCI.MS-PS3.A: Definitions of Energy (heat refers to energy transferred due to temperature difference; temperature is one measure of an object's energy; objects may have kinetic and/or potential energy)

DCI.MS-PS3.B: Conservation of Energy and Energy Transfer (when motion changes, so does energy; energy is transferred from hotter regions to colder; energy required for temperature change depends on the nature and size of matter and its environment)

DCI.MS-ETS1.B: Developing Possible Solutions (evaluate solutions with respect to criteria and constraints; use models to test solutions and then modify a solution based on test results)

DCI.MS-ETS1.C: Optimizing the Design Solution (iterative process of testing and modifying based on test results leads to an optimal solution)

Notes:

Grade 4 Unit Correlations and K–8 Program Storyline

Grades K–2 Storyline	Grades 3–5 Storyline
	Gr 4 Unit 3 Energy and Communication *cont.*
DCI.1PS4.A Wave Properties (sound can make matter vibrate, and vibrating matter can make sound)	Gr 4 **DCI.4-PS4.A: Wave Properties** (waves can be made in water by disturbing the surface; waves can have different wavelengths and amplitudes)
DCI.1-PS4.C: Information Technologies and Instrumentation (people use devices to send and receive information over long distances)	Gr 4 **DCI.4-PS4.C: Information Technologies and Instrumentation** (digitized information can be transmitted over long distances)
	G4 Unit 4 Shaping Landforms
DCI.2-ESS1.C: The History of Planet Earth (on Earth some events happen quickly, others occur slowly)	Gr 3 **DCI.3-LS4.A: Evidence of Common Ancestry and Diversity** (fossils provide evidence of life and environments of long ago) Gr 4 **DCI.4-ESS1.C: History of Planet Earth** (patterns of rock formation provide evidence of changes on Earth over time)
DCI.K-ESS3.A: Natural Resources (living things need water, air, and resources) **DCI.2-ESS1.C: The History of Planet Earth** (on Earth some events happen quickly, others occur slowly) **DCI.2-ESS2.A: Earth Materials and Systems** (wind and water can change the shape of the land	Gr 4 **DCI.4-ESS2.A: Earth's Materials and Systems** (Earth's rocks and landforms can be changed by water, ice, wind, living things, and gravity) Gr 5 **DCI.5-ESS2.A: Earth Materials and Systems** (Earth's major systems are the geosphere, hydrosphere, atmosphere, and biosphere)
DCI.K-ESS2.E: Biogeology (plants and animals can change their environment) **DCI.K-ESS3.C: Human Impacts on Earth Systems** (things people do can affect the world around them.)	Gr 4 **DCI.4-ESS2.E: Biogeology** (living things affect the physical characteristics of their regions) Gr 5 **DCI.5-ESS2.A: Earth Materials and Systems** (Earth's major systems are the geosphere, hydrosphere, atmosphere, and biosphere) Gr 5 **DCI.5-ESS3.C: Human Impacts on Earth Systems** (human activities have had major effects on Earth and even in outer space)
	Gr 4 Unit 5 Earth's Features and Resources
DCI.2-ESS2.B: Plate Tectonics and Large-Scale System Interactions (maps show where things are) **DCI.2-ESS2.C: The Roles of Water in Earth's Surface Processes** (water is found in many forms in oceans, on land, and in the air)	Gr 4 **DCI.4-ESS2.B: Plate Tectonics and Large-Scale System Interactions** (locations of major Earth features such as mountain ranges, etc. occur in patterns) Gr 5 **DCI.5-ESS2.A: Earth Materials and Systems** (Earth's major systems are the geosphere, hydrosphere, atmosphere, and biosphere) Gr 5 **DCI.5-ESS2.C: The Roles of Water in Earth's Surface Processes** (nearly all of Earth's water is in the ocean)

Disciplinary Core Ideas

Grades 6–8 Storyline

DCI.MS-PS4.A: Wave Properties (a simple wave has a repeating pattern; sound waves need a medium to travel through)

DCI.MS-PS4.C: Information Technologies and Instrumentation (digitized signals are a reliable way to transmit information)

DCI.MS-ESS1.C: The History of Planet Earth (the geologic time scale provides a way to organize Earth's history)

DCI.MS-ESS2.A: Earth's Materials and Systems (Earth processes are the result of energy flowing and matter cycling through the planet's systems)

DCI.MS-ESS2.B: Plate Tectonics and Large-Scale System Interactions (maps of ancient land and water patterns show how Earth's plates have moved through time)

DCI.MS-LS4.A: Evidence of Common Ancestry and Diversity (the fossil record documents the change of many life forms throughout Earth's history and provides evidence for evolutionary history)

DCI.MS-ESS2.A: Earth's Materials and Systems (Earth processes are the result of energy flowing and matter cycling through the planet's systems)

DCI.MS-ESS2.B: Plate Tectonics and Large-Scale System Interactions (maps of ancient land and water patterns show how Earth's plates have moved through time)

DCI.MS-ESS2.C: The Roles of Water in Earth's Surface Processes (movement of Earth's water causes changes in all Earth systems, determining weather, shaping landforms, and causing ocean currents)

DCI.MS-ESS3.C: Human Impacts on Earth Systems (as resource consumption increases, so do negative impacts on Earth)

DCI.MS-ESS1.C: The History of Planet Earth (the geologic time scale provides a way to organize Earth's history)

DCI.MS-ESS2.A: Earth's Materials and Systems (Earth processes are the result of energy flowing and matter cycling through the planet's systems)

DCI.MS-ESS2.B: Plate Tectonics and Large-Scale System Interactions (maps of ancient land and water patterns show how Earth's plates have moved through time)

Notes:

Grade 4 Unit Correlations and K–8 Program Storyline

Grades K–2 Storyline	Grades 3–5 Storyline
	Gr 4 Unit 5 Earth's Features and Resources *cont.*
DCI.K-ESS3.A: Natural Resources (living things need water, air, and resources)	Gr 4 **DCI.4-ESS3.A: Natural Resources** (energy and fuels are derived from natural sources) Gr 5 **DCI.5-ESS3.C: Human Impacts on Earth Systems** (human activities have had major effects on Earth and even in outer space)
DCI.K-ESS3.B: Natural Hazards (some kinds of severe weather are more likely than others in a given region)	Gr 3 **DCI.3-ESS3.B: Natural Hazards** (natural hazards result from natural processes) Gr 4 **DCI.4-Ess3.B: Natural Hazards** (natural hazards result from natural processes) Gr 5 **DCI.5-ESS2.A: Earth Materials and Systems** (Earth's major systems are the geosphere, hydrosphere, atmosphere, and biosphere)
	Gr 4 **DCI.4-PS3.D: Energy in Chemical Processes and Everyday Life** (stored energy can be converted into a form for practical use) Gr 5 **DCI.5-PS3.D: Energy in Chemical Processes and Everyday Life** (energy released from food was once energy from the sun) Gr 5 **DCI.5-LS1.C: Organization for Matter and Energy Flow in Organisms** (plants acquire material for growth chiefly from air and water; animals get these materials from food)
DCI.K-2-ETS1.A: Defining and Delimiting Engineering Problems (asking questions, making observations, and gathering information help in thinking about problems to be solved) **DCI.K-2-ETS1.B: Developing Possible Solutions** (designs can be conveyed through sketches, drawings, and physical models) **DCI.K-2-ETS1.C: Optimizing the Design Solution** (there is always more than one possible solution; compare and test designs)	Gr 3 **DCI.3-5-ETS1.C: Optimizing the Design Solution** (test different solutions to determine which best solves the problem) Gr 4 **DCI.3-5 ETS1.B: Developing Possible Solutions** (tests are often designed to identify failure points or difficulties)

Disciplinary Core Ideas

Grades 6–8 Storyline

DCI.MS-ESS3.C: Human Impacts on Earth Systems (as resource consumption increases, so do negative impacts on Earth)

DCI.MS-ESS3.A: Natural Resources (humans depend on Earth's land, ocean, atmosphere, and biosphere for resources)

DCI.MS-ESS3.D: Global Climate Change (human activities are a major factor in the current rise in Earth's mean surface temperature)

DCI.MS-ESS3.B: Natural Hazards (mapping the history of natural hazards in a region helps to forecast future possible occurrences)

DCI.MS-PS3.A: Definitions of Energy (heat refers to energy transferred due to temperature difference; temperature is one measure of an object's energy; objects may have kinetic and/or potential energy)

DCI.MS-PS3.B: Conservation of Energy and Energy Transfer (when motion changes, so does energy; energy is transferred from hotter regions to colder; energy required for temperature change depends on the nature and size of matter and its environment)

DCI.MS-ETS1.B: Developing Possible Solutions (evaluate solutions with respect to criteria and constraints; use models to test solutions and then modify a solution based on test results)

DCI.MS-ETS1.C: Optimizing the Design Solution (iterative process of testing and modifying based on test results leads to an optimal solution)

Notes:

Grade 4 Unit Correlations and K–8 Program Storyline

Grades K–2 Storyline	Grades 3–5 Storyline
	Gr 4 Unit 1 Engineering and Technology
Influence of Engineering, Technology, and Science on Society and the Natural World (human life would be very different without technology; products are designed using knowledge of natural world and natural materials; products are designed using knowledge of natural world and natural materials)	**Influence of Engineering, Technology, and Science on Society and the Natural World** (engineers improve technologies or develop new ones; people's needs, wants, and demands change over time)
	Gr 4 Unit 2 Plant and Animal Structure
Systems and System Models (systems have part that work together)	**Systems and System Models** (system described by its components and their interactions)
Cause and Effect (events have causes that generate patterns; simple tests can provide evidence to support or refute ideas)	**Cause and Effect** (cause-and-effect relationships are identified, tested, and used to explain change)
	Gr 4 Unit 3 Energy and Communication
	Energy and Matter (energy transferred in various ways and between objects)
Influence of Engineering, Technology, and Science on Society and the Natural World (human life would be very different without technology; products are designed using knowledge of natural world and natural materials; using technology has impacts on the world)	**Influence of Engineering, Technology, and Science on Society and the Natural World** (engineers improve technologies or develop new ones)
	Science is a Human Endeavor (scientists and engineers work in teams; science affects everyday life
Patterns (patterns can describe phenomena and be used as evidence)	**Patterns** (patterns can be used to sort, classify, communicate, and analyze rates of change)
	Interdependence of Science, Engineering, and Technology (knowledge and research findings is important to engineering)
Systems and System Models (systems have parts that work together)	**Systems and System Models** (system described by its components and their interactions)
	Gr 4 Unit 4 Shaping Landforms
Patterns (patterns can describe phenomena and be used as evidence)	**Patterns** (patterns can be used as evidence for an explanation)
Cause and Effect (events have causes that generate patterns; simple tests can provide evidence to support or refute ideas)	**Cause and Effect** (cause-and-effect relationships are identified, tested, and used to explain change)
Scientific Knowledge Assumes an Order and Consistency in Natural Systems (natural events happen today as in the past; many events are repeated)	**Scientific Knowledge Assumes an Order and Consistency in Natural Systems** (science assumes consistent patterns)

Crosscutting Concepts

Grades 6–8 Storyline

Influence of Engineering, Technology, and Science on Society and the Natural World (technology use driven by needs, desires, values, research, and other factors; technologies enhance scientific investigations)

Systems and System Models (systems interact; may have subsystems and be part of complex systems)

Cause and Effect (correlation does not necessarily imply causation; cause-and-effect relationships can predict phenomena)

Energy and Matter (transfer of energy drives motion and cycling of matter in a system; energy may take different forms; transfer of energy can be tracked as energy flows through a system)

Influence of Engineering, Technology, and Science on Society and the Natural World (technology use driven by needs, desires, values, research, and other factors; technologies enhance scientific investigations)

Science is a Human Endeavor (scientists and engineers are guided by habits of mind; science and technology influence each other)

Patterns (macroscopic patterns are related to microscopic and atomic-level structure)

Interdependence of Science, Engineering and Technology (engineering advances led to scientific discoveries and vice versa)

Systems and System Models (systems interact; may have subsystems and be part of complex systems)

Patterns (macroscopic patterns are related to microscopic and atomic-level structure; patterns in numerical relationships can provide information about natural and designed systems; patterns can identify cause and effect)

Cause and Effect (correlation does not necessarily imply causation; cause-and-effect relationships can predict phenomena)

Scientific Knowledge Assumes an Order and Consistency in Natural Systems (natural systems and consistent patterns understandable through measurement and observation)

Notes:

Grade 4 Unit Correlations and K–8 Program Storyline

Grades K–2 Storyline	Grades 3–5 Storyline
	Gr 4 Unit 5 Earth's Features and Resources
Cause and Effect (events have causes that generate patterns; simple tests can provide evidence to support or refute ideas).	**Cause and Effect** (cause-and-effect relationships are identified, tested, and used to explain change)
	Interdependence of Science, Engineering, and Technology (knowledge and research findings is important to engineering)
Influence of Engineering, Technology, and Science on Society and the Natural World (human life would be very different without technology; products are designed using knowledge of natural world and natural materials; using technology has impacts on the world)	**Influence of Engineering, Technology, and Science on Society and the Natural World** (engineers improve technologies or develop new ones; people's needs, wants, and demands change over time)
Patterns (patterns can describe phenomena and be used as evidence)	**Patterns** (patterns can be used as evidence for an explanation)

Crosscutting Concepts

Grades 6–8 Storyline

Cause and Effect (correlation does not necessarily imply causation; cause-and-effect relationships can predict phenomena)

Interdependence of Science, Engineering and Technology (engineering advances led to scientific discoveries and vice versa)

Influence of Engineering, Technology, and Science on Society and the Natural World (technology use driven by needs, desires, values, research, and other factors; technologies enhance scientific investigations)

Patterns (macroscopic patterns are related to microscopic and atomic-level structure; patterns in numerical relationships can provide information about natural and designed systems; patterns can identify cause and effect)

Notes:

HMH Into Science™ and the EQuIP Rubric

The **EQuIP Rubric** is an instrument for evaluating a curriculum's conformance with the contours of an authentic NGSS program. As such, one needs to bear in mind the known limitations and proper usages of the rubric:

- The rubric is intended to be applied to lessons or units, not to entire curricula.
- The rubric itself indicates that it is unlikely that a single lesson will lead to mastery of a Performance Expectation. High-Quality Units may do so.
- The evaluation process is intended to be done in a group, not by an individual.
- The rubric requires familiarity with the Performance Expectation and its supporting Dimensions of Learning. The ***HMH Into Science Trace Tool to the NGSS*** can help provide this orientation.

Throughout the ***HMH Into Science Teacher Guide***, you will find features to help you orient toward the critical dimensions of the EQuIP Rubric. Using the book, you are well beyond the evaluation phase of considering a program, but these features will demonstrate the best practices of NGSS summarized by the evaluation instrument. Highlights of critical EQuIP Rubric evaluation points are summarized in the reduced pages you see here.

UNIT OPENER PAGES

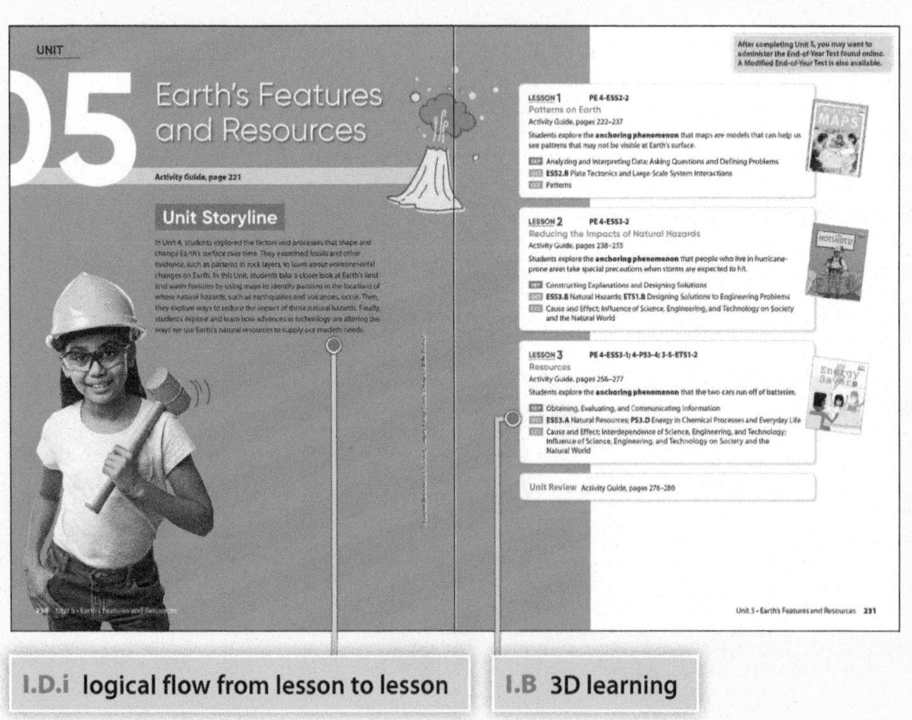

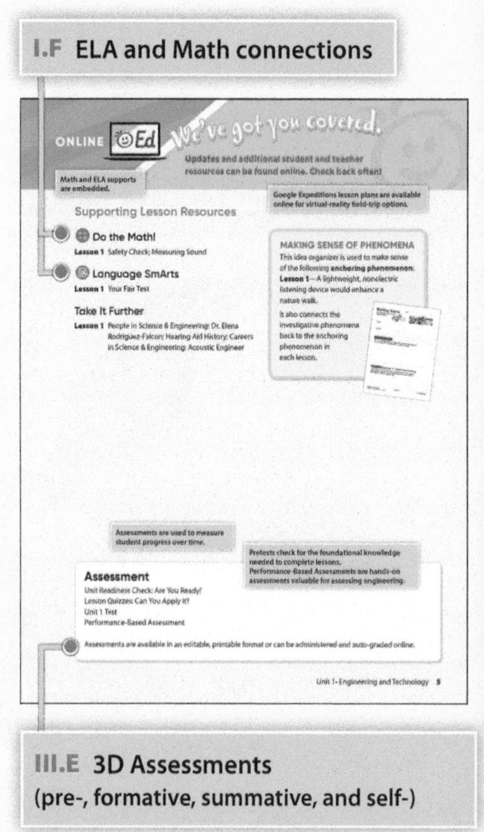

LESSON OPENER PAGES

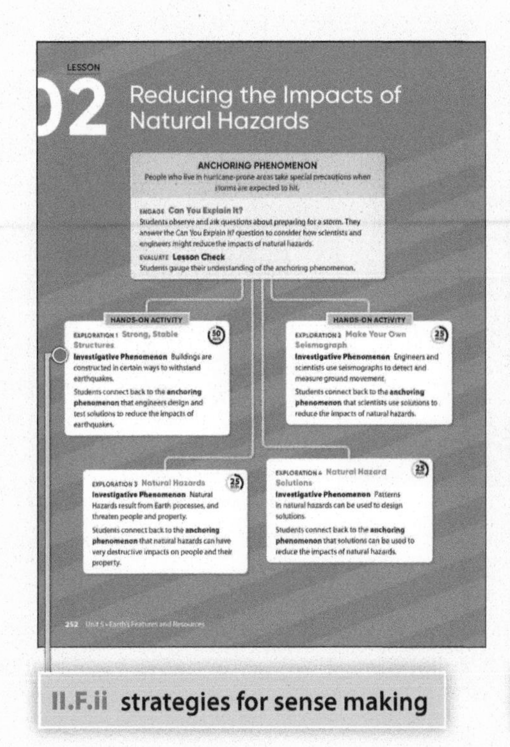

II.F.ii strategies for sense making

II.A.i authentic and meaningful scenarios

FUNonemal READER

II.C prior knowledge

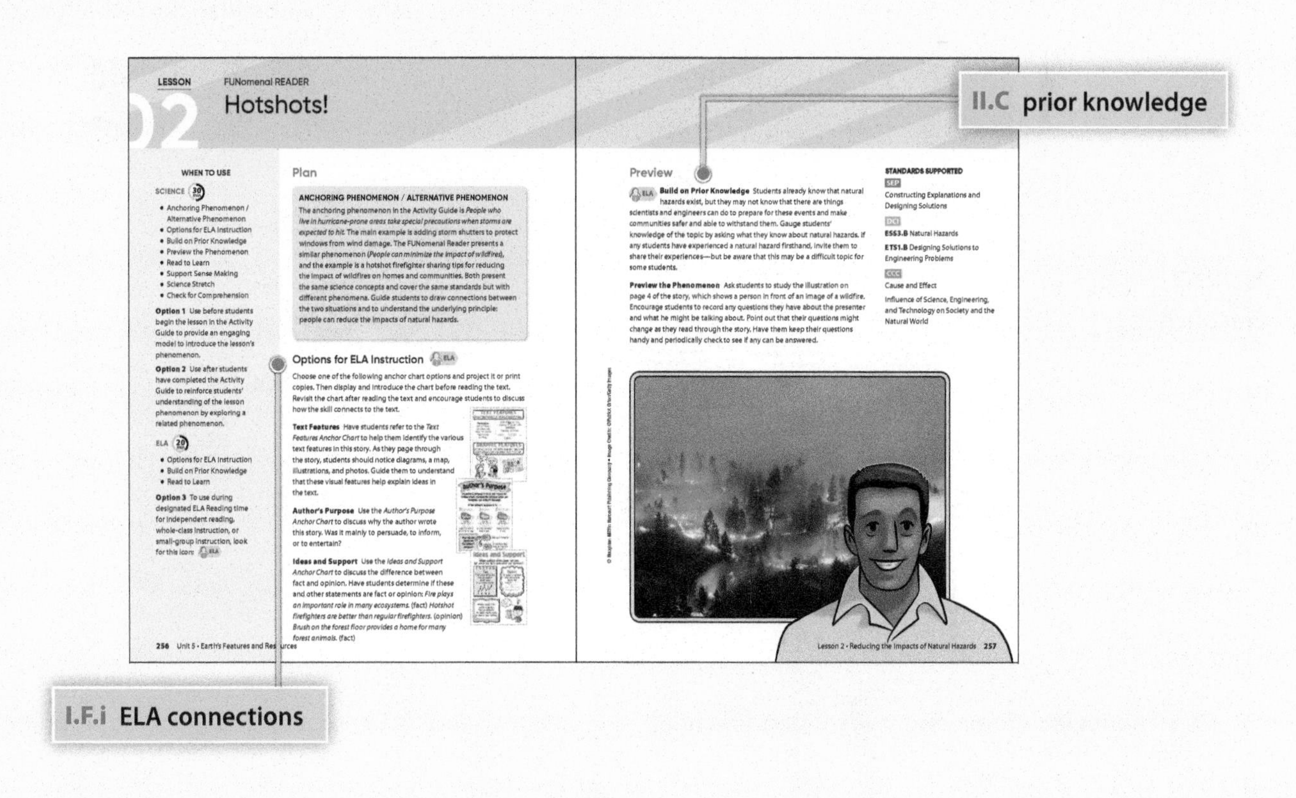

I.F.i ELA connections

ONLINE RESOURCES

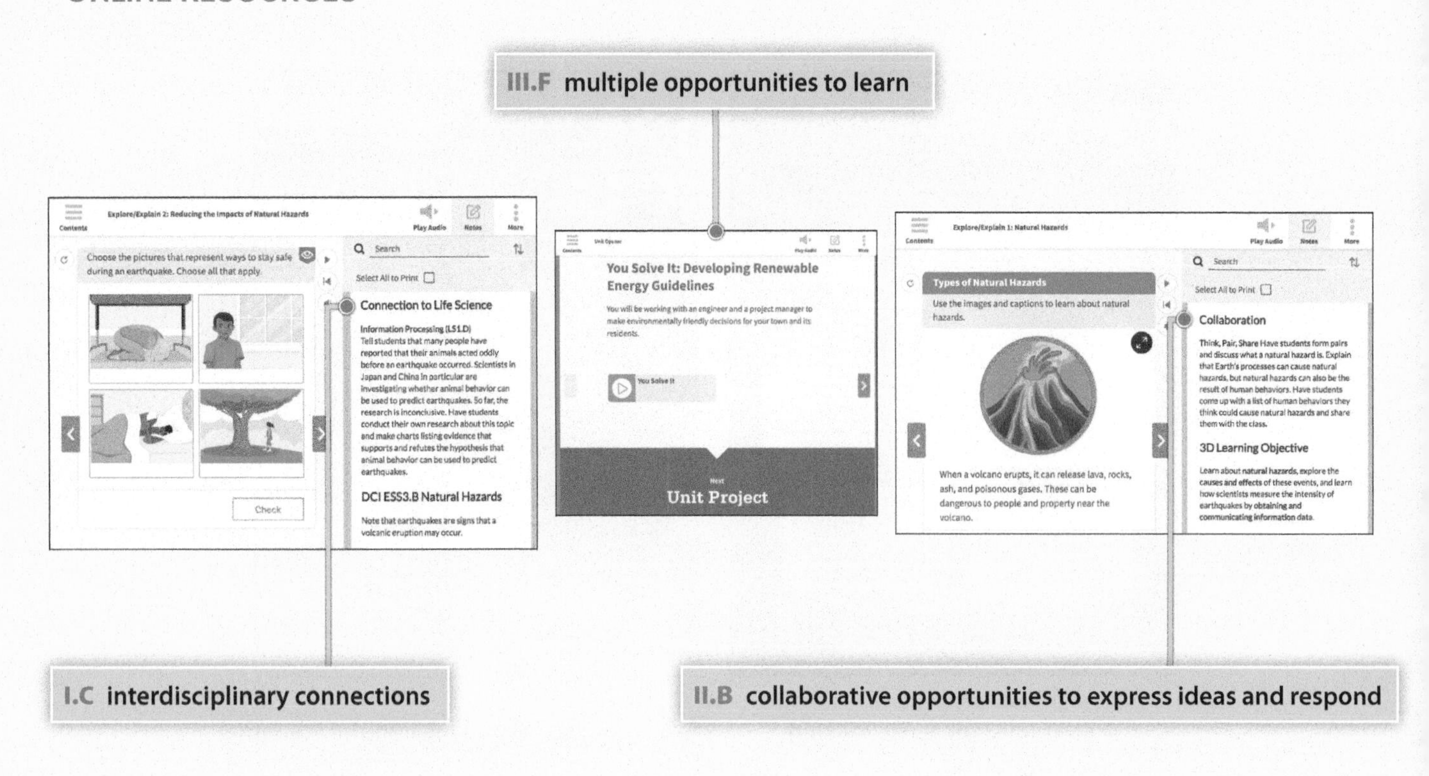

LESSON PAGES

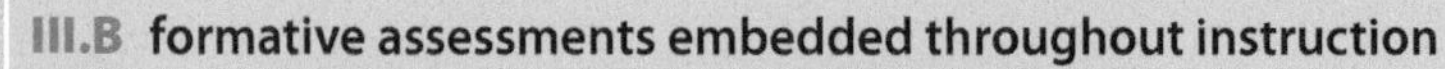

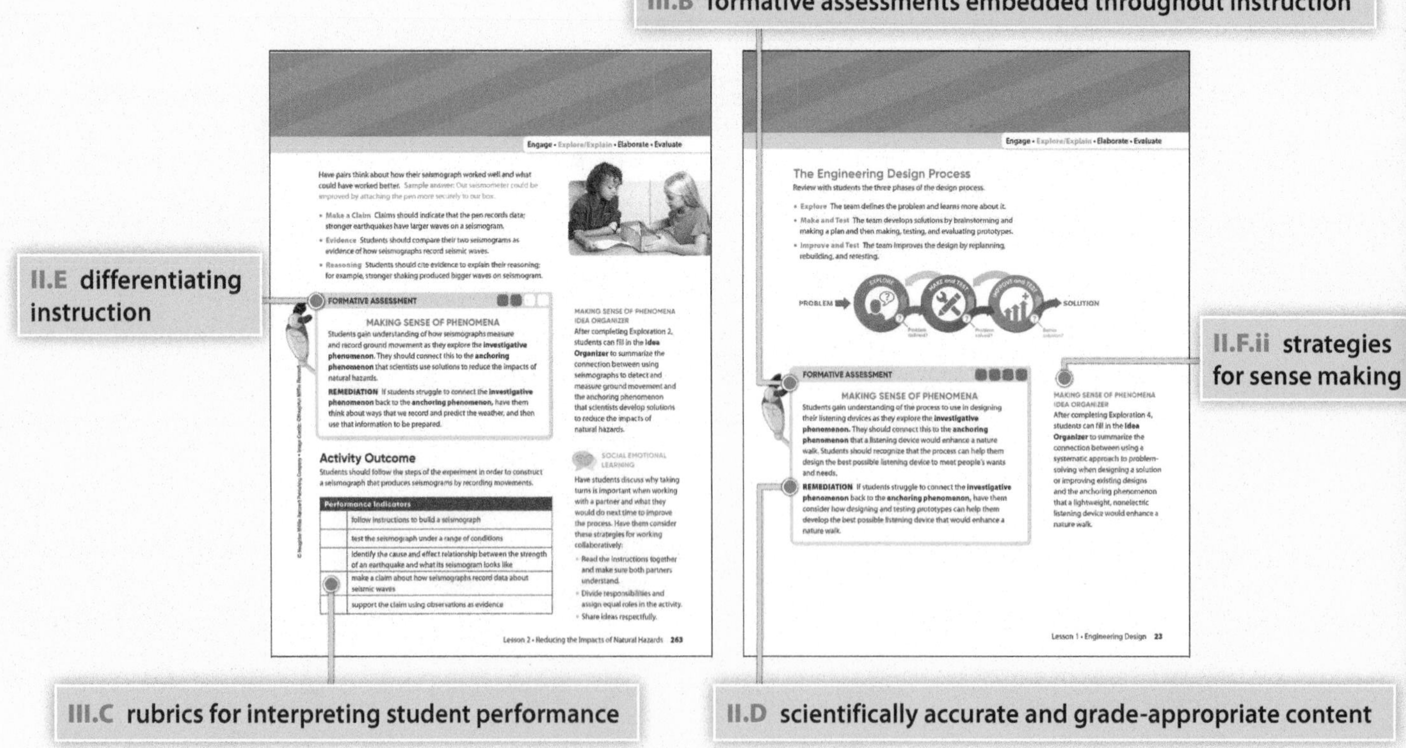

LESSON CLOSER PAGES

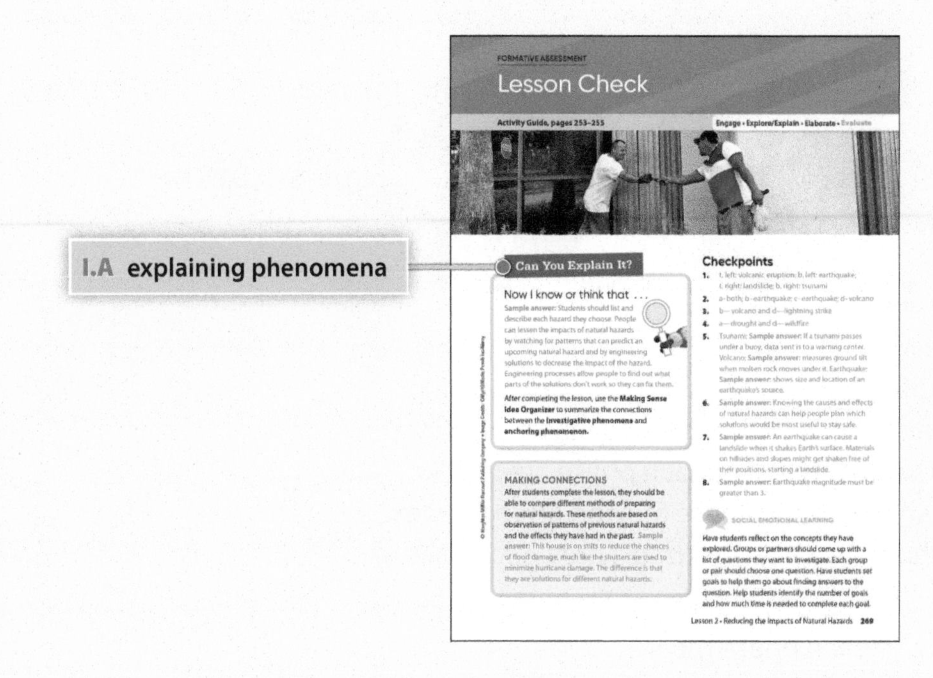

UNIT CLOSER PAGES

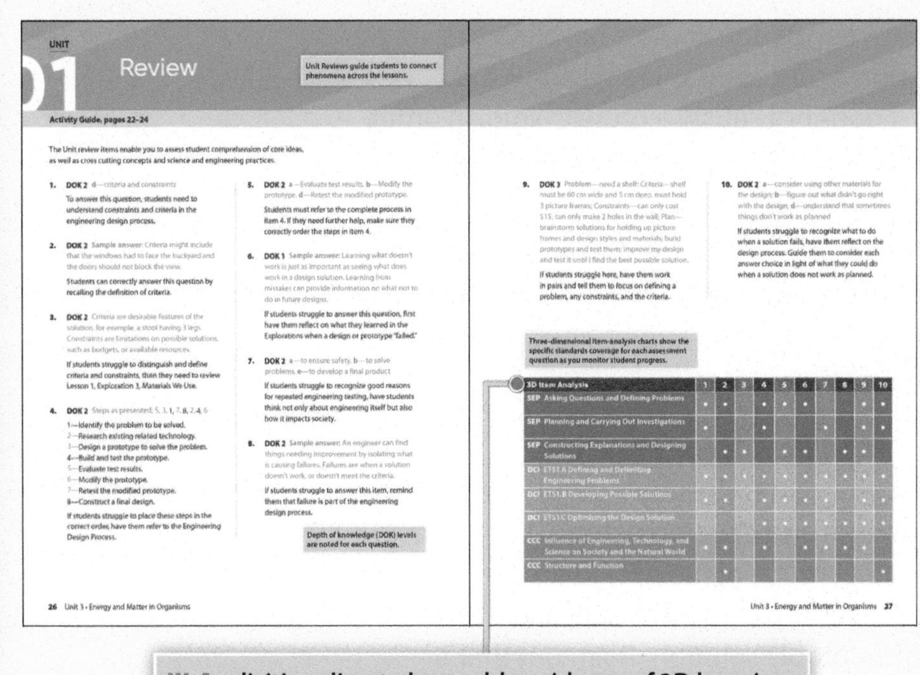

Engineering

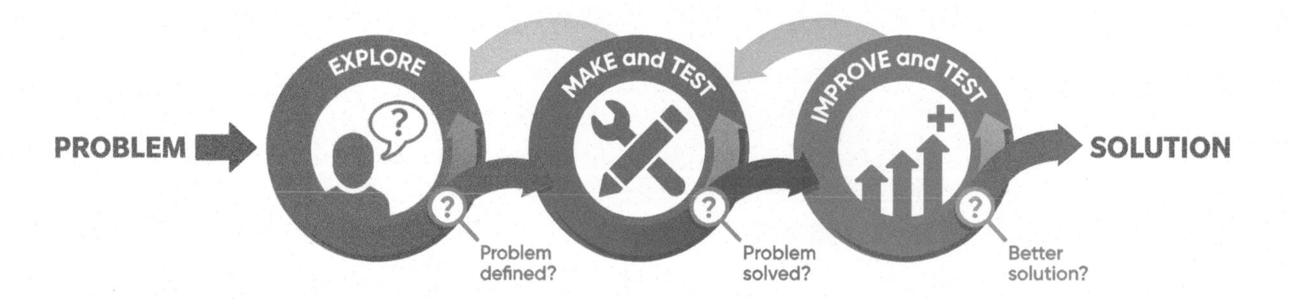

Have students examine the diagram by looking at the icons and tracing the arrows. The arrows within each phase show how you may repeat steps within a phase multiple times. The questions for each phase are checks to help identify what result you should have before moving on to the next phase. The return arrows show how you may return to a previous phase at any time.

Ask: What do you think the icons in each phase mean? Students may notice that in the first phase a person is asking questions. In the second phase, there is a pencil representing the idea of using a pencil to plan, but also to record data from tests. The wrench indicates making changes to a possible solution. The icon in the third phase shows repeated improvements by the arrows increasing to a plus sign.

EXPLORE

Discuss with students how to gather information about a problem to understand it and identify what features an acceptable solution would have. A solution is unacceptable if it does not satisfy all constraints. In order to define a problem, one must state the problem clearly and identify the criteria and constraints for an acceptable solution.

Ask: Look at the diagram. What should you do when you answer 'yes' to the question "Problem defined"? Students should identify that if the problem is defined, they go on to the Make and Test phase. If not, they should repeat the steps in the Explore phase to gather the necessary information.

MAKE and TEST

Discuss with students how to brainstorm and develop potential solutions in the Make and Test phase. Explain that much of the design time may be spent in the Make and Test phase. Students can modify, test, and evaluate one or more prototypes to find an acceptable solution. Point out that a solution can be a tool or process that solves a problem.

Discuss with students how testing is needed to gather the data needed to make decisions. New information might arise during this phase that makes it necessary to return to the Explore phase. During testing, students may realize that even though a solution seems to satisfy the criteria, it doesn't really solve their problem. This may mean that they need to adjust their problem definition.

Ask: How are criteria and constraints used during the MAKE and TEST phase? Criteria and constraints are used to evaluate a solution. If a solution satisfies the criteria and constraints it should solve the problem.

Remind students that multiple solutions may solve the problem. One solution may work better than another, and features of different solutions may be combined to make a better solution.

IMPROVE and TEST

Discuss with students why you should repeat the steps of changing, testing, and evaluating a prototype to improve it. Each change should improve how well the solution satisfies the criteria to get the best possible solution. If new information makes it necessary, you may return to the Explore or Make and Test phase.

Discuss with students that engineers often work in groups and design solutions for other people. They need to communicate during all phases of the process to gather and share information. This includes presenting a solution so that other people can use it.

Ask: How might you communicate a solution to other people? Students may say that a model can be used to explain how a solution works or what it looks like so that other people can use it.

Hana wants to attract pretty birds to her backyard. Talk with a partner about how Hana might use an engineering design process to solve this problem. Sample answer: Students should consider all the parts of the engineering design process presented here and discuss how Hana might use this process to solve the problem of attracting birds to her backyard.

Claims, Evidence, and Reasoning

Use the following discussion points to introduce the Claims, Evidence, and Reasoning strategy that will be used throughout the program.

Materials

Prepare the following materials before starting:

- clear container, 50 mL vinegar
- clear container, 100 mL vinegar
- clear container, 200 mL vinegar
- tablespoon
- baking soda, 3 tablespoons
- safety goggles

Procedure

Ask for three volunteers. Before you begin the activity, have students write a claim about which amount of vinegar will react the most.

1. Have one volunteer put one tablespoon of baking soda in the 50 mL of vinegar. Pause to observe.
2. Have the next volunteer put one tablespoon of baking soda in the 100 mL of vinegar. Pause to observe.
3. Have the last volunteer put one tablespoon of baking soda in 200 mL of vinegar. Pause to observe.
4. Have students share their observations.

Discuss with students that a claim can be made about an observation either before or after you do a scientific investigation or solve an engineering problem.

Have students work independently to formulate questions and identify one to investigate. Students should use this investigation to practice making a claim, supporting it with evidence, and using reasoning to connect and explain the evidence. They can use sentence frames such as, The evidence supports my claim because ______.

Ask: In a scientific investigation, what can you use as evidence to support a claim? Sample answer: Data collected from the investigation, observations, research or things you read about

Find more support in the **Claims, Evidence, and Reasoning** section of the online Science and Engineering Practices Handbook.

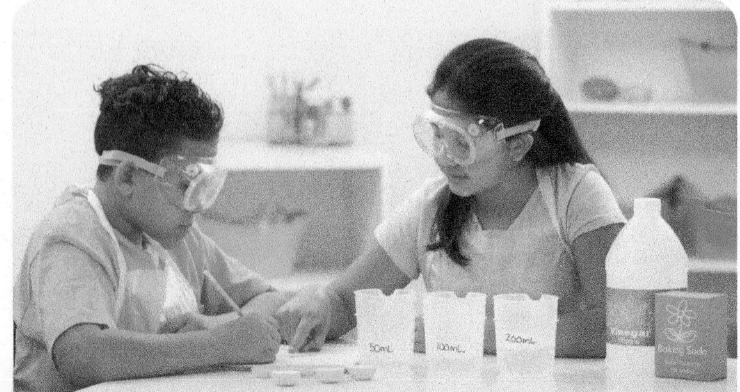

Safety in Science

Safety in the Lab

Use the following discussion points to emphasize key safety rules for indoor science activities.

Ask: Why is it important to understand safety reminders before you begin an activity? You may get hurt if you don't follow the reminders during the activity.

Ask: Why do you need to keep long sleeves and hair out of the way during science activities? Hair and clothes can snag equipment and get stained. They can also catch fire.

Ask: Tell me what you would do if you spilled some water. Students should mention informing the teacher and helping clean up.

Ask: What could happen if the spill wasn't cleaned up? Students should realize that water makes the floor slippery and increases the risk of falls.

Ask: First, put on a pair of safety goggles. What are the differences between safety goggles and ordinary glasses? Students should recognize the sturdy material and protection all around the sides of the lenses.

Ask: Why are these differences important during science activities? The lenses are less likely to break. The protection on the sides keeps liquid and objects from getting into your eyes.

Ask for a student volunteer. Tell them to walk up to and point at a piece of safety equipment in the classroom, then tell the class when and how you would use it.

Safety in the Field

Use the following discussion points to emphasize key safety rules for outdoor science activities.

Ask: How does your clothing affect your safety outdoors? Covering up your arms and legs protects you from scratches and from the sun.

Ask: Why do you think open-toed or dressy shoes are poor choices for exploring outdoors? Sturdy shoes can protect your feet from sharp objects, plants, and biting insects.

Ask: Why is it unsafe to taste anything outdoors? Many plants and animals are poisonous. Even adults can be fooled.

Ask: Why is it important to stay with your group and stay on marked trails? With a group, someone will be there to help if you get hurt or have a problem. Marked trails are safer; walking through wild areas may damage habitats.

Ask: Why are running and horseplay riskier outdoors? You don't know the area. The ground level may change quickly. If you're moving fast, it's easier to fall and get hurt before you can stop.

Ask: Why is it especially important to wash your hands when you come back indoors? It helps keep you from getting sick and from rubbing grit into your eyes by accident.

Safety Symbols

Safety symbols will appear in the instructions for each Hands-On Activity to emphasize important notes of caution. Make sure students learn what they represent and understand the appropriate precautions to take.

Use the following discussion points to emphasize key safety rules for each Hands-On Activity.

Ask: How are safety goggles different from regular eyeglasses? Safety goggles are made of sturdy material and have protection around the sides of the lenses.

Ask: Why should you tie back long hair? Loose, long hair could obstruct the materials in the activity or become contaminated.

Ask: If chemicals get on your skin, clothing, or in your eyes, why is it important to rinse it immediately? Chemicals can burn or stain skin or clothing. Rinsing immediately helps to reduce the impact of the chemicals.

Ask: Why should you wash your hands thoroughly after each activity? Hands can get contaminated from the materials in the activity. Washing hands helps to ensure that materials from the activity are not ingested when eating. Washing hands also keeps you from rubbing things into your eyes.

Dress Code

Glassware and Sharp Object Safety

Electrical Safety

Chemical Safety

Heating and Fire Safety

Plant and Animal Safety

Cleanup

Safety Quiz

Use this quiz to check student understanding of lab safety practices and procedures.

It is important that students take responsibility for their safety and the safety of others. Be sure to discuss with students each question and answer to help them understand the importance of safe conduct during an activity.

1. At the end of any activity you should
   a—wash your hands thoroughly before leaving the lab.
2. If you get hurt or injured in any way, you should
   a—tell your teacher immediately.
3. Before starting an activity, you should
   c—read all directions and make sure you understand them
4. When working with materials that might fly into the air and hurt someone's eye, you should wear
   a—goggles.
5. If you get something in your eye you should
   d—tell your teacher right away.

Find more support in the online **Lab Safety Handbook**.

Notes:

UNIT

Engineering and Technology

Activity Guide, page 1

Unit Storyline

In this Unit, students explore a design problem. They learn how to ask questions and define problems in order to design a hearing-enhancing device. By exploring the engineering process, students come to understand the Influence of Engineering, Technology, and Science on Society and the Natural World. They will learn about the importance of prototypes, learn to define and evaluate criteria and constraints, and use models to examine how to test and improve designs.

Before starting Unit 1, you may want to administer the Beginning-of-Year Readiness Check found online.

LESSON 1 **PE 3-5-ETS1-1, 3-5-ETS1-2, 3-5-ETS1-3**

Engineering Design

Activity Guide, pages 2–21

Students explore the **anchoring phenomenon** that a lightweight, nonelectric listening device would enhance a nature walk.

SEP Asking Questions and Defining Problems; Planning and Carrying Out Investigations; Constructing Explanations and Designing Solutions

DCI **ETS1.A** Defining and Delimiting Engineering Problems; **ETS1.B** Developing Possible Solutions; **ETS1.C** Optimizing the Design Solution

CCC Influence of Engineering, Technology, and Science on Society and the Natural World

Unit Review Activity Guide, pages 22–24

Engineering is embedded throughout each grade level and covered in depth in the first unit to provide a solid foundation for students.

Engineering Design Process

PROBLEM → EXPLORE → MAKE and TEST → IMPROVE and TEST → SOLUTION

Problem defined?

Problem solved?

Better solution?

UNIT 01

AT A GLANCE

Online-Only Resources

Online, the NGSS Trace Tool unpacks the standards and displays the connectedness and spiraling within and across grade levels.

Supporting Unit Resources

You Solve It SUPPORTS LESSON 1

Keeping It Warm and Cool is a virtual lab that offers practice in support of **Performance Expectations 3-5-ETS1-1**, **3-5-ETS1-2** and **3-5-ETS1-3.** Students apply the design process to evaluate building materials and consider cost constraints while finding a solution to a problem.

SEP Asking Questions and Defining Problems; Constructing Explanations and Designing Solutions

DCI **ETS1.A** Defining and Delimiting Engineering Problems; **ETS1.B** Developing Possible Solutions

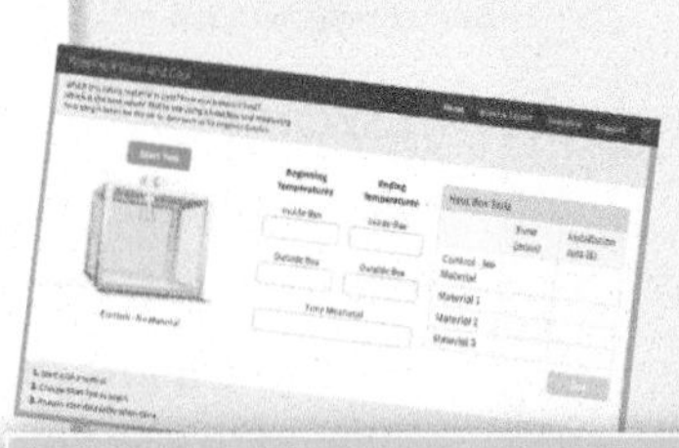

You Solve It activities are engagin open-ended computer simulation that offer alternative, easy lab options.

Unit Project SUPPORTS LESSON 1

90 min

Extend a Sense provides students an opportunity to practice aspects of **Performance Expectation 3-5-ETS1-1** and **3-5-ETS1-2.** Students identify a sense to improve, then design a device to enhance the sense.

SEP Asking Questions and Defining Problems; Constructing Explanations and Designing Solutions

DCI **ETS1.A** Defining and Delimiting Engineering Problems; **ETS1.B** Developing Possible Solutions

CCC Influence of Engineering, Technology, and Science on Society and the Natural World

Optional Unit Projects can be usec to tie together bigger concepts across the unit.

Unit Performance Task SUPPORTS LESSON 1

90 min

Designing a Portable Chair provides an opportunity for students to practice aspects of and demonstrate their understanding of the **Performance Expectations 3-5-ETS1-1** and **3-5-ETS1-2.** Students develop models of a more comfortable chair. They identify problems with the old design and propose solutions for new designs.

SEP Defining Problems; Developing and Using Models

DCI **ETS1.A** Defining and Delimiting Engineering Problems; **ETS1.B** Developing Possible Solutions; **ETS1.C** Optimizing the Design Solution

CCC Influence of Engineering, Technology, and Science on Society and the Natural World; Structure and Function

Hands-On Unit Performance Tasks provide tactile assessment option

Language Development

This worksheet is used as students progress through the unit's lessons. As they come to a highlighted vocabulary term, they should come back to this chart and fill in the blanks with words or phrases.

Embedded ELA best practices and strategies allow teachers to cover both science and ELA in the same lesson.

ONLINE 

We've got you covered.

Updates and additional student and teacher resources can be found online. Check back often!

Math and ELA supports are embedded.

Google Expeditions lesson plans are available online for virtual-reality field-trip options.

Supporting Lesson Resources

 Do the Math!

Lesson 1 Safety Check; Measuring Sound

 Language SmArts

Lesson 1 Your Fair Test

Take It Further

Lesson 1 People in Science & Engineering: Dr. Elena Rodriguez-Falcon; Hearing Aid History; Careers in Science & Engineering: Acoustic Engineer

MAKING SENSE OF PHENOMENA

This idea organizer is used to make sense of the following **anchoring phenomenon**:

Lesson 1—A lightweight, nonelectric listening device would enhance a nature walk.

It also connects the investigative phenomena back to the anchoring phenomenon in each lesson.

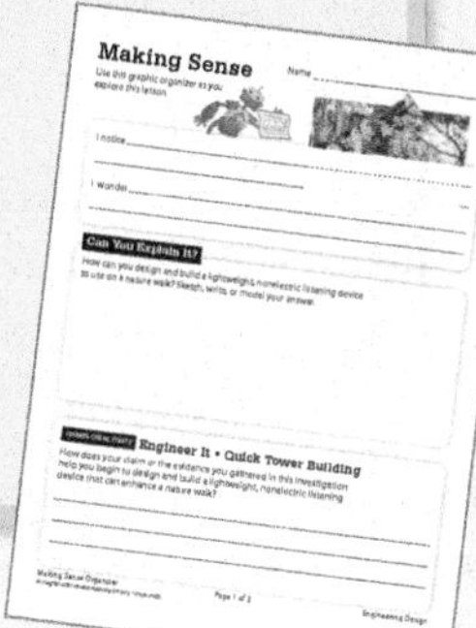

Assessments are used to measure student progress over time.

Pretests check for the foundational knowledge needed to complete lessons.
Performance-Based Assessments are hands-on assessments valuable for assessing engineering.

Assessment

Unit Readiness Check: Are You Ready?
Lesson Quizzes: Can You Apply It?
Unit 1 Test
Performance-Based Assessment

Assessments are available in an editable, printable format or can be administered and auto-graded online.

LESSON

01 Engineering Design

ANCHORING PHENOMENON

A lightweight, nonelectric listening device would enhance a nature walk.

ENGAGE **Can You Explain It?**
Students observe and ask questions about a field researcher's special equipment, a listening device. They answer the Can You Solve It? question to design a lightweight and nonelectric listening device.

EVALUATE **Lesson Check**
Students gauge their understanding of the anchoring phenomenon.

Lessons begin with phenomena- and problem-driven three-dimensional learning.

Every lesson clearly shows how the phenomena relate to a coherent storyline.

HANDS-ON ACTIVITY

EXPLORATION 1 **Quick Tower Building** 20 min
Investigative Phenomenon Part of designing solutions to problems is defining criteria and constraints.

Students connect back to the **anchoring phenomenon** that a lightweight, nonelectric listening device would enhance a nature walk.

HANDS-ON ACTIVITY

EXPLORATION 2 **Designing a Listening Device** 60 min
Investigative Phenomenon Engineers make and improve designs to meet needs or wants and solve problems.

Students connect back to the **anchoring phenomenon** that a lightweight, nonelectric listening device would enhance a nature walk.

EXPLORATION 3 **What is Engineering?** 30 min
Investigative Phenomenon Engineers apply science and math ideas to make technology that solves problems like the desire for a listening device.

Students connect back to the **anchoring phenomenon** that engineers develop solutions to meet everyday needs and wants, such as the desire for a listening device to enhance a hike.

EXPLORATION 4 **How Engineers Solve Problems** 60 min
Investigative Phenomenon Engineers use a systematic approach to problem-solving when designing listening devices or improving existing designs.

Students connect back to the **anchoring phenomenon** of a need for a listening device.

Making 3D Connections

The **anchoring phenomenon** in this lesson supports students' understanding of and application of these Next Generation Science Standards.

Building to the Performance Expectations

3-5-ETS1-1 Define a simple design problem that includes specified criteria and constraints.

3-5-ETS1-2 Generate and compare multiple possible solutions to a problem.

3-5-ETS1-3 Plan and carry out fair tests in which variables are controlled and failure points are considered to identify aspects of a model or prototype that can be improved.

SEP

Asking Questions and Defining Problems Define a simple design problem that can be solved. *(Explorations 1, 2, 3, 4)*

Planning and Carrying Out Investigations Plan and conduct an investigation collaboratively. *(Explorations 1, 2, 3, 4)*

Constructing Explanations and Designing Solutions Generate and compare multiple solutions to a problem. *(Explorations 1, 2, 3, 4)*

DCI

ETS1.A Defining and Delimiting Engineering Problems Different proposals for solutions can be compared. *(Explorations 1, 2, 3, 4)*

ETS1.B Developing Possible Solutions Research on a problem should be carried. Testing solutions involves investigating performance. Tests are designed to identify failure points. *(Explorations 1, 2, 3, 4)*

ETS1.C Optimizing the Design Solution Solutions need to be tested to find which solves the problem. *(Explorations 2, 4)*

CCC

Influence of Engineering, Technology, and Science on Society and the Natural World People's needs and wants change over time. Engineers improve existing technologies or develop new ones. *(Explorations 1, 2, 3, 4)*

Focal points of the three dimensions of learning for each lesson are defined.

Vocabulary

Word Wall A word wall, anchor chart, or Language Development chart can be used to support vocabulary.

constraint a limit on possible solutions, such as cost or material

criteria the desirable features of a solution

engineering the process of designing new or improved technology

fair test a test that does not give any advantage to the conditions or objects being tested

prototype an early version of a design

technology how humans change the natural world to meet a want or a need

You may want to include additional academic terms such as *revert* and *variable*, and any other terms students might struggle with.

Language Development Prompt students to complete the chart and add their own terms as they progress through the lesson.

Anchor Chart You may want to make a vocabulary-based anchor chart.

Language development support options are embedded for students, and strategies are called out for teachers.

LESSON

01 Engineering Design

Activity Guide, pages 2–3

Online, students can view videos, play animations, and interact with instructional images and text.

Students can engage in the Can You Solve It? content by observing the photograph or by exploring the corresponding video online.

ONLINE 

View a video about collecting animal audio data.

ANCHORING PHENOMENON
A lightweight, nonelectric listening device would enhance a nature walk.

PHENOMENON EXPLAINED
By using the engineering design process, someone can build a lightweight, comfortable, portable, and battery-free device that enhances our sense of hearing.

Explanations of lesson phenomena provide useful instructional background information.

Lessons supported by the 5E instructional model are flexible so you can adjust them to your classroom needs.

Lesson Objective

Students will learn to define a design problem and identify the constraints and criteria for a design solution. They will also research and design possible solutions to a problem, and investigate how well the solution performs.

Support Discovery

The following prompts can be used to guide student-led discovery.

Discussion prompts allow teachers to easily facilitate classroom explorations.

I notice . . .

After observing the photograph or watching the video, students should record what they noticed about the equipment being used. If students struggle to record observations, ask them what the scientist is doing.

Sample answer: I notice that the person is using equipment to listen better. She appears to be outside.

I wonder . . .

After observing the photograph or watching the video, students should record what they want to find out more about how and why the scientist is using the special equipment.

Sample answer: I wonder what the equipment she is using does. I wonder if the equipment is effective.

Alternative phenomena provide additional instructional flexibility or can be used as an assessment to measure students' ability to apply learning to a new situation.

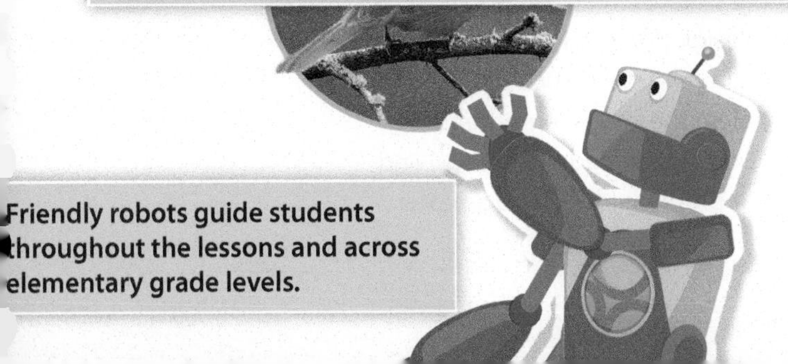

Friendly robots guide students throughout the lessons and across elementary grade levels.

Can You Solve It?

In the Can You Solve It?, students make an initial claim that explains the **Anchoring Phenomenon.** Student responses can be sketched, written or modeled. Their solutions should indicate the materials they will use and how their solution will work.

Students will learn about the engineering design process. This will enable them to give a more complete explanation of the **Anchoring Phenomenon** at the end of the lesson.

Alternative Phenomenon

If students are unfamiliar with listening devices, remind them about headphones or microphones and megaphones. Discuss the advantages of these devices and when, where, and how they might use one but not the other. Consider inviting the school nurse to demonstrate how to use a stethoscope and letting students listen to their own hearts. If you have a stethoscope available, explain how the device lets the listener hear the heart and the lungs. Point out that you do not have to press an ear against the chest when you use the device.

SOCIAL EMOTIONAL LEARNING

Have each student set a personal goal for this lesson and make a plan for how to achieve the goal. Throughout the lesson, take daily breaks for students to track their progress in meeting their goals. As students move through the lesson, they can continue to work towards their initial goals or set new ones. If students struggle setting goals for this lesson, share with them some of the following ideas: identifying problems, brainstorming ideas, providing constructive feedback, and being respectful when working in a group.

LESSON 01

FUNomenal READER

Desk Designers

The FUNomenal Leveled Readers model how students should use scientific processes to resolve phenomena.

WHEN TO USE

SCIENCE 

- Anchoring Phenomenon / Alternative Phenomenon
- Options for ELA Instruction
- Build on Prior Knowledge
- Preview the Phenomenon
- Read to Learn
- Support Sense Making
- Science Stretch
- Check for Comprehension

Option 1 Use before students begin the lesson in the Activity Guide to provide an engaging model to introduce the lesson's phenomenon.

Option 2 Use after students have completed the Activity Guide to reinforce students' understanding of the lesson phenomenon by exploring a related phenomenon.

ELA 

- Options for ELA Instruction
- Build on Prior Knowledge
- Read to Learn

Option 3 To use during designated ELA Reading time for independent reading, whole-class instruction, or small-group instruction, look for this icon: ELA

Options on when to use your FUNomenal Readers can be found here.

Plan

ANCHORING PHENOMENON / ALTERNATIVE PHENOMENON

The anchoring phenomenon in the Activity Guide is *A lightweight, nonelectric listening device would enhance a nature walk*, and the main example is a field researcher using a listening device to amplify bird calls. The FUNomenal Reader presents a similar phenomenon (*We need better school desks*), and the example is a classroom challenge to design the ideal desk. Both present the same science concepts and cover the same standards but with different phenomena. Guide students to draw connections between the two situations and to understand the underlying principle: the engineering design process can be used to solve problems.

Follow the ELA icon to use readers during your reading time.

Options for ELA Instruction 

Choose one of the following anchor chart options and project it or print copies. Then display and introduce the chart before reading the text. Revisit the chart after reading the text and encourage students to discuss how the skill connects to the text.

Ask and Answer Questions Use the *Ask and Answer Questions Anchor Chart* when introducing, developing, or reviewing those skills. Have students consider how asking questions helps the students in the story define and delimit the problem they want to solve.

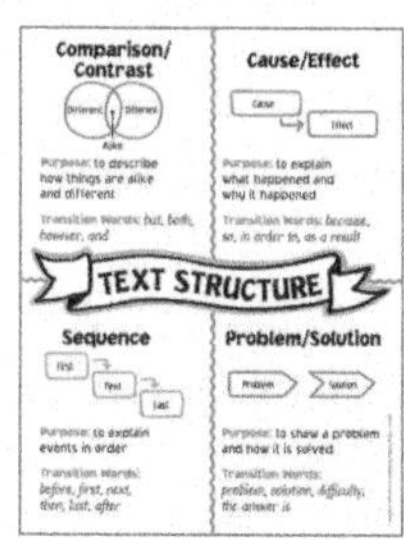

Text Structure Refer to the *Text Structure Anchor Chart* when discussing text structure in the context of this story. Guide students to an understanding of the problem-solution structure of the story. Have them identify the problem and the solution.

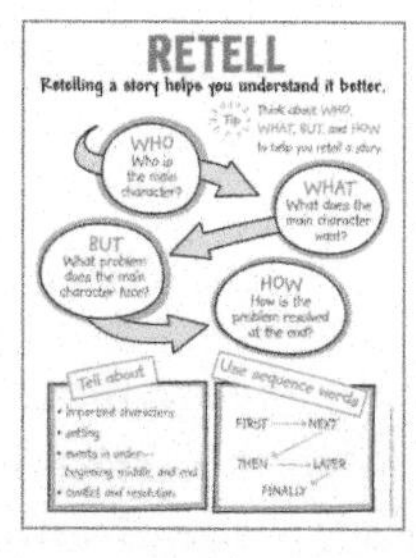

Retell Use the *Retell Anchor Chart* after reading to help gauge students' understanding of the steps in the engineering design process. Have student pairs take turns retelling the story. Encourage partners to focus on the problem the characters address (school desks that don't meet students' needs) and the resolution of that problem (designing a better school desk).

Preview

ELA **Build on Prior Knowledge** Have students make a quick list of five technologies that affect their everyday lives. Then have them prioritize the technologies that have the most impact on their lives. Ask volunteers to present their top priority. Discuss how it might have been developed and who developed it, along with how and why the technology has changed over the years.

Preview the Phenomenon Have students study the illustration on pages 2–3 of the story, which shows a classroom, students, and a teacher. Encourage students to record any questions they have, reminding them that this story is part of a lesson on engineering design. Is there anything in the illustration that might benefit from a new design? Point out that their questions might change as they read through the story. Have them keep their questions handy and periodically check to see if any can be answered.

STANDARDS SUPPORTED

SEP

Asking Questions and Defining Problems

Planning and Carrying Out Investigations

DCI

ETS1.A Defining and Delimiting Engineering Problems

ETS1.B Developing Possible Solutions

ETS1.C Optimizing the Design Solution

CCC

Influence of Engineering, Technology, and Science on Society and the Natural World

Desk Designers (continued)

Discover

Read to Learn

The **Read to Learn** suggestions inside the book's front cover encourage students to interact with the book multiple times for different purposes.

Preview Students look for unfamiliar words and share them with a partner. New terms may include *engineering design process, criteria,* and *constraint.* Have students look up words they aren't sure about and notice how they are used in the context of the story.

Skim Students skim the illustrations in the story. Have them turn to a partner and share their predictions of what the story will be about.

Read As students read the story, ask them to look for connections to one of the following anchor chart skills. **Ask and Answer Questions, Text Structure, Retell**

Support Sense Making

Choose one or more of the following:

- Be sure students can identify the phenomenon presented on the opening pages of the story: Omar is frustrated because his books won't all fit in his desk and his tablet keeps sliding down the slanted desktop. The story follows his class's efforts to design the ideal school desk.
- Discuss the criteria and constraints Omar and his classmates identify. Project the *Engineering Design Process* graphic from the Teacher Guide introduction to this unit, and have students list the steps in the engineering design process that Omar's class follows under the three heads: Explore, Make and Test, Improve and Test.
- Encourage a student-led discussion of why Mr. Choppa had the students build prototypes of their desk designs. Guide students to an understanding that a prototype is usually made with cheaper materials than the final version. It allows you to test how your design will work and get feedback before spending a lot of time and money. Interested students can do research to find photos of prototypes of well-known buildings or everyday items and share them with the class.
- Remind students that engineers learn from their failures. In the engineering design process, there are no "right answers." Instead, getting things wrong is an important part of problem solving. Invite volunteers to describe failures they have experienced that led to a new understanding or other breakthrough.

Extend

Science Stretch

The **Science Stretch** suggestions inside the book's back cover help students think about what they read. Students can complete one or more as time allows.

Think of other criteria and constraints Omar and his classmates could have had for their design. **Sample answer:** Adjustable desk height could be another criteria.

Identify the steps the class took. Think of one more step they could have taken to improve their designs. **Sample answer:** We could redesign and retest our solution again.

What would be the criteria for an improved design of a technology in your classroom? **Sample answer:** If we improved what we write with, it would have to be easy to use and fit in our hands.

SOCIAL EMOTIONAL LEARNING

How would you tell someone in a nice way that you weren't going to use their idea? **Sample answer:** "I really like your idea, but this other solution better addresses the criteria."

Check for Comprehension Ask: *Why is it important that multiple solutions be developed and tested?* Be sure students understand that an engineering design solution might not actually work when tested. It is important to try several alternatives to improve the chances of success.

EXPLORATION 1 HANDS-ON ACTIVITY

Engineer It • Quick Tower Building

Activity Guide, pages 4–5

TIME ESTIMATE

SHORT ON TIME?

This activity can be done as a class exhibition with different volunteers coming up to try their luck.

Time-saving tips provide greater instructional flexibility.

POSSIBLE MATERIALS

- ☐ 10 sheets of construction paper
- ☐ 30 cm tape

PREPARATION

You might discuss how adjusting the criteria and constraints can help make the activity more successful or how adjusting the criteria and constrains can make the activity more difficult to complete. Ask what they would discover using different materials to build the tower, such as construction paper versus tissue paper or newspaper.

Preparation notes and easy-to-source materials typify each hands-on activity.

INVESTIGATIVE PHENOMENON
Part of designing solutions to problems is defining criteria and constraints.

Phenomenon Explained Students explore the **investigative phenomenon** in the context of a speed design challenge. They work together to build a paper structure quickly and then examine the criteria and constraints involved in building it.

Form a Question After reading the introductory paragraph, students should form a question about how criteria and constraints affect engineering design solutions. If students struggle to form a question, review that criteria are the features needed in the design and constraints are the limits on what the design can use. **Sample question:** How do criteria and constraints affect or limit design solutions?

Make and Test

Students work with partners to build the tallest structure they can in 10 minutes using 10 sheets of paper and 30 cm of tape. They then list the criteria and constraints, explaining which was hardest to meet and why. **Sample answers:** Our criteria was to build the tallest structure that wouldn't fall over and could support the weight of one book. Our constraints were that we only had 10 sheets of paper, 30 cm of tape, and 10 minutes. The hardest to meet were the criteria because the book was so heavy.

Remind students that a claim makes a statement that evidence and reasons must then show to be true.

- **Make a Claim** Students should state a claim about whether or not their designs met the criteria and constraints of the activity.
- **Evidence** Students should give details about the outcome of their activity to support their claim.
- **Reasoning** Students should explain why the evidence they give supports the claim they made.

Having students make claims aids in gathering student background knowledge.

FORMATIVE ASSESSMENT

MAKING SENSE OF PHENOMENA

Students gain understanding for an engineering design to meet criteria and constraints as they explore the **investigative phenomenon.** They should connect this to the **anchoring phenomenon** that a lightweight, nonelectric listening device would enhance a nature walk. Students should recognize that their listening device will have criteria and constraints to be met.

REMEDIATION If students struggle to connect the **investigative phenomenon** back to the **anchoring phenomenon,** have them consider what the words *lightweight* and *nonelectric* suggest about the criteria or constraints of the listening device they will design.

MAKING SENSE OF PHENOMENA IDEA ORGANIZER

After completing Exploration 1, students can fill in the **Idea Organizer** to summarize the connection between defining criteria and constraints as part of designing solutions to problems and the anchoring phenomenon that a lightweight, nonelectric listening device would enhance a nature walk.

Activity Outcome

Students should design and follow the steps of an engineering activity to determine if they have met criteria and constraints.

	Performance Indicators
	design a paper tower that meets certain criteria and constraints
	make a claim about whether their design met the criteria and constraints
	support the claim using evidence and reasoning

SOCIAL EMOTIONAL LEARNING

Have students think about how communication skills and teamwork helped them complete the hands-on activity. Encourage them to discuss how they communicated ideas, such as what their designs should look like, and how they divided up tasks, such as meeting criteria and constraints and finding the right language to identify them in their answers.

Embedded Social Emotional Learning activities and strategies build student confidence and healthy learning environments.

EXPLORATION 2 HANDS-ON ACTIVITY

Engineer It • Designing a Listening Device

Engineer It explorations allow students to apply the engineering design process.

Activity Guide, pages 6–9

TIME ESTIMATE

day 1 day 2

SHORT ON TIME?

The activity can be done as a whole-class activity to save the time individual groups would take to conduct it.

POSSIBLE MATERIALS

- ☐ plastic cups
- ☐ paper cups
- ☐ cloth scraps
- ☐ duct tape
- ☐ masking tape
- ☐ string
- ☐ scissors
- ☐ rubber tubing

Hands-on materials kits are available and easy to use.

PREPARATION

Rearrange the room to make space for students to spread out their designs and materials. Supply materials or have students themselves collect plastic and paper cups and cloth scraps from home for reuse in the activity.

Materials Alert Ensure that the materials students have selected are appropriate and will be used safely. Verify that students will not insert any materials into their ears, and observe head-lice precautions.

INVESTIGATIVE PHENOMENON
Engineers make and improve designs to meet needs or wants and solve problems.

Phenomenon Explained Students explore the **investigative phenomenon** by investigating how engineers design a solution to a particular problem that meets particular criteria and constraints.

Form a Question After reading the introductory paragraph about a hearing-enhancing device, students should form a question about designing such a device. If they have trouble forming a question, ask them to think about what their device needs to do. **Sample answer:** How can I make a hearing-enhancing device that satisfies the constraints and criteria?

STEP 1 Have students brainstorm in a group to identify criteria and constraints but then work independently to complete their sketches. **Sample answers:** Constraints: no batteries, does not go in ear; Criteria: enhances hearing, comfortable, durable, lightweight

STEP 2 Have students work independently to identify which materials they will use and explain how those materials will help meet the criteria and constraints. **Sample answer:** I will use plastic cups because they are more durable than paper cups and lighter than cloth scraps.

STEPS 3 and 4 Circulate around the room as students test and improve their devices. Check to make sure students accurately record and explain any design changes and improvements.

STEP 5 Have students evaluate their devices and even consider making second ones. Encourage students to discuss why they chose certain materials and how the type of materials affected the way their solution functioned.

- **Make a Claim** Students make a claim about how effective their designs were at meeting the activity goals.
- **Evidence** Students should support their claim with evidence about the device's operation.
- **Reasoning** Students should explain how their devices met constraints and criteria.

Each activity guides students through using evidence to either support or refute a claim.

FORMATIVE ASSESSMENT

MAKING SENSE OF PHENOMENA

Students gain understanding that engineers can make and improve designs to meet goals as they explore the **investigative phenomenon.** They should connect this to the **anchoring phenomenon** that a lightweight, nonelectric listening device would enhance a nature walk. Students should recognize that the listening device they design meets particular constraints and criteria to enhance a nature walk.

REMEDIATION If students struggle to connect the **investigative phenomenon** back to the **anchoring phenomenon,** have them think about how they used their designs to develop a listening device that met the criteria and constraints they listed.

MAKING SENSE OF PHENOMENA IDEA ORGANIZER

After completing Exploration 2, students can fill in the **Idea Organizer** to summarize the connection between engineers making and improving designs to meet needs or solve problems and the anchoring phenomenon that a lightweight, nonelectric listening device would enhance a nature walk.

Formative assessment and remediation options are provided at point of use.

Activity Outcome

Students should follow steps of an activity to design and improve a listening device that meets particular criteria and constraints.

Performance Indicators	
	design a listening device
	make a claim about how effective the device is
	support the claim using evidence of device performance

Activity rubrics aid in grading.

EXPLORATION 3

What Is Engineering?

Activity Guide, pages 10–11

TIME ESTIMATE

INVESTIGATIVE PHENOMENON
Engineers apply science and math ideas to make technology that solves problems like the desire for a listening device.

Phenomenon Explained Students explore the **investigative phenomenon** by learning how engineering contributes to new technology that meets human needs and desires.

Kitchen Tech

Direct students' attention to the photo of the kitchen. Help them recognize that the engineering contributions in choice *a* led to the glass panels in the door; those in choice *b* led to the cardboard box on the table; those in choice *c* led to the microwave oven and the stove.

Everyday Phenomenon **Engineers design everyday items to meet human needs and wants.**

Discuss how a paper towel holder like the one in the kitchen photo meets the desire of someone in the kitchen. Discuss and explore design elements the holder needs: sturdy wall mounting, roller rolling smoothly, room for a thick roll, and so on.

Have students read the text about engineering. Note that different types of engineers specialize in different types of design—electrical engineers, mechanical engineers—and that the first part of designing a solution is identifying what it must do.

Everyday Phenomenon **Engineering can improve the design of everyday items used in school.**

Have students identify an everyday problem involving something they use in school, such as trying to fit and organize items in a backpack. Discuss ideas for solving the problem.

FORMATIVE ASSESSMENT

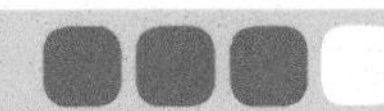

MAKING SENSE OF PHENOMENA

Students gain understanding of the role of engineering in designing and improving technology as they explore the **investigative phenomenon.** They should connect this to the **anchoring phenomenon** that engineers develop solutions to meet everyday needs and wants, such as the desire for a listening device to enhance a nature walk. Students should recognize that the first step of designing a solution is identifying the human needs and wants it must meet.

REMEDIATION If students struggle to connect the **investigative phenomenon** back to the **anchoring phenomenon,** have them consider how the items in the kitchen photo meet everyday needs and wants.

SOCIAL EMOTIONAL LEARNING

Brainstorm with students different sentence starters that they can use to provide constructive feedback.

- I like the way you ...
- You should continue to ...
- Can you tell me how you ...
- Next time you should ...
- You might want to ...
- I'm confused by ...

MAKING SENSE OF PHENOMENA IDEA ORGANIZER

After completing Exploration 3, students can fill in the **Idea Organizer** to summarize the connection between engineers making or improving technology to solve problems and the anchoring phenomenon that engineers develop solutions to meet everyday needs and wants, such as the desire for a listening device to enhance a hike.

EXPLORATION 4

How Engineers Solve Problems

Activity Guide, pages 12–18

TIME ESTIMATE

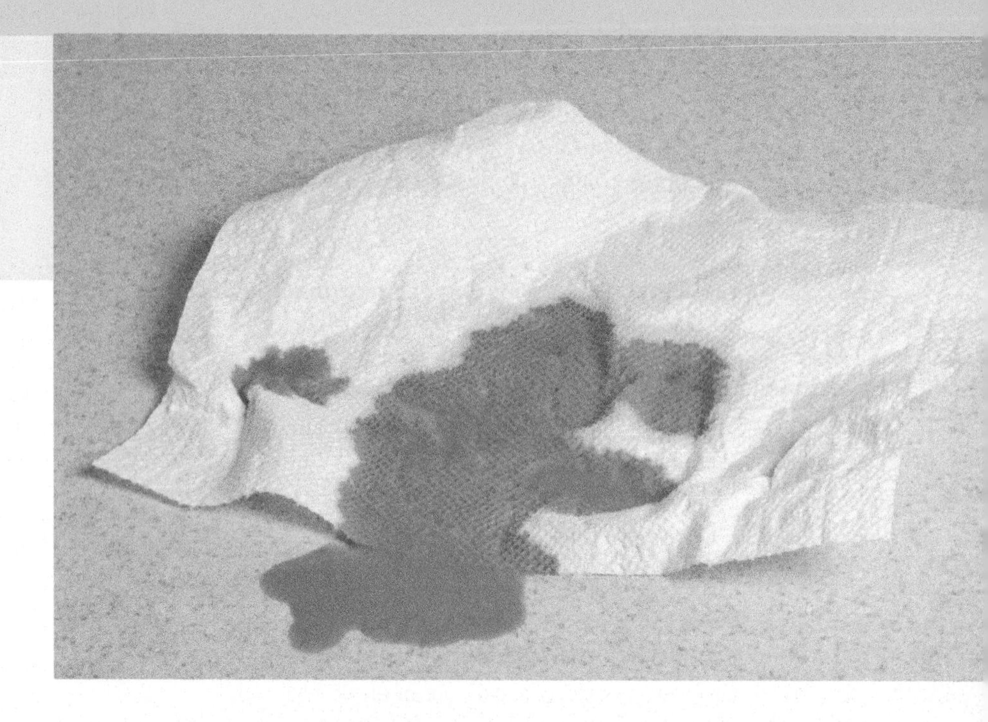

INVESTIGATIVE PHENOMENON
Engineers use a systematic approach to problem solving when designing listening devices or improving existing designs.

Phenomenon Explained Students explore the **investigative phenomenon** by going through the process engineers go through to solve problems when designing or improving technology.

Explore

Work with students to identify more items in the kitchen photo and the problems they solve. **Sample answer:** refrigerator, keeps food cool so it doesn't spoil; door, provides a way to get in and out of the house; table, provides a flat surface on which to eat and place items

Explain that throwaway paper towels were considered an improvement because rags had to be cleaned for reuse. Then ask in what way the three-bin laundry basket could be considered an improvement, and what constraints might keep people from buying one. **Sample answer:** It allows people to sort laundry. They may be constrained by cost or space considerations, or they may want something lightweight and portable.

Looking Back to Look Forward

Everyday Phenomenon **People use hearing aids to help them hear.**

Have students read about hearing devices and study the accompanying photos. Point out that today, instead of ear trumpets, many people use hearing aids. Discuss the design features people might look for in a hearing aid—small size, comfortable fit, good sound magnification, unnoticeable appearance, and so on.

SOCIAL EMOTIONAL LEARNING

Ask students how they manage disagreements about information when they brainstorm answers in a group. Help students recognize that they do not need to agree on the same answers and that different members of the group may offer valuable input when they give different responses.

Make

Stress that brainstorming means coming up with as many ideas as possible, even if some won't work. Engineers can consider how criteria and constraints will be accounted for by making a plan prior to making a prototype.

Test

Discuss why making and testing a prototype is important: Engineers would not want to move too far ahead with a design that doesn't work or isn't safe. Have students study the photo of the sound system test room and the three captions explaining its parts.

How Engineers Solve Problems (continued)

Activity Guide, pages 12–18, *cont.*

Your Fair Test

Ask how students would test only one variable in the sound system shown to make the test fair. **Sample answer:** I would test only one speaker system at a time. I would use the same source, sit in the same place, listen at the same volume, and keep other variables in the room setup as similar as possible.

Improve and Test

Stress that in the *Improve and Test* phase of design, engineers keep testing to improve the design as much as possible. **Sample answer:** Communication helps people consider more than one possible solution or strategy. It can help improve a design or plan.

Everyday Phenomenon **Communication between team members can help a team win a game.**

Students should connect the need for communication between members of an engineering design team to the same need in everyday situations, such as that of teammates on a volleyball or other sports team. Have students consider the ways sports team members communicate—hand signals, verbal signals, body movements, and so on.

The Engineering Design Process

Review with students the three phases of the design process.

- **Explore** The team defines the problem and learns more about it.
- **Make and Test** The team develops solutions by brainstorming and making a plan and then making, testing, and evaluating prototypes.
- **Improve and Test** The team improves the design by replanning, rebuilding, and retesting.

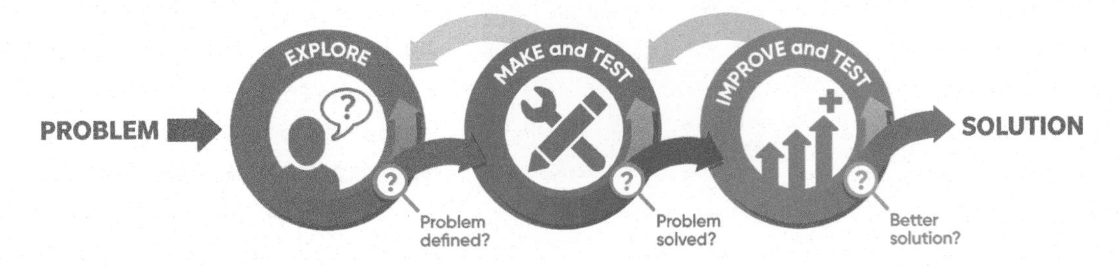

FORMATIVE ASSESSMENT

MAKING SENSE OF PHENOMENA

Students gain understanding of the process to use in designing their listening devices as they explore the **investigative phenomenon.** They should connect this to the **anchoring phenomenon** that a listening device would enhance a nature walk. Students should recognize that the process can help them design the best possible listening device to meet people's wants and needs.

REMEDIATION If students struggle to connect the **investigative phenomenon** back to the **anchoring phenomenon,** have them consider how designing and testing prototypes can help them develop the best possible listening device that would enhance a nature walk.

MAKING SENSE OF PHENOMENA IDEA ORGANIZER

After completing Exploration 4, students can fill in the **Idea Organizer** to summarize the connection between using a systematic approach to problem-solving when designing a solution or improving existing designs and the anchoring phenomenon that a lightweight, nonelectric listening device would enhance a nature walk.

LESSON

01

ONLINE-ONLY RESOURCES

Take It Further

The Take it Further section of each lesson showcases diverse People and Careers in Science & Engineering. These features show students the real-world applications of what they're learning.

Engage • Explore/Explain • Elaborate • Evaluate

TIME ESTIMATE

These Take It Further paths may be completed to enrich and extend students' comprehension of content covered within this lesson.

Online, students have different pathways from which to choose, increasing differentiation options.

ONLINE

People in Science & Engineering: Dr. Elena Rodriguez-Falcon

Students learn about Dr. Elena Rodriguez-Falcon, a Chief Academic Officer and Distinguished Professor in Engineering Education, and develop a lesson plan to teach an Engineering Design Process to younger students.

Hearing Aid History

Students explore the history of hearing aids and how their technology has developed over the years.

Careers in Science & Engineering: Acoustic Engineer

Students will learn about the careers of acoustic engineers. Acoustic engineers use their knowledge of sound and sound transmission to design spaces such as performance venues and recording studios.

FORMATIVE ASSESSMENT

Lesson Check

Activity Guide, pages 19–21

Engage • Explore/Explain • Elaborate • Evaluate

Online, self-checks are autograded, so students get immediate feedback.

Can You Explain It?

Now I know or think that . . .

Sample answer: Knowing about previous solutions can help prompt new solutions to a problem; engineering solutions need to meet a set of criteria and constraints; solutions are tested and retested to make sure they meet design goals.

After completing the lesson, use the **Making Sense Idea Organizer** to summarize the connections between the **investigative phenomena** and **anchoring phenomenon.**

MAKING CONNECTIONS

After students complete the lesson, they should be able to answer a question about how the need to protect eyes when the sun is high is similar to the need to enhance hearing. **Sample answer:** The solution is similar because it can be resolved with technology. Possible solutions are to wear a cap with a brim to shield the eyes or to wear sunglasses to block out the worst of the sun's rays.

Making Connections helps students apply what they have learned to a new real-world phenomenon.

Checkpoints

1. Good Design Practice: first, third, and fifth box; Poor Design Practice: second and forth box.
2. a—test solutions to design problems more than once; d—create more than one solution to the same problem
3. a—The lunchbox should be comfortable to carry for long periods of time; b—The lunchbox could keep the food colder; c—The lunchbox could use a special pocket for water bottles.
4. **Sample answer:** Karl should keep all other variables constant for the test to be fair.
5. test, retesting, many tries
6. **Sample answer:** Now that I have a functioning prototype, I will test it in a variety of different conditions. Since I know what my criteria and constraints are, I will find the materials that best meet the conditions in which my device will mainly be used and try different materials to see if they are the best choices.
7. **Sample answer:** multiple prototypes, retest them many times, one part

SOCIAL EMOTIONAL LEARNING

Have students reflect on the goals they set at the beginning of the lesson. Allow them to discuss how successful they were in meeting their goals.

UNIT

01 Review

Unit Reviews guide students to connect phenomena across the lessons.

Activity Guide, pages 22–24

The Unit review items enable you to assess student comprehension of core ideas, as well as cross cutting concepts and science and engineering practices.

1. **DOK 2** **d**—criteria and constraints

To answer this question, students need to understand constraints and criteria in the engineering design process.

2. **DOK 2** **Sample answer:** Criteria might include that the windows had to face the backyard and the doors should not block the view.

Students can correctly answer this question by recalling the definition of criteria.

3. **DOK 2** Criteria are desirable features of the solution, for example, a stool having 3 legs. Constraints are limitations on possible solutions, such as budgets, or available resources.

If students struggle to distinguish and define criteria and constraints, then they need to review Lesson 1, Exploration 3, Materials We Use.

4. **DOK 2** Steps as presented; 5, 3, 1, 7, 8, 2, 4, 6

1—Identify the problem to be solved.
2—Research existing related technology.
3—Design a prototype to solve the problem.
4—Build and test the prototype.
5—Evaluate test results.
6—Modify the prototype.
7—Retest the modified prototype.
8—Construct a final design.

If students struggle to place these steps in the correct order, have them refer to the Engineering Design Process.

5. **DOK 2** **a**—Evaluate test results. **b**—Modify the prototype. **d**—Retest the modified prototype.

Students must refer to the complete process in item 4. If they need further help, make sure they correctly order the steps in item 4.

6. **DOK 1** **Sample answer:** Learning what doesn't work is just as important as seeing what does work in a design solution. Learning from mistakes can provide information on what not to do in future designs.

If students struggle to answer this question, first have them reflect on what they learned in the Explorations when a design or prototype "failed."

7. **DOK 2** **a**—to ensure safety, **b**—to solve problems, **e**—to develop a final product

If students struggle to recognize good reasons for repeated engineering testing, have students think not only about engineering itself but also how it impacts society.

8. **DOK 2** **Sample answer:** An engineer can find things needing improvement by isolating what is causing failures. Failures are when a solution doesn't work, or doesn't meet the criteria.

If students struggle to answer this item, remind them that failure is part of the engineering design process.

Depth of knowledge (DOK) levels are noted for each question.

9. **DOK 3** Problem—need a shelf; Criteria—shelf must be 60 cm wide and 5 cm deep, must hold 3 picture frames; Constraints—can only cost $15, can only make 2 holes in the wall; Plan—brainstorm solutions for holding up picture frames and design styles and materials; build prototypes and test them; improve my design and test it until I find the best possible solution.

   If students struggle here, have them work in pairs and tell them to focus on defining a problem, any constraints, and the criteria.

10. **DOK 2** **a**—consider using other materials for the design; **b**—figure out what didn't go right with the design; **d**—understand that sometimes things don't work as planned

    If students struggle to recognize what to do when a solution fails, have them reflect on the design process. Guide them to consider each answer choice in light of what they could do when a solution does not work as planned.

Three-dimensional item-analysis charts show the specific standards coverage for each assessment question as you monitor student progress.

3D Item Analysis	1	2	3	4	5	6	7	8	9	10
SEP Asking Questions and Defining Problems	•	•		•	•	•			•	•
SEP Planning and Carrying Out Investigations	•			•			•		•	•
SEP Constructing Explanations and Designing Solutions		•	•		•	•		•	•	
DCI ETS1.A Defining and Delimiting Engineering Problems	•	•	•	•	•	•	•	•	•	•
DCI ETS1.B Developing Possible Solutions	•	•		•	•	•	•		•	•
DCI ETS1.C Optimizing the Design Solution				•	•	•	•	•	•	•
CCC Influence of Engineering, Technology, and Science on Society and the Natural World	•	•		•		•	•	•	•	

UNIT

02 Plant and Animal Structure and Function

Activity Guide, page 25

Unit Storyline

In Unit 1, students explored engineering design and learned about form and function. In Unit 2 they explore plant and animal structures and their functions. They develop and use models to explore how organism structures support survival, growth, and reproduction. Then they use their findings to engage in argument from evidence. By exploring how senses work, students can explain how an organism's senses help it to survive.

LESSON 1 **PE 4-LS1-1**

Plant Parts and How They Function

Activity Guide. pages 26–43

Students explore the **anchoring phenomenon** that the apple tree has structures that change through the seasons.

SEP Engaging in Argument from Evidence; Developing and Using Models

DCI **LS1.A** Structure and Function

CCC Systems and System Models

LESSON 2 **PE 4-LS1-1**

Animal Parts and How They Function

Activity Guide, pages 44–63

Students explore the **anchoring phenomenon** that the glass frog has structures and behaviors that allow it to live, survive, and reproduce in the rain forest.

SEP Engaging in Argument from Evidence

DCI **LS1.A** Structure and Function

CCC Systems and System Models

LESSON 3 **PE 4-LS1-1, 4-LS1-2, 4-PS4-2**

How Senses Work

Activity Guide, pages 64–83

Students explore the **anchoring phenomenon** that bats use their senses to find food.

SEP Engaging in Argument from Evidence; Developing and Using Models

DCI **LS1.A** Structure and Function; **LS1.D** Information Processing; **PS4.B** Electromagnetic Radiation

CCC Systems and System Models; Cause and Effect

Unit Review Activity Guide, pages 84–86

UNIT 02

AT A GLANCE

Online-Only Resources

Supporting Unit Resources

You Solve It SUPPORTS LESSON 2

Break It Down is a virtual lab that offers practice in support of **Performance Expectation 4-LS1-1.** Students will investigate the internal structures of animals and explore how digestive systems adapt to the foods that animals eat.

- SEP Analyzing and Interpreting Data
- DCI **LS1.A** Structure and Function
- CCC Systems and System Models

Unit Project SUPPORTS LESSONS 1 AND 2

Plant and Animal Partnerships provides students an opportunity to practice aspects of **Performance Expectation 4-LS1-1.** Small groups of students will research and then present ways that plant and animal structures work together to allow pollination to occur.

- SEP Analyzing and Interpreting Data; Engaging in Argument from Evidence
- DCI **LS1.A** Structure and Function
- CCC Systems and System Models

Unit Performance Task SUPPORTS LESSON 3

Communication of the Wild provides an opportunity for students to practice or be assessed on aspects of **Performance Expectations 4-LS1-1** and **4-LS1-2.** Students analyze data to look for observable patterns that can tell them more about how animals use their senses.

- SEP Analyzing and Interpreting Data; Constructing Explanations and Designing Solutions
- DCI **LS1.A** Structure and Function; **LS1.D** Information Processing
- CCC Patterns

Language Development

This worksheet is used as students progress through the unit's lessons. As they come to a highlighted vocabulary term, they should come back to this chart and fill in the blanks with words or phrases.

Updates and additional student and teacher resources can be found online. Check back often!

Supporting Lesson Resources

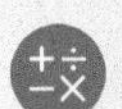

Do the Math!

Lesson 1 Reason Quantitatively
Lesson 2 Heart Beat; One Fish, Two Fish
Lesson 3 Senses

Language SmArts

Lesson 1 Writing Opinion Pieces; Interpreting Visual Information; Multiple Sources
Lesson 2 Compare External Structure; Compare and Contrast Body Systems; Form an Opinion; Interpret Information
Lesson 3 Identifying Main Ideas and Detail; Present It! Opinion

Take It Further

Lesson 1 Careers in Science & Engineering: Botanist; People in Science & Engineering: Clayton Anderson; Brrr!
Lesson 2 People in Science & Engineering: Henry Gray and Vanessa Ruiz; Careers in Science & Engineering: Biomimetic Engineering; Balanced Parts
Lesson 3 Extreme Senses; Careers in Science & Engineering: Optometrist; People in Science & Engineering: Dr. Kale Edmiston

MAKING SENSE OF PHENOMENA

This idea organizer is used to make sense of the following **anchoring phenomena**:
Lesson 1—The apple tree has structures that change through the seasons.
Lesson 2—The glass frog has structures and behaviors that allow it to live, survive, and reproduce in the rain forest.
Lesson 3—Bats use their senses to find food.

This organizer also connects the investigative phenomena back to the anchoring phenomenon in each lesson.

Assessment

Unit Readiness Check: Are You Ready?
Lesson Quizzes: Can You Apply It?
Unit 2 Test
Performance-Based Assessment

Assessments are available in an editable, printable format or can be administered and auto-graded online.

LESSON 01

Plant Parts and How They Function

ANCHORING PHENOMENON

The apple tree has structures that change through the seasons.

ENGAGE Can You Explain It?
Students observe and ask questions about an apple tree. They answer the Can You Explain It? question to describe what they observe about the tree's structure and how it produces fruit.

EVALUATE Lesson Check
Students gauge their understanding of the anchoring phenomenon.

HANDS-ON ACTIVITY

EXPLORATION 1 Flower Power 50 min

Investigative Phenomena Flowers have different structures involved in reproduction.

Students connect back to the **anchoring phenomenon** by investigating the structures of a flower and their role in plant reproduction.

HANDS-ON ACTIVITY

EXPLORATION 2 Slurp! 60 min

Investigative Phenomena Plants have internal structures that allow them to take in and transport water.

Students connect back to the **anchoring phenomenon** by investigating and modeling the structures involved in the transport of water in a plant.

EXPLORATION 3 Plant Structures Have Special Functions 60 min

Investigative Phenomena Plants have external and internal structures that support survival and growth.

Students connect back to the **anchoring phenomenon** by understanding that plants have internal and external structures with specific functions.

EXPLORATION 4 How Plants Change 30 min

Investigative Phenomena Plants react to their environments.

Students connect back to the **anchoring phenomenon** by understanding that plants have behaviors that allow them to react to changes in their environment.

Making 3D Connections

The anchoring phenomenon in this lesson supports students' understanding of and application of this Next Generation Science Standard.

Building to the Performance Expectations

4-PE-LS1-1 Construct an argument that plants and animals have internal and external structures that function to support survival, growth, behavior, and reproduction.

SEP

Engaging in Argument from Evidence Construct an argument with evidence, data, and/or a model. *(Explorations 1, 2, 3, 4)*

Developing and Using Models Use a model to test interactions concerning the functioning of a natural system. *(Exploration 2)*

DCI

LS1.A Structure and Function Plants and animals have both internal and external structures that serve various functions in growth, survival, behavior, and reproduction. *(Explorations 1, 2, 3, 4)*

CCC

Systems and System Models A system can be described in terms of its components and their interactions. *(Explorations 1, 2, 3)*

Vocabulary

Word Wall A word wall, anchor chart, or Language Development chart can be used to support vocabulary.

structure a physical part of living things

spore a reproductive structure of some plants, such as mosses and ferns, that can form a new plant.

You may want to include additional academic terms such as *absorb, conditions, infer, transport,* and *visible* and any other terms students might struggle with.

Language Development Prompt students to complete the chart when they come to these highlighted terms within the lesson and to add their own terms as they come across unknown science terms.

Anchor Chart As you progress through the unit, you may want to make a vocabulary-based anchor chart using the Language Development chart as a guide that can be displayed and filled out as a whole group during each lesson.

LESSON

01 Plant Parts and How They Function

Activity Guide, pages 26–43

Students can engage in the Can You Explain It? content by observing the photograph or by exploring the corresponding video online.

ONLINE

View a video of apple picking in an orchard.

ANCHORING PHENOMENON

The apple tree has structures that change through the seasons.

PHENOMENON EXPLAINED

Apple trees change as seasons change. In the spring, apple trees sprout new leaves and flowers, and these external changes are supported by internal structures that plants have.

Lesson Objective

Students will gather evidence about the function and structure of plant parts. They will use this evidence to construct an argument that these parts work together in a system in order for the plant to grow, reproduce and survive.

Support Discovery

The following prompts can be used to guide student-led discovery.

I notice . . .

After observing the photograph or watching the video, students should record what they noticed about the tree.

Sample answer: I notice that the tree has green leaves and red fruit.

I wonder . . .

After observing the photograph or watching the video, students should record what they want to find out more about the apples on the trees.

Sample answers: I wonder how/when/why a tree makes apples.

Can You Explain It?

In the Can You Explain It?, students make an initial claim that explains the **Anchoring Phenomenon.**

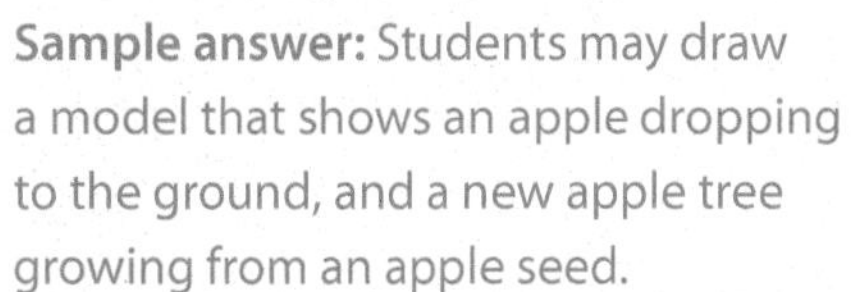

Sample answer: Students may draw a model that shows an apple dropping to the ground, and a new apple tree growing from an apple seed.

In the lesson, students gather evidence about plant structures and their functions. This will enable them to give a more complete explanation of the **Anchoring Phenomenon** at the end of the lesson.

Alternative Phenomenon

If students are unfamiliar with the concept of seasonal changes, you could use dandelions as an example of how plants change according to environmental conditions. Most students know about the yellow flowers that turn into white puffs. Dandelions open in the morning when there is light, and close up at night when it is dark and usually cooler. Show a short time-lapse video of a dandelion as the flower turns into a seed head. How soon dandelions grow and turn to seed depends on conditions such as temperature and precipitation in their environment. Their life cycle lasts from 9 to 15 days.

SOCIAL EMOTIONAL LEARNING

Guide students to reflect on their goals from previous lessons and on any feedback they received from their teachers or peers. Then have each student set a personal goal for this lesson and make a plan for how to achieve the goal. Throughout the lesson, take daily breaks for students to track their progress in meeting their goals. As students move from lesson to lesson, they can continue to work towards their initial goals or set new ones.

LESSON 01

FUNomenal READER

Sugaring Season

WHEN TO USE

SCIENCE 

- Anchoring Phenomenon / Alternative Phenomenon
- Options for ELA Instruction
- Build on Prior Knowledge
- Preview the Phenomenon
- Read to Learn
- Support Sense Making
- Science Stretch
- Check for Comprehension

Option 1 Use before students begin the lesson in the Activity Guide to provide an engaging model to introduce the lesson's phenomenon.

Option 2 Use after students have completed the Activity Guide to reinforce students' understanding of the lesson phenomenon by exploring a related phenomenon.

ELA 20 min

- Options for ELA Instruction
- Build on Prior Knowledge
- Read to Learn

Option 3 To use during designated ELA Reading time for independent reading, whole-class instruction, or small-group instruction, look for this icon: ELA

Plan

ANCHORING PHENOMENON / ALTERNATIVE PHENOMENON

The anchoring phenomenon in the Activity Guide is *The apple tree has structures that change through the seasons,* and the main example is a boy picking an apple from a tree. The FUNomenal Reader presents a similar phenomenon (*Maple trees produce sap, which can be made into syrup*), and the example is "sugaring season" in a maple grove. Both present the same science concepts and cover the same standards but with different phenomena. Guide students to draw connections between the two situations and to understand the underlying principle: plant parts are used for survival, growth, reproduction, and behavior.

Options for ELA Instruction 

Choose one of the following anchor chart options and project it or print copies. Then display and introduce the chart before reading the text. Revisit the chart after reading the text and encourage students to discuss how the skill connects to the text.

Ask and Answer Questions Use the *Ask and Answer Questions Anchor Chart* to discuss how Eleanor and her brother learn about sugaring season by asking questions. Help students notice how one question and its answer lead to another question.

Following and Giving Instructions Display the *Following and Giving Instructions Anchor Chart* as student pairs write out the steps involved in tapping a maple tree to get its sap. Then partners can take turns reading the instructions and acting them out.

Text Features Have students refer to the *Text Features Anchor Chart* to help them identify the various text features in this story. As they page through the story, students should notice photos, diagrams, and illustrations. Guide them to understand that these visual features help explain ideas in the text.

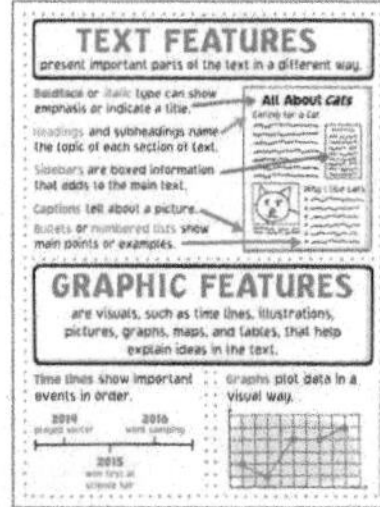

Preview

ELA **Build on Prior Knowledge** Ask if any students have seen "helicopter seeds" twirling to the ground. Invite volunteers to share their experiences. Students may know that these seeds come from maple trees, but they may not realize they are the fruit of the maple. The winged shape is known as a double samara. The papery tissue around the seed helps carry it away from the tree as the wind blows.

Preview the Phenomenon Ask students to study the illustration on page 6 of the story, which shows a group of people at a maple syrup festival. Guide students to notice the setting (a wooded area) and season (late winter / early spring). Encourage students to record the first questions that come into their minds. Point out that their questions might change as they read through the story. Have them keep their questions handy and periodically check to see if they can answer any.

STANDARDS SUPPORTED

SEP

Engaging in Argument from Evidence

Developing and Using Models

DCI

LS1.A Structure and Function

CCC

Systems and System Models

Sugaring Season (continued)

Discover

Read to Learn

The **Read to Learn** suggestions inside the book's front cover encourage students to interact with the book multiple times for different purposes.

Preview Students look for unfamiliar words and share them with a partner. New terms may include *sap, lobe, notch,* and *spile.* Have students look up words they aren't sure about and notice how they are used in the context of the story.

Skim Students skim the illustrations, photos, and diagrams. Have them turn to a partner and share their predictions of what the story will be about.

Read As students read the story, ask them to look for connections to one of the following anchor chart skills. **Ask and Answer Questions, Following and Giving Instructions, Text Features**

Support Sense Making

Choose one or more of the following:

- Encourage students to pay attention to plants in their homes, at school, or in their neighborhood. Ask them to make a list of plants they observe in a day or on their commute to school. Challenge them to identify the leaves, stems, roots, and other plant parts. Invite volunteers to share their findings with the class.
- Ask students why the maple syrup festival in the story takes place in late winter. Discuss how daytime and nighttime temperatures affect the flow of sap in maple trees. Sap usually starts to flow in February and March, when daytime temperatures rise above freezing and nighttime temperatures fall below freezing. Help students understand that as temperatures increase in the spring, the sugar content decreases.
- Do a demonstration of (or have student groups perform) the experiment Eleanor describes in the story. Place carnations or stalks of celery in containers of water with red dye. Help students see how the dye moves from the water through the stems to the flowers or leaves. Relate this to sap moving through a maple tree.
- Help students understand that the Ojibwe people originally lived along the east coast of North America, from the Carolinas and into Canada. Have interested students do research to learn more about Ojibwe culture and traditions and report their findings to the class.

Extend

Science Stretch

The **Science Stretch** suggestions inside the book's back cover help students think about what they read. Students can complete one or more as time allows.

Make a drawing of a fruit tree and identify three different structures. Provide gardening books and magazines for students to use as resources.

Make a model of a plant structure and explain how the structure is related to its function. **Sample answer:** I made a model of a stem, which connects the plant's roots to its leaves.

Write a one-page essay about another plant that is used to make a sweetener. Student research may lead to sugar beets, agave, birch trees, coconuts, sorghum grasses, and other plants.

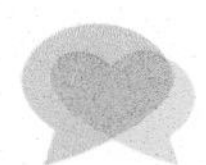

SOCIAL EMOTIONAL LEARNING

What are two things you learned from this story? Share your answer with a classmate. Remind students to listen respectfully to their classmate's ideas. **Sample answer:** I learned that maple syrup comes from maple trees. I also learned that it takes a lot of sap to make a bottle of syrup.

Check for Comprehension Have students refer to the diagrams on pages 6 and 7 and make a claim about which part of a maple tree they think is most important for plant growth. They should cite three facts as evidence to support their claim.

EXPLORATION 1 | HANDS-ON ACTIVITY

Flower Power

Activity Guide, pages 28–31

TIME ESTIMATE

SHORT ON TIME?

This activity can be done as a whole class activity to save time.

POSSIBLE MATERIALS

- ☐ flowers on a stem
- ☐ newspaper or paper plates
- ☐ scissors
- ☐ tweezers
- ☐ gloves
- ☐ hand lens

Materials Alert Ask students about any plant allergies before conducting this activity. Tulips or lilies work best for dissection.

PREPARATION

Review safety precautions with students before they begin. Remind them to wear gloves when handling the flowers and to be careful with sharp objects such as scissors and tweezers.

INVESTIGATIVE PHENOMENON

Flowers have different structures involved in reproduction.

Phenomenon Explained Students explore the **investigative phenomenon** by observing and recording the structures found in flowers. Students use their observations to support a claim about how the flower structures work together as a system.

Form a Question After they learn about pollination, students should form a question about the structures that make up a flower. If students struggle to form a question, have a class brainstorming session. **Sample answers:** What are the different parts that make up a flower? What are their functions? How does a flower help a plant reproduce?

Parts of a Flower

Students choose words from a diagram of flower structures to complete sentences. sepals; anther; ovule.

STEP 1 Students observe a flower and identify its parts.

STEP 2 Students use the recording space to draw the flower structures they identified. Student drawings should show and properly identify sepals, petals, stamen, anther, pistil, and ovule.

Student groups share and explain differences or similarities among the data. **Sample answers:** Although we identified the same structures in each of our flowers, some of them looked different depending on what type of flower we had.

- **Make a Claim** Claims should indicate that a flower is made up of many different parts that protect it or help the plant to reproduce.
- **Evidence** Students should cite their observations from the activity as evidence, such as identifying male and female flower parts.
- **Reasoning** Students should explain that identifying male and female parts indicates that their function is to help the plant to reproduce.

FORMATIVE ASSESSMENT

MAKING SENSE OF PHENOMENA

Students gain understanding that flowers have different structures involved in reproduction as they explore the **investigative phenomenon.** They should connect this to the **anchoring phenomenon** that plants have various parts that work together in a system. Students should understand that, before a tree makes fruit, it makes flowers that attract insects that help it to reproduce.

REMEDIATION If students struggle to connect the **investigative phenomenon** back to the **anchoring phenomenon,** ask them if they have ever seen flowers on trees and how they think they might compare to the flowers they observed in this activity.

MAKING SENSE OF PHENOMENA IDEA ORGANIZER

After completing Exploration 1, students can fill in the **Idea Organizer** to summarize the connection between flowers having different structures involved in reproduction and the anchoring phenomenon that plants have various parts.

Activity Outcome

Students should record observations about the structures in flowers in order to observe that flowers have different structures involved in reproduction.

Performance Indicators	
	record observations about the structures in flowers
	make a claim that flowers have different structures involved in reproduction that work together as a system
	support the claim using observations as evidence

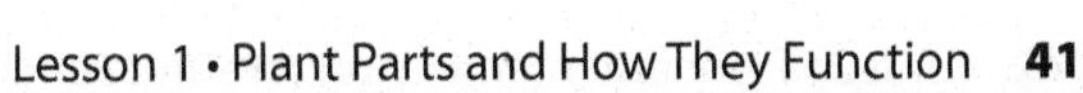

EXPLORATION 2 HANDS-ON ACTIVITY

Slurp

Activity Guide, pages 32–34

TIME ESTIMATE

day 1 day 2

SHORT ON TIME?

Have different group members take on different roles during the two days of the investigation, then work together as a team to build their 3D model.

POSSIBLE MATERIALS

- ☐ celery
- ☐ food dye
- ☐ plastic knife
- ☐ water
- ☐ clear plastic cup
- ☐ newspaper
- ☐ arts and crafts materials

Materials Alert Red or blue food coloring works best for this activity. A fresh cut should be made on the bottom of the stalk to remove any clogged or collapsed vessels. Tall cups should be used. Cut the stalks so that they are not so top heavy that they will tip the cups over. Warn students that food coloring stains clothes and skin.

PREPARATION

In advance, gather arts and crafts materials, including straws, clay, or small bits of plastic tubing. Make them available to students for use in making 3D models.

INVESTIGATIVE PHENOMENON
Plants have internal structures that allow them to take in and transport water.

Phenomenon Explained Students explore the **investigative phenomenon** by planning a fair test to explain how plants transport water. Students gather evidence to support their explanation and make a 3D model of a plant's water system.

Form a Question After they consider how plants use water, students should form a question about the transportation of water and nutrients through a plant. If students struggle to form a question, suggest that they review the different parts of a plant with which they are already familiar. **Sample answer:** How does a plant move water and nutrients from its roots to its leaves? What does the inside of a plant stem look like?

STEP 1 Students plan a fair test to investigate how plants transport water, listing needed materials and writing or drawing the procedure. Review and approve students' plans before they conduct their tests. **Sample answer:** 1. Fill a cup with water. 2. Add several drops of food coloring. 3. Place a celery stalk in the water. 4. Make observations 24 hours later. 5. Use a plastic knife to cut the celery in half cross-wise and make observations.

Make Observations Students record how the celery appears before and after they investigate. **Sample answer:** Before I placed the celery in the water, the stem and leaves were green. After I placed it in the water with the blue dye, the stem and leaves had a blue tint.

- **Make a Claim** Claims should indicate that water moves through the stem of a plant up to its leaves through tube-shaped structures.
- **Evidence** Students should cite as evidence that they observed the tube-shaped structures containing dye when they cut the celery stalk.
- **Reasoning** Students should explain that seeing dye concentrated in the tube-shaped structures suggests that the colored water made its way inside the plant through those structures.

Make a Model Students make a 3D model of a plant's water transport system. Remind students that this does not have to be a working model, but that they should identify the system's structure and function.

FORMATIVE ASSESSMENT

MAKING SENSE OF PHENOMENA

Students gain understanding that plants have internal structures that allow them to take in and transport water as they explore the **investigative phenomenon.** They should connect this to the **anchoring phenomenon** that plants have internal structures that support change throughout the seasons. Students should understand that, in order to grow fruit, a tree needs nutrients and water. A plant must be able to transport this water and nutrients from its roots up to the branches where fruit grows.

REMEDIATION If students struggle to connect the **investigative phenomenon** back to the **anchoring phenomenon,** remind them that an apple tree has structures such as stems that have the same function as similar structures in a celery plant.

Activity Outcome

Students should design and follow the steps of a fair test in order to observe that plants have a tube system that transports water throughout the plant. They state and support a claim, and make a 3D model of a plant's water system.

Performance Indicators	
	plan and conduct a fair test to explain how plants transport water
	make and support a claim that plants have a tube system that transports water throughout the plant
	make a 3D model of a plant's water transport system

MAKING SENSE OF PHENOMENA IDEA ORGANIZER

After completing Exploration 2, students can fill in the **Idea Organizer** to summarize the connection between plants having internal structures that allow them to take in and transport water and the anchoring phenomenon that plants have internal structures that support change throughout the seasons.

SOCIAL EMOTIONAL LEARNING

As a class, discuss why good communication and teamwork is important. Help students understand that being able to effectively verbalize their thoughts and work with others to solve problems can help them in achieving their goals. **Sample answer:** We took turns speaking when we came up with our fair test and decided what each group member would do during the investigation.

EXPLORATION 3

Plant Structures Have Special Functions

Activity Guide, pages 35–38

TIME ESTIMATE

INVESTIGATIVE PHENOMENON
Plants have external and internal structures that support survival and growth.

Phenomenon Explained Students explore the **investigative phenomenon** by exploring the functions of external and internal structures of plants that together create a system to help the plant survive. Students also use evidence gathered to support their claim about why trees make fruit.

What Do Plant Parts Do?

Students explore similar structures in plants and their similar functions. Have students discuss why it is important that the structures work together to help the plant survive and reproduce.

Similar but Different

Students compare sets of plant structures and identify their main functions.

Roots, leaves (needles), and stems growth

Flowers, cones, and spores reproduction

Thorns, bark, and spines protection

It's What's Inside that Counts

Students explore the tube system inside plants that transports water and food. Discuss the diagrams and, if needed, clarify that the arrows show the direction of movement of water and/or food.

Everyday Phenomenon **A plant is a system of many parts.**

Have students work with a partner to discuss the **everyday phenomenon** of a plant being a whole system made up of many different parts that work together. Have partners identify what other parts besides the tubes help a plant get water and make food. (Roots get water from the soil and leaves make food.) Help them as needed to connect this to the **anchoring phenomenon** that plants have structures that support changes through the seasons.

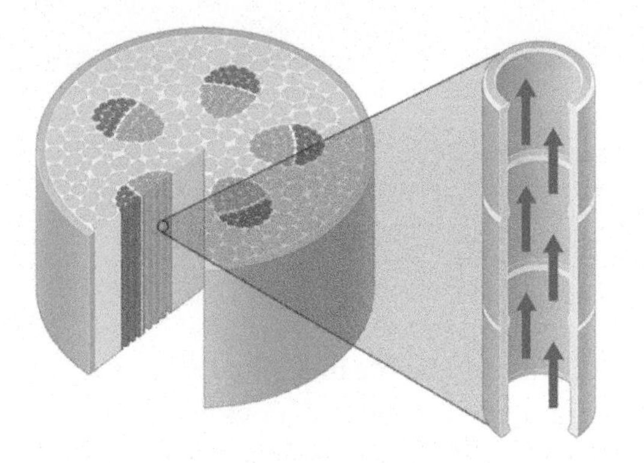

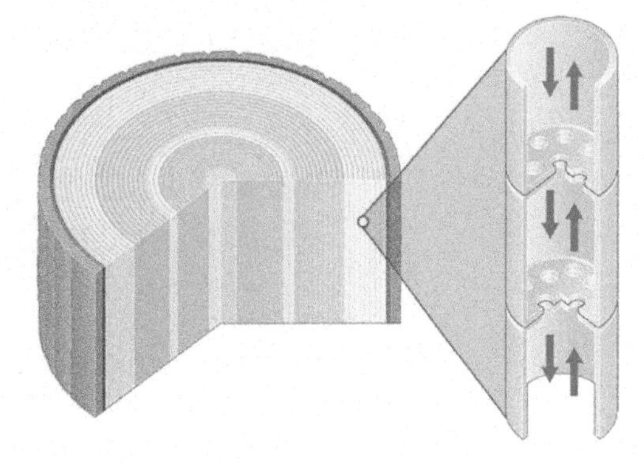

FORMATIVE ASSESSMENT

MAKING SENSE OF PHENOMENA

Students gain understanding that plants have external and internal structures that support survival and growth as they explore the **investigative phenomenon**. They should connect this to the **anchoring phenomenon** that plants have structures that support changes through the seasons. Students should understand that fruit develops from a flower on a plant, and its function is to protect and help spread seeds for reproduction.

REMEDIATION If students struggle to connect the **investigative phenomenon** back to the **anchoring phenomenon**, have them identify the structures of the apple tree pictured on Activity Guide page 26.

MAKING SENSE OF PHENOMENA IDEA ORGANIZER

After completing Exploration 3, students can fill in the **Idea Organizer** to summarize the connection between plants having external and internal structures that support survival and growth and the anchoring phenomenon that plants have structures that support changes through the seasons.

EXPLORATION 4

How Plants Change

Activity Guide, pages 39-40

TIME ESTIMATE

winter

summer

spring

autumn

INVESTIGATIVE PHENOMENON
Plants react to their environments.

Phenomenon Explained Students explore the **investigative phenomenon** by investigating how plants react and move in response to their environments. They also use evidence gathered to support their claim about why trees make fruit.

Seasonal Changes

Everyday Phenomenon **Some trees drop their leaves in the fall.**

Use the images in this Exploration to discuss the **everyday phenomenon** of seasonal changes, and guide students in connecting it to the **anchoring phenomenon** that plants have structures that change through the seasons. Ask students if they have noticed differences in how trees look from one season to the next. Have students discuss their answers. If you live in a climate that lacks distinct seasons, ask students why the trees that live there might not change dramatically in appearance.

Students infer factors that cause a tree to lose its leaves. Sample answer: Fewer hours of daylight might cause a tree to drop its leaves.

SOCIAL EMOTIONAL LEARNING

Have students work together in small groups to brainstorm ideas to answer the question. Encourage students to listen respectfully to others even when their opinions or ideas differ.

How Do You Grow?

Students learn about and predict how plants respond to light and gravity.

Response to light: students should circle image a

Response to gravity: students should circle image b

Everyday Phenomenon **A plant's structures help it survive.**

Use the images in this Exploration to discuss the **everyday phenomenon** of plant structures and survival, and guide students in connecting it to the **anchoring phenomenon** that plants have structures that change through the seasons.

Remind students that the parts of a plant's system work together to help it survive.

Ask: How do a plant's movements help it survive? Sample answer: Roots move toward a water source and leaves move toward a light source so the plant can produce food.

Materials Alert Encourage students to use free online resources to find additional evidence of plants responding to light and gravity. Suggest they search "free slow motion (or time-lapse) phototropism" and "free slow motion geotropism."

FORMATIVE ASSESSMENT

MAKING SENSE OF PHENOMENA

Students gain understanding that plants react to their environments as they explore the **investigative phenomenon.** They should connect this to the **anchoring phenomenon** that plants have structures that change through the seasons. Students should understand that trees only have fruit at certain times of the year because they need certain conditions such as day length and temperature to flower and make fruit.

REMEDIATION If students struggle to connect the **investigative phenomenon** back to the **anchoring phenomenon,** have a class discussion about seasonal changes students have observed in your local area and in local plants.

MAKING SENSE OF PHENOMENA IDEA ORGANIZER

After completing Exploration 4, students can fill in the **Idea Organizer** to summarize the connection between plants reacting to their environments and the anchoring phenomenon that plants have structures that change through the seasons.

LESSON 01

ONLINE-ONLY RESOURCE

Take It Further

Engage • Explore/Explain • **Elaborate** • Evaluate

TIME ESTIMATE

These Take It Further paths may be completed to enrich and extend students' comprehension of content covered within this lesson.

ONLINE 

Careers in Science & Engineering: Botanist

Botany is a broad science. There are nearly 400,000 known species of plants, with more discovered each year. Botanists are called by different names based on the plants they study. Jenny Xiang, PhD is an Asian American botanist who studies plant responses to climate change. Marie-Ann Van Sluys, PhD and Mariana Cabral de Oliveira, PhD are Latin American botanists who used genetics to determine how Pierce's disease was being spread. Pedro Acevedo, PhD is a Latin American botanist who studies soapberry plants and develops field guides.

People in Science & Engineering: Clayton Anderson

In this feature, students learn about scientist and engineer Clayton Anderson's work with plants in zero gravity.

Brrr!

Students explore what happens to help some plants to survive the winter.

FORMATIVE ASSESSMENT

Lesson Check

Activity Guide, pages 41–43

Can You Explain It?

Now I know or think that . . .

Sample answer: Structures are the physical parts of living things. Plants respond to seasonal changes, such as amount of daylight. As seasons change, a plant begins budding new leaves, forming flower buds, or dropping leaves. The roots, stem and leaves work together as a system to help the plant grow.

After completing the lesson, use the **Making Sense Idea Organizer** to summarize the connections between the **investigative phenomena** and **anchoring phenomenon.**

MAKING CONNECTIONS

After students complete the lesson, they should be able to answer a question about an alternative phenomenon to explain how the structures of a plant that grows low to the ground might compare to the structures found on a tree. **Sample answer:** A plant that grows closer to the ground probably has similar structures to those found in a tree, but it doesn't need the same structural support (longer roots, thick bark) that a tree does.

Checkpoints

1. a—food; c—water
2. a—Roots absorb water, which plants need to make food.
3. b—Leaves produce food using sunlight, and food moves down the tubes to the rest of the plant.
4. light; gravity
5. a—bark; c—spines; d—thorns
6. stem—growth; roots—growth; flowers—reproduction; spines—protection
7. **Sample answer:** Both thorns and spines protect the plant. They are sharp and can injure an animal that tries to eat the plant.
8. **Sample answer:** Roots absorb water that plants need to grow.

SOCIAL EMOTIONAL LEARNING

Have students reflect on the concepts they have explored about plant parts and their functions. With a partner, have students discuss one or more concepts they were surprised to learn during their various explorations. Have volunteers take turns sharing the key points of their discussion.

LESSON

02 Animal Parts and How They Function

ANCHORING PHENOMENON

The glass frog has structures and behaviors that allow it to live, survive, and reproduce in the rain forest.

ENGAGE **Can You Explain It?**
Students observe and ask questions about the structures and behaviors of glass frogs. They answer the Can You Explain It? question to identify what they will gather evidence about in the lesson.

EVALUATE **Lesson Check**
Students gauge their understanding of the anchoring phenomenon.

HANDS-ON ACTIVITY

EXPLORATION 1 **Dinner Is Served**

Investigative Phenomenon Animals have different structures they use to catch and eat food.

Students connect back to the **anchoring phenomenon** by designing an investigation to explore the structures that animals use to eat.

HANDS-ON ACTIVITY

EXPLORATION 2 **Courtship Displays**

Investigative Phenomenon Animals have external structures that function to support behavior and reproduction.

Students connect back to the **anchoring phenomenon** by investigating the decorative external structures and behaviors of animals and their relation to reproduction.

EXPLORATION 3 **Body Building**

Investigative Phenomenon Animals have external structures that serve functions in growth and survival.

Students connect back to the **anchoring phenomenon** by exploring the external structures that function to allow animals to grow, survive, and reproduce.

EXPLORATION 4 **Inside Out**

Investigative Phenomenon Animals have internal structures that serve functions in growth, survival, and reproduction.

Students connect back to the **anchoring phenomenon** by exploring the internal structures that function to allow animals to grow, survive, and reproduce.

Making 3D Connections

The anchoring phenomenon in this lesson supports students' understanding of and application of these Next Generation Science Standards.

Building to the Performance Expectations

4-PE-LS1-1 Construct an argument that plants and animals have internal and external structures that function to support survival, growth, behavior, and reproduction.

SEP

Engaging in Argument from Evidence Construct an argument with evidence, data and/or a model. *(Explorations 1, 2, 3, 4)*

DCI

LS1.A Structure and Function Animals have both internal and external structures that serve various functions in growth, survival, behavior, and reproduction. *(Explorations 1, 2, 3, 4)*

CCC

Systems and System Models A system can be described in terms of its components and their interactions. *(Explorations 1, 3, 4)*

Vocabulary

Word Wall A word wall, anchor chart, or Language Development chart can be used to support vocabulary.

You may want to include academic terms such as *behavior, circulatory, courtship, determine, display, digestive, external, flexible, internal, respiratory, spiral, transparent,* and other terms students might struggle with.

Language Development Prompt students to complete the chart when they come to these academic terms within the lesson and to add their own terms as they come across unknown science terms.

Anchor Chart As you progress through the unit, you may want to make a vocabulary-based anchor chart using the Language Development chart as a guide that can be displayed and filled out as a whole group during each lesson.

LESSON

02 Animal Parts and How They Function

Activity Guide, pages 44–63

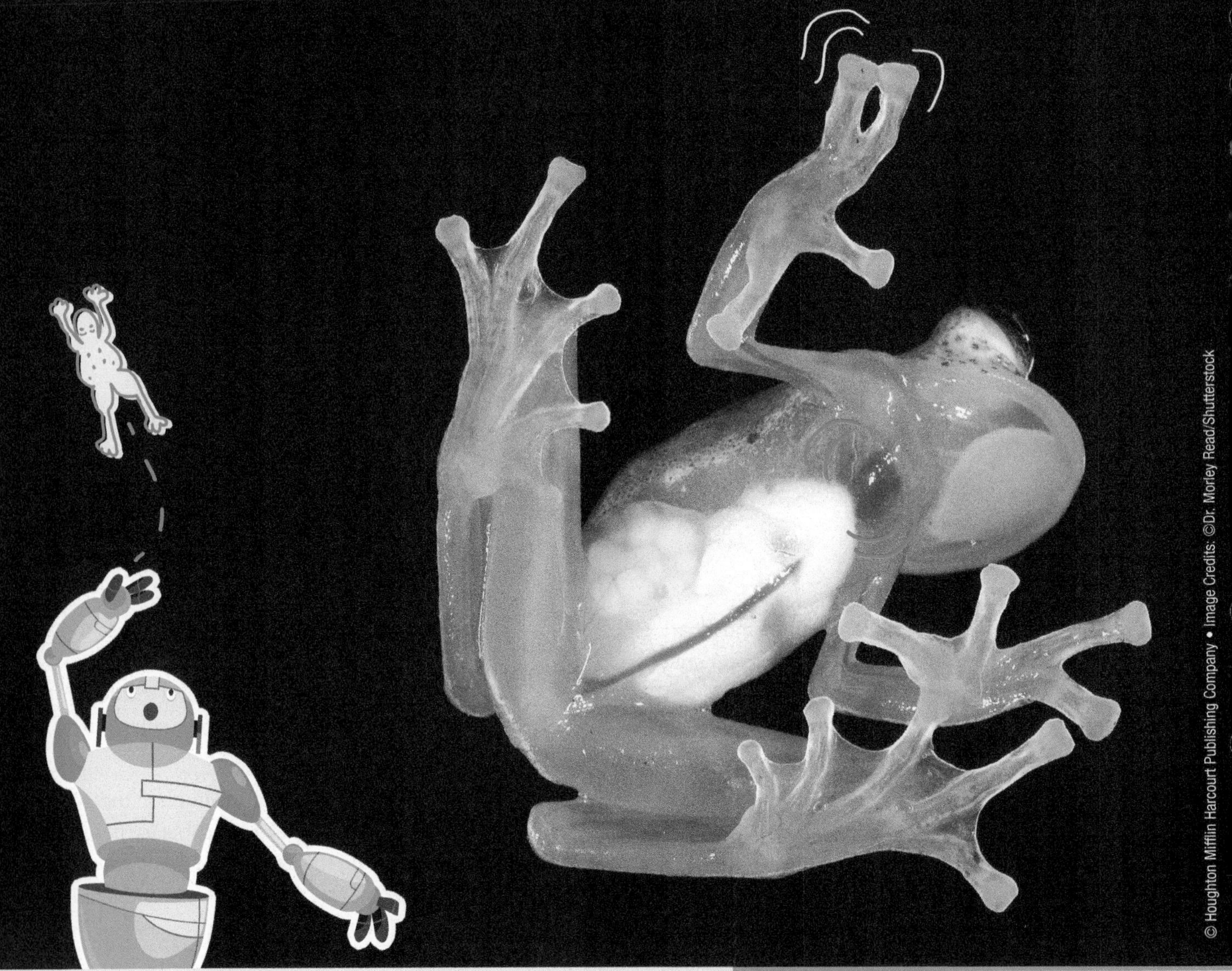

Students can engage in the Can You Explain It? content by observing the photograph or by exploring the corresponding video online.

ONLINE

View a video related to glass frogs in the rain forest.

ANCHORING PHENOMENON

The glass frog has structures and behaviors that allow it to live, survive, and reproduce in the rain forest.

PHENOMENON EXPLAINED

The glass frog has external and internal structures and behaviors that serve various functions in growth, survival, and reproduction.

Lesson Objective

Students will gather evidence about the function and structure of animal parts in order to construct an argument that these parts work together as a system to enable the animal to survive, grow, reproduce, and behave.

Support Discovery

The following prompts can be used to guide student-led discovery.

I notice . . .

After observing the photograph or watching the video, students should record what they noticed about the glass frogs. If students struggle to record observations, ask them to think about how the glass frog hides from predators.

Sample answer: Because you can see through the frog's skin, a predator might not recognize it's a frog.

I wonder . . .

After observing the photograph or watching the video, students should record what they want to find out more about the internal and external structures of glass frogs.

Sample answer: I wonder how the structures inside and outside the frog work together.

Alternative Phenomenon

If students are unfamiliar with glass frogs, guide them to think of other animals that use obvious structures to survive in unique environments, such as the lion in the African savanna, or the prairie dog in the American grasslands. You can bring examples via video clips or magazine pictures so that students can make observations of how these animals use their internal and external structures to live and survive.

Can You Explain It?

In the Can You Explain It?, students make an initial claim that explains the **Anchoring Phenomenon.**

Sample answer: Students may draw a doodle that shows a glass frog using its translucent coloration to hide on a large tropical leaf. Or they might model how a frog uses its mouth and tongue to capture food to eat.

Students will gather evidence about animal parts and how they function. This will enable them to give a more complete explanation of the **Anchoring Phenomenon** at the end of the lesson.

SOCIAL EMOTIONAL LEARNING

Guide students to reflect on their goals from previous lessons and on any feedback they received from their teachers or peers. Then have each student set a personal goal for this lesson and make a plan for how to achieve the goal. Throughout the lesson, take daily breaks for students to track their progress in meeting their goals. As students move from lesson to lesson, they can continue to work towards their initial goals or set new ones. If students struggle setting goals for this lesson, share with them some of the following ideas: identifying animal parts and their functions, or ensuring everyone in the group has a chance to share an idea, or persevering when a topic is difficult.

LESSON 02

FUNomenal READER

Sea Star Survival

WHEN TO USE

SCIENCE 30 min 

- Anchoring Phenomenon / Alternative Phenomenon
- Options for ELA Instruction
- Build on Prior Knowledge
- Preview the Phenomenon
- Read to Learn
- Support Sense Making
- Science Stretch
- Check for Comprehension

Option 1 Use before students begin the lesson in the Activity Guide to provide an engaging model to introduce the lesson's phenomenon.

Option 2 Use after students have completed the Activity Guide to reinforce students' understanding of the lesson phenomenon by exploring a related phenomenon.

ELA 20 min

- Options for ELA Instruction
- Build on Prior Knowledge
- Read to Learn

Option 3 To use during designated ELA Reading time for independent reading, whole-class instruction, or small-group instruction, look for this icon: ELA

Plan

ANCHORING PHENOMENON / ALTERNATIVE PHENOMENON

The anchoring phenomenon in the Activity Guide is *The glass frog has structures and behaviors that allow it to live, survive, and reproduce in the rain forest.* The main example is a glass frog with its visible internal structures. The FUNomenal Reader presents a similar phenomenon (*Sea stars have internal and external structures that help them grow, survive, and reproduce in their environment*) and features a girl who wants to learn more about sea stars. Both present the same science concepts and cover the same standards but with different phenomena. Guide students to draw connections between the two situations and to understand the underlying principle: animals have parts that are used for growth, survival, behavior, and reproduction.

Options for ELA Instruction 

Choose one of the following anchor chart options and project it or print copies. Then display and introduce the chart before reading the text. Revisit the chart after reading the text and encourage students to discuss how the skill connects to the text.

Research In the story, Simone does online research to learn more about sea stars. Have students refer to the *Research Anchor Chart* as a reminder of reliable sources to use when doing their own research.

Context Clues Use the *Context Clues Anchor Chart* if students struggle to understand the meaning of some words or terms in the story. Remind them to break each one down into its basic components. For example, *carnivore* can be broken down into *carni-*, which means "flesh," and *vore,* which means "eater."

Visualize Use the *Visualize Anchor Chart* to help draw students into the content of the story. Have them take two minutes to close their eyes and think of what it would feel like to touch a sea star, as Simone does in the story. Discuss how the photos, illustrations, and text give them clues.

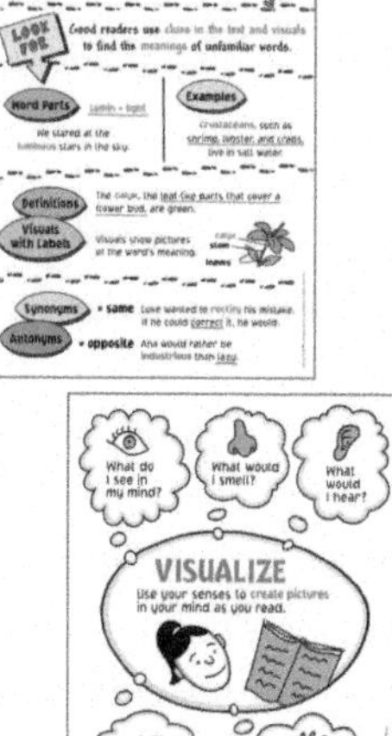

Preview

ELA **Build on Prior Knowledge** Ask students what they already know about sea stars, sometimes erroneously called starfish. Have volunteers share what they know. Explain that a sea star is an echinoderm (ih-KY-nuh-duhrm), not a fish. Ask if students can name any other animals with more than four arms or legs. (Examples include octopus, millipede, spider, and crab.)

Preview the Phenomenon Ask students to study the illustration on page 2 of the story, which shows a mother and daughter exploring a tide pool. The daughter is holding a sketch pad. Encourage students to record any questions they have about what the characters might be doing. Point out that their questions might change as they read through the story. Have them keep their questions close by and periodically check to see if they can answer any.

STANDARDS SUPPORTED

SEP

Engaging in Argument from Evidence

DCI

LS1.A Structure and Function

CCC

Systems and System Models

Sea Star Survival (continued)

Discover

Read to Learn 

The **Read to Learn** suggestions inside the book's front cover encourage students to interact with the book multiple times for different purposes.

Preview Students look for unfamiliar words and share them with a partner. New terms may include *invertebrate, carnivore,* and *zooplankton.* Have students look up words they aren't sure about and notice how they are used in the context of the story.

Skim Students skim the illustrations and photos in the story. Have them turn to a partner and share their predictions of what the story will be about.

Read As students read the story, ask them to look for connections to one of the following anchor chart skills. **Research, Context Clues, Visualize**

Support Sense Making

Choose one or more of the following:

- Be sure students can identify the phenomenon presented on the opening pages of the story: Simone is exploring a tide pool and wonders how sea stars are able to survive there. The story is about her efforts to learn more about sea stars and how they use their body parts for growth, survival, behavior, and reproduction.
- Encourage a student-led discussion of how a sea star finds its prey and eats. Have them focus on the sea star's body parts, such as its tube feet and unusual stomach structure. Students can pantomime how the sea star catches and eats food.
- Simone finds out that sea stars can grow a new arm to replace a missing one. Have small groups learn more about limb regeneration in animals. Groups can present their findings to the class.
- Have students identify an animal that is common to the local environment. Discuss and then have students investigate how the internal structures of the animal are adapted to the available food that animal eats. Have students determine how each animal would be affected as a result of direct and indirect changes to the natural system due to the growth of human populations.

Extend

Science Stretch

The **Science Stretch** suggestions inside the book's back cover help students think about what they read. Students can complete one or more as time allows.

Make a model of one of the structures described in this story. Provide paper, markers, clay, and other supplies for students to use.

Identify one internal and one external structure of your favorite animal. Describe its function in growth, survival, or reproduction. **Sample answer:** A hamster has very sharp hearing so it can sense danger from predators. It has cheek pouches that let it store food to help it survive.

Write a blog post about another animal that lives in tidal pools. Compare it with a sea star. Provide print and online resources for students to use for research.

SOCIAL EMOTIONAL LEARNING

What is the most interesting fact you learned in this story? Share your answer with a classmate. **Sample answer:** The most interesting fact was that 97% of all animals don't have backbones.

Check for Comprehension Have students write several sentences that explain how a sea star's body parts help it survive.

EXPLORATION 1 HANDS-ON ACTIVITY

Dinner Is Served

Activity Guide, pages 46–49

TIME ESTIMATE

SHORT ON TIME?
Assign each pair of students one set of materials to model how animal mouth structures relate to their feeding habits.

POSSIBLE MATERIALS

- ☐ plastic spoons
- ☐ paper clips
- ☐ paper
- ☐ chopsticks
- ☐ marbles
- ☐ cup
- ☐ tweezers
- ☐ paper straws
- ☐ eye droppers
- ☐ paper plates

PREPARATION
Gather materials in advance. The materials listed in the Activity Guide are a starting point to represent different ways of taking in food. Students can use a broad variety of materials to model external animal structures for their investigation. Expand provided materials based on what is available, and honor student requests for other materials as appropriate.

INVESTIGATIVE PHENOMENON
Animals have different structures that they use to catch and eat food.

Phenomenon Explained Students explore the **investigative phenomenon** by classifying the structures animals use for feeding. They plan and execute a fair test to explain the relationship between animals' external structures and how and what they eat. Students gather evidence to support their explanation.

Form a Question After observing the photograph, students should form a question about the structures an animal uses to eat. If students struggle to form a question, ask them to consider what structures common household pets use to eat. **Sample answer:** How is the structure of an animal's mouth parts related to the food it eats?

Time to Eat!

Help students connect the specialized mouth structures (or lack thereof) of the six animals on the page with what they eat.

Animal	What does it eat?	What's your evidence?
mountain lion	animals	sharp teeth
antelope	plants	flat teeth
female mosquito	blood	piercing mouth part
golden eagle	animals	sharp beak
frog	insects	large mouth/sticky tongue
giant tubeworm	nutrients in the water	no mouth

STEP 1 Students make a plan to answer a question about how external structures are involved in the way animals catch and eat food. Procedures should include a plan to model an animal's mouth parts and how the model mouth will be used to "eat" food.

STEP 2 Students carry out their plan and record their results, then develop a presentation tool to best display their findings.

- **Make a Claim** Claims should indicate how an animal's mouth structure relates to its feeding habits.
- **Evidence** Students should cite as evidence observations from the activity that show how mouth parts help animals catch and eat food.
- **Reasoning** Students should explain their reasoning by connecting a claim about how an animal's survival is related to its mouth and how and what it eats.

FORMATIVE ASSESSMENT 

MAKING SENSE OF PHENOMENA

Students gain understanding that the structure of an animal's mouth aids how it catches and eats food in the **investigative phenomenon.** They should connect this to the **anchoring phenomenon** that animals have parts, or structures, that allow them to catch and eat food, and thus survive. The glass frog has a wide mouth to help it catch and eat food in the rain forest.

REMEDIATION If students struggle to connect the **investigative phenomenon** back to the **anchoring phenomenon**, have them consider what structures they use to eat, such as jaws and teeth.

MAKING SENSE OF PHENOMENA IDEA ORGANIZER

After completing Exploration 1, students can fill in the **Idea Organizer** to summarize the connection between external structures involved in animal feeding and the anchoring phenomenon that the glass frog has external structures that help it live and survive in the rain forest.

Activity Outcome

Students should design and follow the steps of a fair test in order to observe how mouth structures affect how animals catch and eat food.

Performance Indicators	
	record observations about how mouth structures function
	use presentation tools to share results
	make a claim that external structures help animals survive
	support the claim using data as evidence

EXPLORATION 2 **HANDS-ON ACTIVITY**

Courtship Displays

Activity Guide, pages 50–51

TIME ESTIMATE

SHORT ON TIME?

To save on research time, consider assigning each pair of students one specific animal ahead of time. Alternatively, students could pick one animal to present about rather than two.

PREPARATION

In advance, establish allotments of computer and technology time for research and multimedia work. Consider developing a set of class rules to govern the use of these shared materials. Finally, prior to class presentations, initiate a class discussion about the behavior of good audience members.

INVESTIGATIVE PHENOMENON
Animals have external structures that function to support behavior and reproduction.

Phenomenon Explained Students explore the **investigative phenomenon** by planning and conducting research about animals that use internal and external structures as well as courtship displays to find a mate. Students make a multimedia presentation about their findings.

Form a Question After observing the photographs, students should form a question about different ways animals attract mates. If students struggle to form a question, ask them to name characteristics that would suggest a mate's ability to survive in the environment—such as signs of health or strength. **Sample answer:** What are some unusual courtship displays that animals perform?

Research Student partners research other animals that use courtship displays to find a mate. Then they choose two and develop a multimedia presentation to share their discoveries with the class.

- **Make a Claim** Claims should indicate that specific animals use particular courtship displays to help them attract a mate.
- **Evidence** Students should cite evidence from their research that shows how specific animals use courtship displays to attract mates.
- **Reasoning** Students should explain their reasoning that survival of the species becomes possible when courtship displays help animals select the strongest and healthiest mate for reproduction.

FORMATIVE ASSESSMENT 

MAKING SENSE OF PHENOMENA

Students gain understanding that animals have external structures that function to support courtship displays that aid reproduction as they explore the **investigative phenomenon.** They should connect this to the **anchoring phenomenon** that animals have external structures and behaviors that aid in reproduction—and thus survival. Male glass frogs have a specific vocal call that they use to attract females for reproduction.

REMEDIATION If students struggle to connect the **investigative phenomenon** back to the **anchoring phenomenon,** have them discuss attributes of glass frogs—size, weight, etc.—most likely to attract mates.

Activity Outcome

Students should research courtship displays and develop a multimedia presentation to share their discoveries.

Performance Indicators	
	record details about how animals' courtship displays aid in finding a mate in order to reproduce
	make a claim that these courtship displays help animals reproduce
	support the claim using collected research as evidence
	use presentation tools to share findings in an interesting way

MAKING SENSE OF PHENOMENA IDEA ORGANIZER

After completing Exploration 2, students can fill in the **Idea Organizer** to summarize the connection between the external structures that animals use for courtship displays and the anchoring phenomenon that animals including glass frogs have structures that govern their behaviors and allow them to survive and reproduce in their environments.

SOCIAL EMOTIONAL LEARNING

Students contemplate examples of good communication and teamwork during the exploration. Sample answers: We took turns when talking and split up tasks equally.

Have students discuss how they can use their communication skills to give good feedback on other students' presentations. The following sentence frames promote positive feedback after presentations:

- One thing that the team did really well was ___________.
- I think the team could improve their presentation if they ___________.

EXPLORATION 3

Body Building

Activity Guide, pages 52–57

TIME ESTIMATE

Materials Alert Consider providing groups of students with additional photos of wildlife. Based on the photos, have them draw inferences about how these animals might use structures, such as external covering and limbs to help them survive in the environments in which they live.

INVESTIGATIVE PHENOMENON
Animals have external structures that serve functions in growth, survival, and reproduction.

Phenomenon Explained Students explore the **investigative phenomenon** by examining how animals use external structures to protect themselves, move, and reproduce within their environments.

Take Cover

Everyday Phenomenon **Camouflage helps a person or animal blend into different environments.**

Students should connect the **everyday phenomenon** about the function of camouflage with the **anchoring phenomenon** that the glass frog's translucent skin is one of the structures that helps it hide from predators and survive in the rain forest. Have students list or research other animals that use camouflage to survive in their environment.

Discuss how the body covering of each pictured animal helps it survive in its habitat. Have students compare and contrast the frog and the polar bear. Ask them to explain how fur and feathers help animals stay warm in a way that other animal coverings do not. Remind students that skin—or fur or feathers—are structures that protect animals in their habitat.

Moving Parts

Discuss how external structures such as legs, wings, and fins, help animals move. Ask students how the ability to move—and move quickly—might help animals survive.

Moving through the Environment

Students identify whether certain animals move best on land, in air, or in water. air, water, land

Discuss the difference in limbs of each of the animals pictured. Have students use evidence to argue why the legs of the okapi are better adapted to land that those of the other two animals. For example, the thin, long leg structures enable the okapi to move quickly on land but would not be useful for flying or swimming.

How Animals Reproduce

Student explore different methods that animals use to reproduce.

Comparing Reproduction Methods

Students compare the reproduction methods of different animals by completing a fill-in-the-blank activity. reproduction, fertilizes, internal

SOCIAL EMOTIONAL LEARNING

Have students discuss their answers to the *Land, Water, or Air?* activity in their groups. Encourage groups to come up with other examples of animals that are well-suited to moving on land, in air, or in the water. Remind them to respectfully listen to others even when their opinions or ideas differ. The following questions can help students self-evaluate their work within the group:

- What ideas did you share with the group?
- How did you encourage other group members to share their ideas?
- How did you resolve any conflicts in the group?

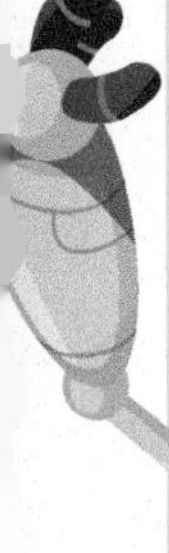

FORMATIVE ASSESSMENT

MAKING SENSE OF PHENOMENA

Students gain understanding of how body structures protect animals, help them move, and help them reproduce as they explore the **investigative phenomenon.** They should connect this to the **anchoring phenomenon** that animal structures have functions that help animals grow, survive, and reproduce. The glass frog has an outer covering that protects it from predators and parts that help it move and reproduce.

REMEDIATION If students struggle to connect the **investigative phenomenon** back to the **anchoring phenomenon,** have them choose an animal featured in the exploration and detail its parts and their functions.

MAKING SENSE OF PHENOMENA IDEA ORGANIZER

After completing Exploration 3, students can fill in the **Idea Organizer** to summarize the connection between the internal and external structures animals use to live, grow, move, and reproduce in their environments and the anchoring phenomenon that the glass frog has structures, both internal and external, that help it stay protected, grow, move, and reproduce in its environment.

EXPLORATION 4

Inside Out

Activity Guide, pages 58-60

TIME ESTIMATE

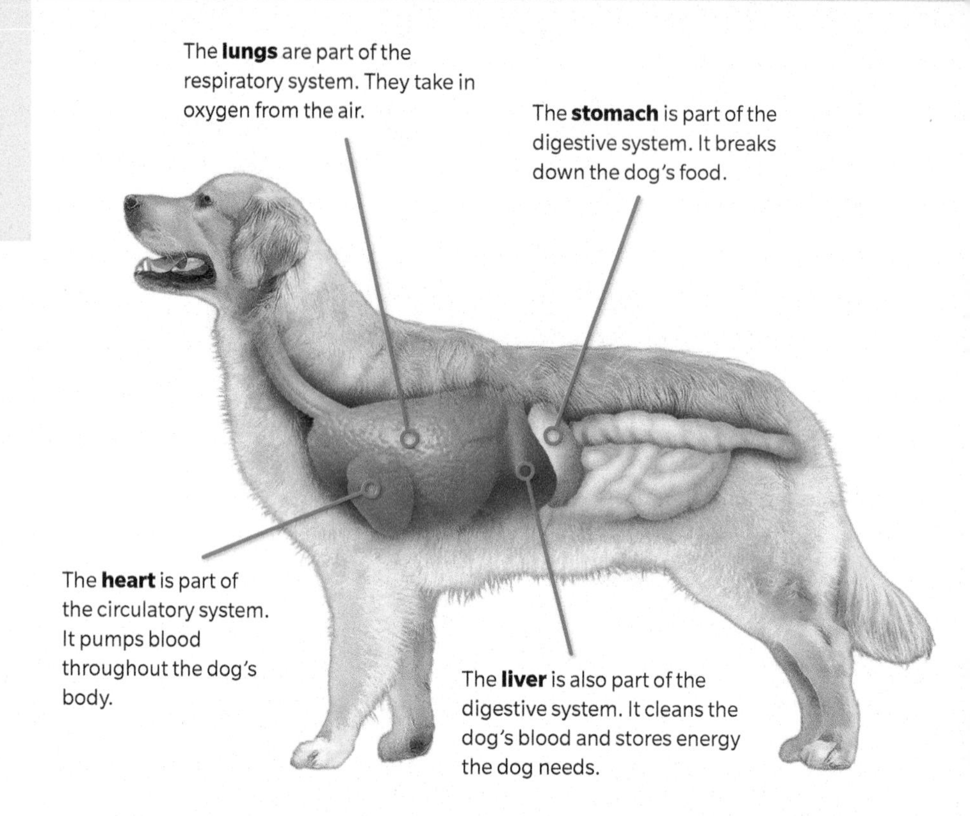

INVESTIGATIVE PHENOMENON
Animals have internal structures that serve functions in growth, survival, and reproduction.

Phenomenon Explained Students explore the **investigative phenomenon** by observing and describing the internal structures that make up bodily systems, including the circulatory, respiratory, and digestive systems. They explore the ways these systems vary among different types of animals. As a starting point, students look at a dog's lungs, stomach, heart, and liver—internal structures that humans share.

Get In My Belly!

Make sure that students understand digestion as the means of extracting needed nutrients from food. Remind them that the digestive system is made up of components, or parts, that have individual functions. Together the components carry out a function that the individual parts could not.

Encourage students to write or articulate sentences comparing and contrasting the digestion of the featured animals. Have them use the terms *stomach*, *intestine*, and *liver* in their descriptive sentences.

Heart to Heart

After students investigate the circulatory system of the featured animals, initiate a discussion about the human heart. How is it alike and different from the other animals' hearts? For example, how many chambers does the human heart have? Does it help to regulate temperature? Does it have arteries and veins that carry blood around the body?

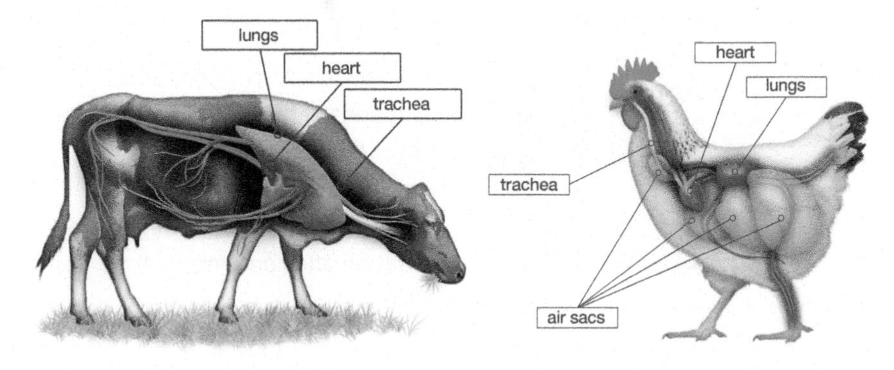

SOCIAL EMOTIONAL LEARNING

Have small groups discuss food allergies, such as nut allergies and lactose- and gluten-intolerance, as well as food preferences, including veganism, vegetarianism, and general food aversions. Then ask:

- How can you make sure that everyone feels welcome at the table?
- How does communication about food help prevent conflicts, even sickness?
- How do you show respect for other people's food choices and traditions?

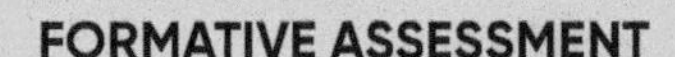

FORMATIVE ASSESSMENT

MAKING SENSE OF PHENOMENA

Students gain understanding of animals' internal structures and systems that serve functions in growth and survival as they explore the **investigative phenomenon.** They should connect this to the **anchoring phenomenon** that animals such as the glass frog have internal structures that make up its circulatory, respiratory, and digestive systems, which serve functions in growth and survival.

REMEDIATION If students struggle to connect the **investigative phenomenon** back to the **anchoring phenomenon,** have them recall what internal processes a glass frog depends on for survival and how these processes relate to internal systems.

MAKING SENSE OF PHENOMENA IDEA ORGANIZER

After completing Exploration 4, students can fill in the **Idea Organizer** to summarize the connection between the internal structures and systems that animals depend on for survival and the anchoring phenomenon that glass frogs have internal structures and systems, including circulatory, respiratory, and digestive systems, that allow them to live and grow so they can survive and reproduce.

LESSON

ONLINE-ONLY RESOURCE

02 Take It Further

Engage • Explore/Explain • **Elaborate** • Evaluate

TIME ESTIMATE

These Take It Further paths may be completed to enrich and extend students' comprehension of content covered within this lesson.

ONLINE 

People in Science & Engineering: Henry Gray and Vanessa Ruiz

In this feature, students read about Henry Gray, famous for publishing *Gray's Anatomy* in 1858. Still in use as a medical reference, the book gives detailed descriptions and illustrations of human body structures and systems. They also learn about Vanessa Ruiz, a medical illustrator and artist who combines medical illustration and contemporary art.

Careers in Science & Engineering: Biomimetic Engineering

In this activity, students learn about biomimetics, the study of using the structures of living things to design human-made devices. They research and design a biomimetic device.

Balanced Parts

Students will distinguish between and answer questions about bilateral and radial symmetry in animals.

FORMATIVE ASSESSMENT

Lesson Check

Activity Guide, pages 61–63

Engage • Explore/Explain • Elaborate • Evaluate

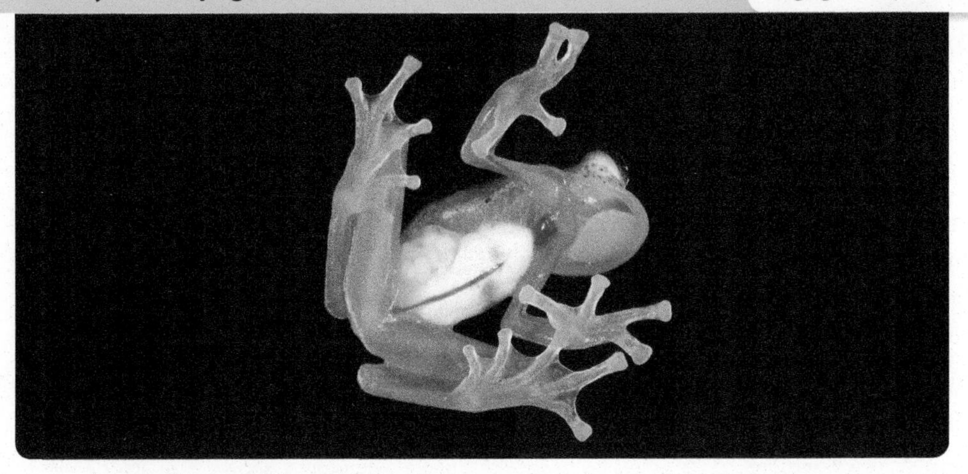

Can You Explain It?

Now I know or think that . . .

Sample answer: The glass frog has legs to jump and thin skin that helps it breathe air in the rain forest. It also has a wide mouth that it uses to eat, and a heart that moves blood through its body.

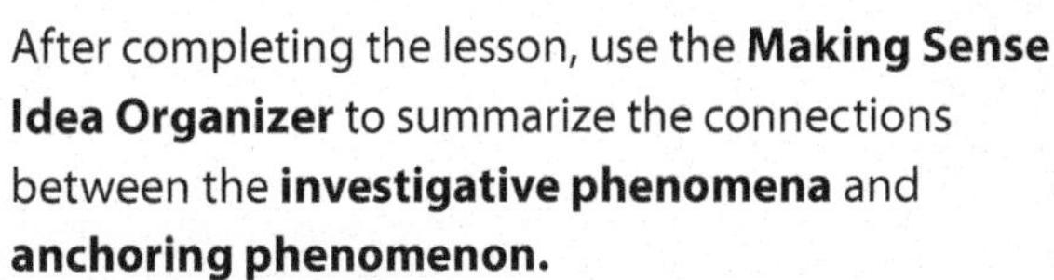

After completing the lesson, use the **Making Sense Idea Organizer** to summarize the connections between the **investigative phenomena** and **anchoring phenomenon.**

MAKING CONNECTIONS

After students complete the lesson, they should be able to answer a question about an alternative phenomenon to compare and contrast the body structures of a parrot fish with a glass frog.

Sample answer: A parrot fish and a glass frog have similar body structures. But a parrot fish has structures that help it live and survive underwater, such as gills and fins, that a glass frog does not have.

Checkpoints

1. Circulatory system: heart, lungs, arteries, veins; Digestive system: intestines, liver, stomach
2. Student drawings should show spines, thick skin, or some other structure that functions to support protection in animals.
3. eating: a snake's fangs, an ant's mouth parts, a frog's tongue; movement: a seagull's wings, a tiger's padded feet, an ostrich's long legs
4. male/female, fertilized
5. L–R, top–bottom: a, d, b, c
6. **Sample answer:** If the shark was missing any part of its digestive system, it wouldn't be able to survive because it needs the full system in order to eat, break down, and digest food.

SOCIAL EMOTIONAL LEARNING

Have students reflect on the concepts they have explored about animal structures and systems and how these structures serve various functions in growth, survival, and reproduction. Have groups of partners develop a list of additional questions they would like to investigate. Then have each group or pair choose one. Have students set short-term goals to help them find answers to the question. Help students identify the number of goals and the amount of time needed to complete each one.

LESSON

03 How Senses Work

ANCHORING PHENOMENON

Bats use their senses to find food.

ENGAGE **Can You Explain It?**
Students observe and ask questions about a bat feeding from a plant. They answer the Can You Explain It? question to explore what they know about how a bat uses its senses.

EVALUATE **Lesson Check**
Students gauge their understanding of the anchoring phenomenon.

HANDS-ON ACTIVITY

EXPLORATION 1 **Touch Test** 50 min

Investigative Phenomenon Touch receptors are specialized for particular kinds of information.

Students connect back to the **anchoring phenomenon** that bats use their senses to find food by exploring how touch receptors work in their own body.

HANDS-ON ACTIVITY

EXPLORATION 2 **No Smell, No Taste, No See**

Investigative Phenomenon Smell, taste, and sight receptors are specialized to smelling, tasting, and seeing.

Students connect back to the **anchoring phenomenon** that bats use their senses to find food by investigating their own senses of smell, taste, and sight.

EXPLORATION 3 **Nerves and Receptors** 60 min

Investigative Phenomenon Perceptions and memories can be used to guide actions.

Students connect back to the **anchoring phenomenon** that bats uses their senses to find food by exploring how information is processed by the brain.

EXPLORATION 4 **Sights and Sounds** 60 min

Investigative Phenomenon Animals can see an object when light reflected from its surface enters the eyes.

Students connect back to the **anchoring phenomenon** that bats uses their senses to find food by exploring how the senses of sight and hearing function.

Making 3D Connections

The anchoring phenomenon in this lesson supports students' understanding of and application of these Next Generation Science Standards.

Building to the Performance Expectations

4-PE-LS1-1 Construct an argument that plants and animals have internal and external structures that function to support survival, growth, behavior, and reproduction.

4-PE-LS1-2 Use a model to describe that animals receive different types of information through their senses, process the information in their brain, and respond to the information in different ways.

4-PE-PS4-2 Develop a model to describe that light reflecting from objects and entering the eye allows objects to be seen.

SEP

Engaging in Argument from Evidence Construct an argument with evidence, data, and/or a model. *(Explorations 1, 2, 3, 4)*

Developing and Using Models Use a model to test interactions concerning the functioning of a natural system. *(Explorations 1, 4)*

DCI

LS1.A Structure and Function Plants and animals have structures that serve various functions. *(Explorations 1, 2, 3, 4)*

LS1.D Information Processing Different sense receptors are specialized for particular kinds of information. Animals use their perceptions and memories to guide their actions. *(Explorations 1, 2, 3, 4)*

PS4.B Electromagnetic Radiation An object can be seen when light reflected from its surface enters the eyes. *(Exploration 4)*

CCC

Systems and System Models A system can be described in terms of its components and their interactions. *(Explorations 2, 3, 4)*

Cause and Effect Cause and effect relationships are routinely identified. *(Explorations 1, 2, 3, 4)*

Vocabulary

Word Wall

A word wall, anchor chart, or Language Development chart can be used to support vocabulary.

senses what allows a body to receive information about the environment

receptors special structures that respond to changes inside and outside the body and report them to the body's nervous system

You may want to include additional academic terms such as *arrange, conditions, interpret, perception, sensitivity,* and *vibrations* and any other terms students might struggle with.

Language Development Prompt students to complete the chart when they come to these highlighted terms within the lesson and to add their own terms as they come across unknown science terms.

Anchor Chart As you progress through the unit, you may want to make a vocabulary-based anchor chart using the Language Development chart as a guide that can be displayed and filled out as a whole group during each lesson.

LESSON

03 How Senses Work

Activity Guide, pages 64–83

Students can engage in the Can You Explain It? content by observing the photograph or by exploring the corresponding video online.

ONLINE 

View a video to see a bat feeding from a plant.

ANCHORING PHENOMENON
Bats use their senses to find food.

PHENOMENON EXPLAINED
Animals have structures that allow them to sense stimuli in their environment, and different sense receptors are specialized for particular kinds of information.

Lesson Objective

Students will gather evidence that animals have structures that work together in a system to sense stimuli in their environment. They will use their evidence to construct and argument about the cause and effect relationship between sense receptors and information processing.

Support Discovery

The following prompts can be used to guide student-led discovery.

I notice . . .

After observing the photograph or watching the video, students should record what they noticed about the bat and the plant.

Sample answer: I notice that the bat is feeding from the plant.

I wonder . . .

After observing the photograph or watching the video, students should record what they want to find out more about the conditions in which the bat is feeding.

Sample answer: I wonder how the bat is able to find food at night.

Can You Explain It?

In the Can You Explain It?, students make an initial claim that explains the **Anchoring Phenomenon.**

Sample answer: Students may draw a model indicating that bats use their noses to smell the flowers from which they feed. Or they may indicate that bats use their ears and sounds from their mouth to determine where food sources are located.

Students will gather evidence about how senses in the body work. This will enable them to give a more complete explanation of the **Anchoring Phenomenon** at the end of the lesson.

Alternative Phenomenon

Guide a discussion exploring how people and animals use their senses, and how our senses enable us to interpret the environment and the world around us. Review the five basic senses: hearing, sight, smell, taste, and touch. There is also a sixth sense, balance. Ask which senses students think are most important for survival. Visually impaired students may discuss how hearing, smell, and balance are most important. Hearing impaired students may say sight and smell.

SOCIAL EMOTIONAL LEARNING

Guide students to reflect on their goals from previous lessons and on any feedback they received from their teachers or peers. Then have each student set a personal goal for this lesson and make a plan for how to achieve the goal. Throughout the lesson, take daily breaks for students to track their progress in meeting their goals. If students struggle setting goals for this lesson, share with them some of the following ideas: identifying how their senses work or ensuring everyone in the group has a chance to share an idea.

LESSON 03

FUNomenal READER

Seeing for the First Time

WHEN TO USE

SCIENCE 

- Anchoring Phenomenon / Alternative Phenomenon
- Options for ELA Instruction
- Build on Prior Knowledge
- Preview the Phenomenon
- Read to Learn
- Support Sense Making
- Science Stretch
- Check for Comprehension

Option 1 Use before students begin the lesson in the Activity Guide to provide an engaging model to introduce the lesson's phenomenon.

Option 2 Use after students have completed the Activity Guide to reinforce students' understanding of the lesson phenomenon by exploring a related phenomenon.

- Options for ELA Instruction
- Build on Prior Knowledge
- Read to Learn

Option 3 To use during designated ELA Reading time for independent reading, whole-class instruction, or small-group instruction, look for this icon: ELA

Plan

ANCHORING PHENOMENON / ALTERNATIVE PHENOMENON

The anchoring phenomenon in the Activity Guide is *Bats use their senses to find food,* and the main example is a bat that is feeding from a plant at night. The FUNomenal Reader presents a similar phenomenon *(A person with regular color vision sees things differently than a colorblind person does),* and the example is a boy who discovers he has colorblindness. Both present the same science concepts and cover the same standards but with different phenomena. Guide students to draw connections between the two situations and to understand the underlying principle: animals have structures that allow them to sense stimuli in their environment.

Options for ELA Instruction 

Choose one of the following anchor chart options and project it or print copies. Then display and introduce the chart before reading the text. Revisit the chart after reading the text and encourage students to discuss how the skill connects to the text.

Ask and Answer Questions Use the *Ask and Answer Questions Anchor Chart* when introducing, developing, or reviewing those skills in the context of this story. Point out that Jeremy starts his investigation of colorblindness by making a list of questions and then adds to the list of questions as he learns more.

My Learning Mindset Have student pairs study the *My Learning Mindset Anchor Chart* and then decide which of the traits describe Jeremy, the story's main character. Challenge partners to find where in the story he shows these traits. Have them consider if these are good traits for investigating any phenomenon.

Literary Elements Display the *Literary Elements Anchor Chart* and guide students to identify the characters, setting, plot, and events in the story. What conflict does the main character face and how does he resolve it?

Preview

ELA **Build on Prior Knowledge** Ask students to name the five basic senses: sight, smell, touch, taste, and hearing. Have them give examples of how our senses help us understand the world around us. Explain that our senses send messages through receptors to the brain, using the nervous system to deliver the message.

Preview the Phenomenon Ask students to study the illustration on page 3 of the story, which shows students in a classroom looking at colorful images in their textbooks. Encourage students to record the first questions that come into their minds, focusing on what the kids are looking at. Point out that their questions might change as they read through the story. Have them keep their questions handy and periodically check to see if they can answer any.

STANDARDS SUPPORTED

SEP

Engaging in Argument from Evidence

Developing and Using Models

DCI

LS1.A Structure and Function

LS1.D Information Processing

PS4.B Electromagnetic Radiation

CCC

Systems and System Models

Cause and Effect

Seeing for the First Time (continued)

Discover

Read to Learn 

The **Read to Learn** suggestions inside the book's front cover encourage students to interact with the book multiple times for different purposes.

Preview Students look for unfamiliar words and share them with a partner. New terms may include *ophthalmologist, phoropter, mischievous, perceive,* and *differentiate.* Have students look up words they aren't sure about and notice how they are used in the context of the story.

Skim Students skim the photos. Have them turn to a partner and share their predictions of what the story will be about.

Read As students read the story, ask them to look for connections to one of the following anchor chart skills. **Ask and Answer Questions, My Learning Mindset, Literary Elements**

Support Sense Making

Choose one or more of the following:

- Be sure students can identify the phenomenon presented on the opening pages of the story: Jeremy learns that he likely has colorblindness. The rest of the story follows his attempts to learn more about the condition. Discuss the steps Jeremy takes to investigate the phenomenon.
- Have small groups do research to learn more about Dr. Shinobu Ishihara, who first published his tests for colorblindness in 1917. Are the tests still used today? How are they administered? Have groups report their findings to the class.
- Encourage a student-led discussion about senses beyond the basic five. For example, the inner ear controls the senses of motion, equilibrium, and position in space. Challenge students to identify other senses, such as the sense of time, sense of hunger, and sense of thirst.
- Some students may have disabilities that make discussing the subject of senses difficult. If possible, invite a guest speaker who is blind or deaf to visit the class to speak about his or her experiences. Encourage students to ask questions and engage in a dialogue about the limitations of not being able to rely on certain senses and how people can overcome those limitations.

Extend

Science Stretch

The **Science Stretch** suggestions inside the book's back cover help students think about what they read. Students can complete one or more as time allows.

Make a model of a body system related to the senses. Provide paper, markers, clay, and other materials for students to use.

Make a presentation about another condition that can affect a person's perceptions. Provide books and an approved list of websites for students to use in their research.

Tell how two senses work together. Make a claim that is supported by evidence and reasoning. **Sample answer:** Claim—My senses of hearing and sight often work together. Evidence—When I hear a loud sound, my eyes start searching for the source of the sound. Reasoning—My body systems act quickly to help me survive in my environment.

SOCIAL EMOTIONAL LEARNING

How can you assess your own strengths and weaknesses but still have confidence in your abilities? **Sample answer:** I can ask others to name my strengths and weaknesses. I can build on my strengths and work on my weaknesses. Knowing that I am "a work in progress" will help me feel confident.

Check for Comprehension Have students write three things they found out in the story, two things they found interesting, and one question they still have about colorblindness.

EXPLORATION 1 | HANDS-ON ACTIVITY

Touch Test

Activity Guide, pages 66–69

TIME ESTIMATE

SHORT ON TIME?

Reduce the number of body parts that are tested by eliminating the calf. You might also consider shaping the paper clips yourself in advance.

POSSIBLE MATERIALS

- ☐ 2 paper clips bent into a V shape
- ☐ metric ruler
- ☐ pencil or pen

Materials Alert Be sure that students are careful in handling the bent paper clips, as sharp objects can cause cuts. After students have completed the activity, ask them to return the paper clips to their original shape and reuse them.

PREPARATION

Discuss safety precautions before the activity and give reminders throughout the activity, as accidents can cause skin punctures from the paper clips. Be sure to have enough paper clips and rulers for each pair of students. You may want to allow time for yourself to quickly check students' V-shaped paper clips before they conduct their tests.

INVESTIGATIVE PHENOMENON

Touch receptors are specialized for particular kinds of information

Phenomenon Explained Students explore the **investigative phenomenon** by planning and conducting a fair test to show that their own skin contains touch receptors, and that different parts of the body contain different amounts of receptors.

Form a Question After observing the photograph and reading the text, students should form a question about how their own skin responds to touch and pressure. **Sample answer:** Are different body parts more sensitive to touch and pressure? Why is it important for my skin to detect touch or pressure?

STEP 1 Demonstrate for students how to reshape the paper clip so that it has two ends of equal length. Monitor students to make sure they prepare the paper clips correctly without hurting themselves.

STEPS 2 and 3 Students test touch receptors on their partner's hand. **Sample answer:** If I press down too hard, I might hurt my partner.

STEP 4 As students work to evaluate the pressure points, check student pairs to make certain they are making correct distance measurements and are carrying out the test in a controlled and methodical manner. **Sample answer:** Making both halves the same length makes it easier to apply pressure evenly.

STEPS 5 and 6 Students repeat the test and complete three trials for each body part. Demonstrate how to complete the table if necessary. Ask students to calculate the average distance and ask them what this information can tell them about the sense of touch and how mathematics can model their conclusions. Student responses to the questions may vary, but should match what they record in their data tables. Direct students to study their results in order to answer the questions.

- **Make a Claim** Claims should indicate that hands have the most touch receptors and are the most sensitive part of the body.
- **Evidence** Students should cite as evidence their recorded data.
- **Reasoning** Students should explain their reasoning that the hands have the most touch receptors because the distance at which two points could be detected was smallest on the hands, indicating that the sense of touch was more refined there.

FORMATIVE ASSESSMENT 

MAKING SENSE OF PHENOMENA

As they explore the **investigative phenomenon**, students gain understanding of how touch receptors work in their body. They should connect this to the **anchoring phenomenon** that bats also have receptors that allow them to recognize and process their environments, even in the dark.

REMEDIATION If students struggle to connect the **investigative phenomenon** back to the **anchoring phenomenon,** have them brainstorm ways that animals use their hands, feet, and wings in similar ways to how we use our hands.

Activity Outcome

Students should design and follow the steps of the test in order to observe that touch sensitivity varies in different parts of the body.

Performance Indicators	
	Work in partnership to complete the activity
	Make a claim that the hands have the most touch receptors
	Support the claim using recorded observations as evidence

MAKING SENSE OF PHENOMENA IDEA ORGANIZER

After completing Exploration 1, students can fill in the **Idea Organizer** to summarize the connection between how touch receptors in their skin work and the anchoring phenomenon that bats rely on receptors to find food, often without the direct use of their eyes.

SOCIAL EMOTIONAL LEARNING

Have students discuss the importance of safety when working closely with a partner, especially when touching is involved. Suggest that they ask for permission or let their partner know before they are going to touch, such as "Ready? I'm going to touch your skin now."

Remind students to touch gently, in a way that they would want to be touched.

EXPLORATION 2 HANDS-ON ACTIVITY

No Smell, No Taste, No See

Activity Guide, pages 70–73

TIME ESTIMATE

SHORT ON TIME?

Remind students to switch roles with their partner as sense test administrator and subject.

POSSIBLE MATERIALS

- ☐ blindfold
- ☐ paper plates
- ☐ various scented items
- ☐ various food items
- ☐ various small objects
- ☐ tape
- ☐ shoe box
- ☐ scissors
- ☐ cardboard
- ☐ construction paper

PREPARATION

Prepare for this activity by preassembling an assortment of things for students to smell and see, as well as foods that students can eat/taste. To smell, you might select things such as pencil erasers, flower petals, coffee beans, or blades of grass. Be sure that the foods to taste are relatively commonplace and that the students could recognize them from their smell. To see, you might use small toys.

INVESTIGATIVE PHENOMENON
Smell, taste, and sight receptors are specialized to smelling, tasting, and seeing.

Phenomenon Explained Students explore the **investigative phenomenon** by testing their ability to see, smell, and taste. They use their results to infer how sight, smell, and taste are involved in identifying things in their environment.

Form a Question After they read about their senses of sight, smell, and taste, students should form a question about their abilities to see, smell, and taste. If they have difficulty forming a question, ask them to remember the last time they used one or more of these senses during a meal. **Sample answers:** How are my abilities to see, smell, and taste connected? If I lose one of these senses, are the others affected?

STEP 1 Students blindfold and test a partner's ability to smell, then switch roles and repeat the test. Remind students to test all the scented items, but to vary the order of testing from one partner to the other.

Students describe their results and explain why the results did or did not surprise them. **Sample answer:** I was surprised because I was able to identify three of the five smells, but my partner was able to identify four of the five smells. I was able to identify the orange, apple, and pineapple.

STEP 2 Students blindfold and test their partner's ability to taste, then switch roles and repeat the test. Remind students to test all the food items, but to also vary the order of testing from one partner to the other.

Students describe their results and predict how their life would differ without their sense of smell. **Sample answer:** I wasn't very good at identifying tastes with no sense of smell. If I couldn't smell, my life would be different because my food wouldn't taste very good.

STEP 3 Students build a vision box using a shoebox, cardboard, and construction paper. Circulate among the groups and help students as needed in the construction of their boxes. They should use the scissors to poke holes in the box and cut out the flaps. Remind them to be careful when using the scissors. Demonstrate how to make a flap such that tape acts as a hinge on one side so that the flap can be opened by lifting it on the other side.

STEP 4 Students use the vision box to test their partner's ability to see an object with limited light. Have students choose only one item to place in the box and test, preferably one without a strong scent that could be used to identify it. Remind them to record the number of flaps opened.

STEP 5 Students switch roles and repeat the test. They should choose a different item to place in the box and test, and should record the number of flaps opened.

Students identify their object and that of their partner, as well as the number of flaps that needed to be opened to see the object. **Sample answers:** My object was a toy car. I had to have two flaps open to identify my object. My partner's object was a teddy bear. She had to have four flaps open to identify her object.

Materials Alert Check for any scent allergies students may have and use appropriate substitutions. Make sure that students do not have any food allergies or sensitivities to the foods selected for this activity. You may need to modify the food choices according to special diets. Also be sure that the foods are fresh and edible.

No See, No Smell, No Taste (continued)

Activity Guide, pages 70–73, *cont.*

Students describe what they saw in the box before the flaps were opened. **Sample answer:** It was dark in my box and I couldn't see anything in it until I started opening the flaps.

Students explain why they weren't able to identify their objects unless the flaps were open. Prompt them to look for cause-and-effect relationships in their observations. **Sample answer:** We couldn't identify the objects because it was dark in the box when the flaps were closed. As we opened each flap more light entered the box, so it was easier to see the object.

Students compare their results with their partner's. **Sample answer:** I only needed a little bit of light to see my car, but my partner's toy blocked the light, so she needed more flaps open in order to see it.

- **Make a Claim** Claims should indicate how the student's sight, smell, and taste are involved in identifying things in their environment. For example, sight is used to see things in the environment when there is light. You can use your nose to smell, but the ability to smell also affects taste.
- **Evidence** Students should cite evidence gathered during the activity, such as they were able see objects in the box only when they opened the flaps to let in more light and holding their noses changed how well they could taste foods.
- **Reasoning** Students should explain their reasoning, such as that if light wasn't needed to see something in the environment, they would have been able to see the object in the box even with the flaps closed. And if smell did not affect taste, holding their noses should not have affected their ability to identify foods by taste.

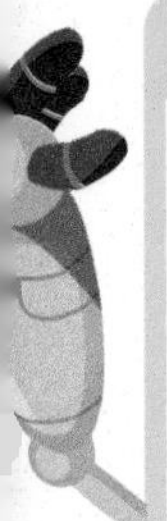

FORMATIVE ASSESSMENT

MAKING SENSE OF PHENOMENA

Students gain understanding that smell and taste receptors are specialized to smelling and tasting as they explore the **investigative phenomenon**. They should connect this to the **anchoring phenomenon** that animals have structures and receptors that allow them to recognize and process different tastes and smells in their environments. Students should understand that bats may use sight to see food and that they may use smell and taste to tell if food is safe to eat.

REMEDIATION If students struggle to connect the **investigative phenomenon** back to the **anchoring phenomenon**, have partners review and discuss their activity results.

MAKING SENSE OF PHENOMENA IDEA ORGANIZER

After completing Exploration 2, students can fill in the **Idea Organizer** to summarize the connection between how smell and taste receptors are specialized to smelling and tasting and the anchoring phenomenon that animals have structures and receptors that allow them to recognize and process different tastes and smells in their environments.

Activity Outcome

Students should test their ability to see, smell, and taste in order to infer that sight, smell, and taste are involved in identifying things in their environment. They should make and support a claim using their observations as evidence.

Performance Indicators	
	record observations about their ability to see, smell, and taste
	make a claim that sight, smell, and taste are involved in identifying things in the environment
	support the claim using observations as evidence

EXPLORATION 3

Nerves and Receptors

Activity Guide, pages 74–76

TIME ESTIMATE

Materials Alert If the anatomical diagram confuses students, have other images ready to display for them. For (a), show pictures of the human skeleton and muscles. For (b), show pictures of the brain, spinal cord, and nerves. For (c), show close-up pictures of nerves. For (d), show pictures of bundles of nerve fibers.

a. Humans and many other animals have a **skeletal system** made mainly of bones. The skeletal system gives structure, support, and protection to the softer parts of the body.

b. The **nervous system** contains the **brain,** the spinal cord, and the nerves. The brain is the central processing organ and is protected by the skeletal system.

c. The nervous system contains two kinds of **nerves**: those that send information to the brain or spinal cord, and those that send information from the brain and spinal cord to the rest of the body.

d. The **spinal cord** is a bundle of nerve fibers and tissues that connect the parts of the body to the brain. It is protected by the backbone. The brain and the spinal cord make up the central nervous system.

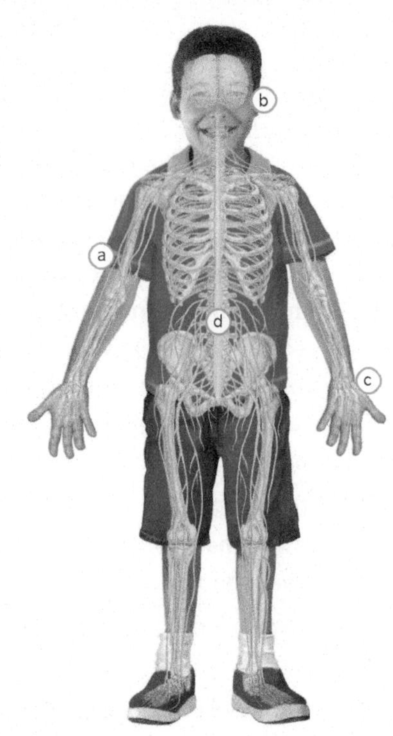

INVESTIGATIVE PHENOMENON
Perceptions and memories can be used to guide actions.

Phenomenon Explained Students explore the **investigative phenomenon** by understanding how systems of the body enable our senses to communicate information to the brain. People and animals remember this sensory information and use it to act in their environment.

Body Senses

Everyday Phenomenon **People who have cut themselves on something sharp know to handle sharp objects carefully in the future.**

When information such as pain is processed by the brain, it can create perceptions and memories. Explain to students how internal and external systems interact with the nervous system to send pain signals to the brain. How does this information change future behavior? Have students discuss how memories and perceptions can guide their actions and ask volunteers to share examples.

Skin Deep

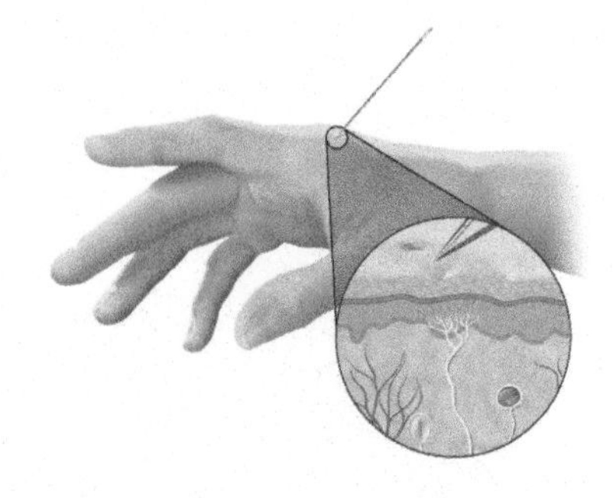

Help students connect this contextual information back to what they experienced in the Touch Test (Exploration 1). Touch receptors sensed when the paper clip was touching their skin. If the paper clip was pressed too hard, pain receptors would have sent that information to the brain. Discuss with students how they should handle sharp objects such as the paper clip given what they now know about receptors.

SOCIAL EMOTIONAL LEARNING

Remind students to take turns and listen quietly when another student is speaking. Help students understand that constructive feedback should be helpful, such as offering suggestions to improve another student's answer. It should refer to the answer, not to students themselves.

Knee-Jerk Response

Everyday Phenomenon **People jump or flinch when they are surprised by a loud sound.**

This is a reflexive response to being startled. Muscles contract, the heart beats faster, and the eyes open wider, all to protect you from possible danger as quickly as possible. Discuss the model diagram and explain that reflexes are another way the body processes information from the senses, with a more immediate response.

FORMATIVE ASSESSMENT

MAKING SENSE OF PHENOMENA

As they explore the **investigative phenomenon**, students gain understanding of the cause and effect relationship between sensory information and how the brain processes it. People retain this information to guide their actions in the future. They should connect this to the anchoring phenomenon that bats can process the information their senses take in and use perceptions and memories to guide actions such as finding food.

REMEDIATION If students struggle to connect the **investigative phenomenon** back to the **anchoring phenomenon**, discuss ways they use sensory information to learn about and respond to their environment. For each example, have students brainstorm a similar example in an animal's behavior.

MAKING SENSE OF PHENOMENA IDEA ORGANIZER

After completing Exploration 3, students can fill in the **Idea Organizer** to summarize the connection between how sensory information is processed by the brain to form perceptions that guide behavior and the anchoring phenomenon that bats use perceptions and memories formed from sensory information to help them find food.

EXPLORATION 4

Sights and Sounds

Activity Guide, pages 77–80

TIME ESTIMATE

Materials Alert Consider printing out a large diagram that shows how the eye works so that you can review it in more detail together as a class.

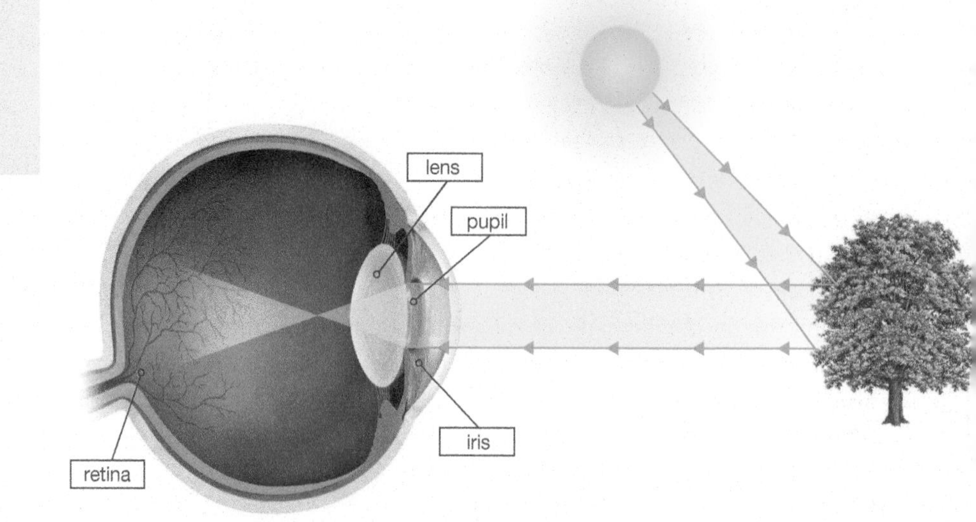

INVESTIGATIVE PHENOMENON
Animals can see an object when light reflected from its surface enters the eyes.

Phenomenon Explained Students explore the **investigative phenomenon** by understanding how eyes function. Eyes can process information about color, shape, depth, and dimension.

Eye See!

Review the diagram together as a class. On their diagram, you might have students number the steps that are discussed in the text.

Reflections of Light

Everyday Phenomenon **Light is necessary to see objects.**

To help students understand why sight requires light, shut off the lights and close the blinds. Place the students in the back of the class, and hold up an object. Then put the object away, turn the lights back on, and open the blinds. Ask students to describe what they saw: its shape, color, surface, etc. Discuss how a lack of light made identification difficult.

Students draw how human eyes use light to see objects. Student drawings should show that light moves from the light source to the object and then reflects off the object into the eye.

Binocular Vision

Students explore why having two or more eyes allows the brain to better process visual information.

Here's to the Ears!

As with the other senses, the ears work together with the brain as a system to process information. Review the diagram with students. Ask them where in the ear sound is perceived (the inner ear) and why (the inner ear contains sensory receptors).

"Seeing" By Hearing

Explain that some animals "see" using senses other than their eyes. Other animals may have senses that are more sensitive than human senses, or that are stronger than their sense of sight. These senses may help them survive. In addition to bats, some examples to discuss are: dogs and cats rely more on scent and sound than vision to find food; some snakes can sense heat, so they know when a living thing is nearby.

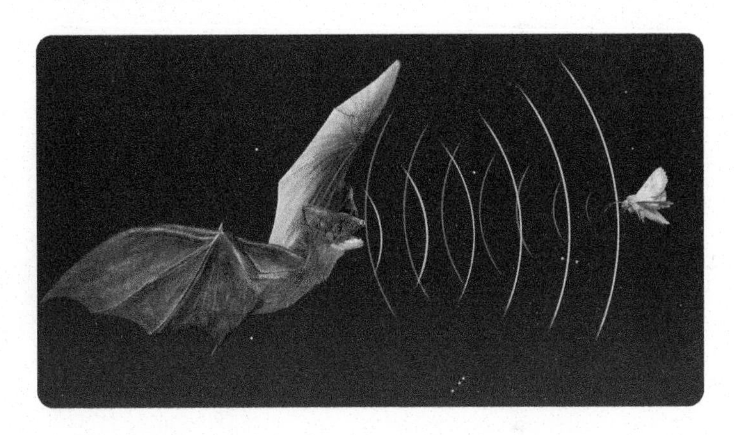

FORMATIVE ASSESSMENT

MAKING SENSE OF PHENOMENA

As they explore the **investigative phenomenon**, students gain understanding that animals can see an object when light reflected from its surface enters the eyes. They also recognize that animals have different sensory abilities, and that some animals, such as certain bat species, rely on senses other than sight to find food. They should connect this to the anchoring phenomenon that bats rely on their senses to find food.

REMEDIATION If students struggle to connect the **investigative phenomenon** back to the **anchoring phenomenon,** have them examine and then describe what is happening in the eyesight diagram at the beginning of this exploration.

MAKING SENSE OF PHENOMENA IDEA ORGANIZER

After completing Exploration 4, students can fill in the **Idea Organizer** to summarize the connection between humans' senses of sight and hearing and the anchoring phenomenon that some bats use these senses differently to find food.

LESSON

03

ONLINE-ONLY RESOURCE

Take It Further

Engage • Explore/Explain • **Elaborate** • Evaluate

TIME ESTIMATE

These Take It Further paths may be completed to enrich and extend students' comprehension of content covered within this lesson.

ONLINE

Extreme Senses

Students explore extreme senses to gain a deeper understanding of some of the unusual sensory processing abilities that help animals survive in their environments.

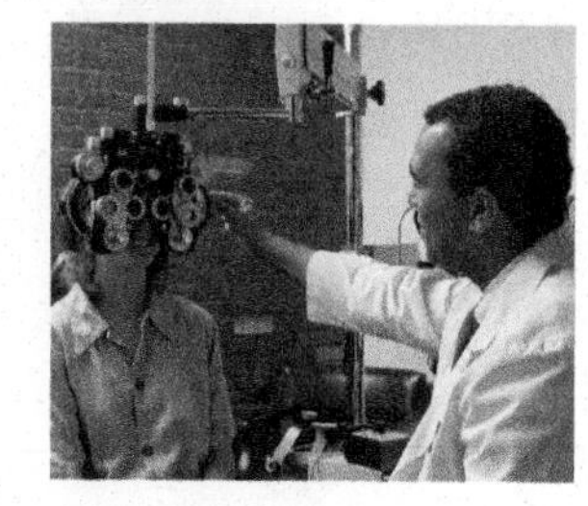

Careers in Science & Engineering: Optometrist

Students explore a career in optometry.

People in Science & Engineering: Kale Edmiston

Students learn about Kale Edmiston, PhD, who studies how the brain processes visual information.

FORMATIVE ASSESSMENT

Lesson Check

Activity Guide, pages 81–83

Engage • Explore/Explain • Elaborate • Evaluate

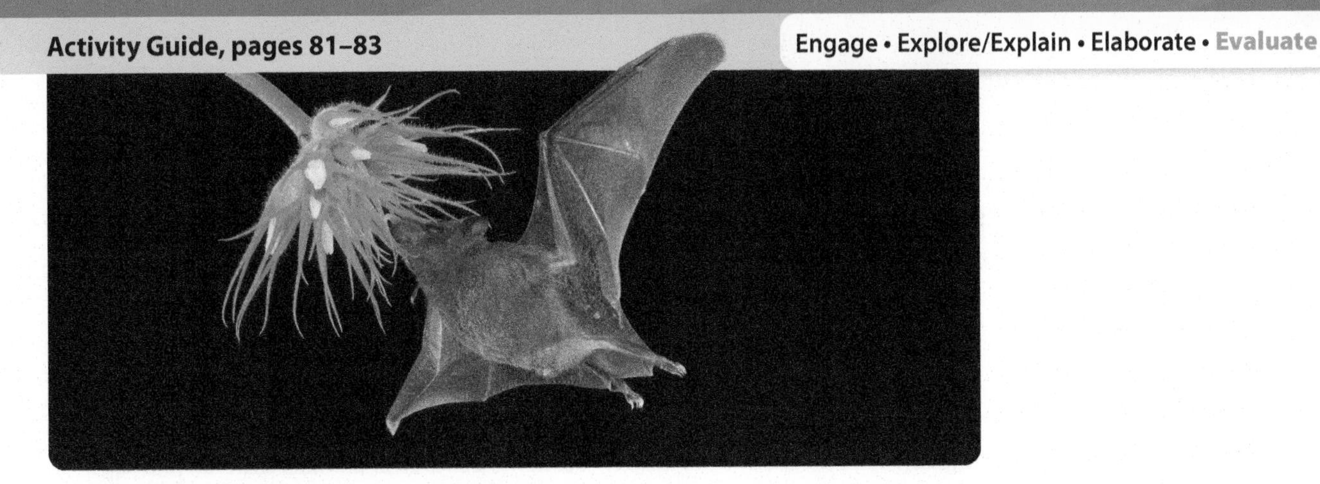

Can You Explain It?

Now I know or think that . . .

Sample answer: Bats use all of their senses to find food. They use their sense of hearing to locate food, sense of touch to detect how they should fly through the air, sense of sight to see foods when there is enough light, and their sense of smell to locate the foods they need. Senses work together by getting different types of information and sending it to the brain. The brain then reacts in different ways to help animals survive.

After completing the lesson, use the **Making Sense Idea Organizer** to summarize the connections between the **investigative phenomena** and **anchoring phenomenon.**

MAKING CONNECTIONS

After students complete the lesson, they should be able to assess how elephant shrews use their senses. Students should draw comparisons with what they have learned about human and bat senses to formulate their answers. **Sample answer:** This shrew probably uses its senses of sight and hearing the most to find food and avoid predators. It probably uses its nose to smell potential food, too. Like the bat, its senses are important to its survival.

Checkpoints

1. seeing a green lizard running—sight receptor; sweet piece of fruit—taste receptor; hand is poked by a sharp object—pain receptor
2. light
3. a—My lunch won't taste as good.
4. b—They make hairs move in the cochlea and c—They are translated by receptors into nerve signals.
5. **Sample answer:** The nervous system helps humans survive by reacting to receptors and sending a message to the brain. The message then tells the brain how the body should react.
6. **Sample answer:** An object can be seen when light reflected off its surface enters the eyes. If there is no light, the effect would be that light could not be reflected off of an object and enter an eye. Cheetahs use sight to find their food, so if there is no light, they cannot see well and cannot catch food.

SOCIAL EMOTIONAL LEARNING

Have students reflect on the concepts they have explored about animal senses. Have them write about what they enjoyed most during the lesson. Then, with a partner, have students discuss something they were surprised to learn during their various explorations. Have volunteers share their responses.

UNIT

02 Review

Activity Guide, pages 84–86

The Unit Review items enable you to assess student comprehension of core ideas as well as crosscutting concepts and science and engineering practices.

1. **DOK 2** **Sample answer:** Leaves capture sunlight. Leaves use the sunlight to make food for the plant. Plants need sunlight, air, nutrients, and water to grow.

   For a quick review on the function of leaves, students can turn back to Lesson 1, Exploration 3.

2. **DOK 3** **Sample answer:** A plant's root and shoot systems work together to transfer water and nutrients from the soil, to the roots, up through the stem and to the plant's leaves. This gives the plant the materials it needs to grow and survive.

   Students can refer back to Lesson 1, Exploration 3 to recall the function of plant parts and systems.

3. **DOK 2** Students should draw a plant that has structures for reproduction or protection. The structures should be labeled. **Sample answer:** Reproduction: cone, flower, spore; Protection: thorns, bark, spines

   Students can refer back to Lesson 1, Explorations 1 and 3, to recall information about which plant structures are involved in reproduction and protection.

4. **DOK 1** **a.** It is thin. **b.** It is slimy. **d.** It is moist.

   To answer this question correctly, students need to understand how external features are adapted to environments. They can find information on external animal parts in Lesson 2, Exploration 3.

5. **DOK 2** Protection: fur, shells, spines; Motion, fins, legs, wings

   Students are asked to classify physical structures. For extra support, it may be helpful to show students pictures of animals with fur, fins, legs, wings, shells, and spines. They can also turn back to Lesson 2, Exploration 3 for a quick review.

6. **DOK 1** **d.** hearing

   Students learned about sights and sounds in Lesson 3, Exploration 4. Remind students about the concept of "seeing by hearing," with the bat as an example. Have them think about some of the similarities between bats and dolphins.

7. **DOK 3** **Sample answer:** Sophia's eyes will see the ball when light is reflected from its surface and signals are sent through her nerves to her brain. Her brain will interpret those images. As the ball gets closer, her eyes will continue to send messages to her brain. Her brain will send signals through her nerves to her arms and hands that will cause her to try to catch the ball.

   Students should make a comprehensive connection among the various senses and structures involved in managing movements. Students can turn back to Lesson 3, Explorations 3 and 4 for a quick review.

8. **DOK 2** **Sample answer:** Animals have different body systems that are made up of different parts. For example, dogs have a digestive system that includes a mouth, esophagus, stomach, and intestines. Without the different parts that have different jobs, the system wouldn't be able to digest food and provide nutrients and energy to other systems..

   If students struggle to answer this question, have them turn back to Lesson 2, Exploration 4.

9. **DOK 2** **Sample answer:** Unlike ferns, apple trees form flowers and fruit (apples) in order to reproduce.

   To answer this question correctly, they will need to know the reproductive differences between ferns, a type of non-seed plant, and other plants. For a review on this material, students can turn back to Lesson 1, Exploration 3.

10. **DOK 2** **Sample answer:** Plants respond to light. If light is only coming from one direction, it will cause the plant to grow toward the light. Plants can also respond to gravity. If a planter is knocked over, the stem and leaves will continue to grow upward and the roots grow downward, instead of sideways.

    Students should recall that the structures of plants support their behaviors as well as their functions. Have students think about some of the behaviors they have seen in plants based on their own observations and what they learned in the lessons. To review, students can refer to Lesson 1, Exploration 4

3D Item Analysis	1	2	3	4	5	6	7	8	9	10
SEP Engaging in Argument from Evidence	●						●	●	●	
SEP Developing and Using Models			●							
DCI LS1.A Structure and Function	●	●	●	●	●	●	●	●	●	●
DCI LS1.D Information Processing						●	●			●
DCI PS4.B Electromagnetic Radiation							●			
CCC Cause and Effect							●			●
CCC Systems and System Models	●	●	●	●	●	●	●	●	●	●

UNIT

03 Energy and Communication

Activity Guide, page 87

Unit Storyline

In Unit 2, students explored how plants and other organisms use and transform matter and energy to live and grow. They identified the structures that allow animals to receive, process, and respond to information. In this unit, students further their investigations in energy and information transfer. They explore how waves are evidence that energy is transferred and how energy and information can be transferred through waves. They also explore and identify the devices and systems—from cell phones to satellites and from binary codes to global networks—that enable humans to transmit information across vast distances.

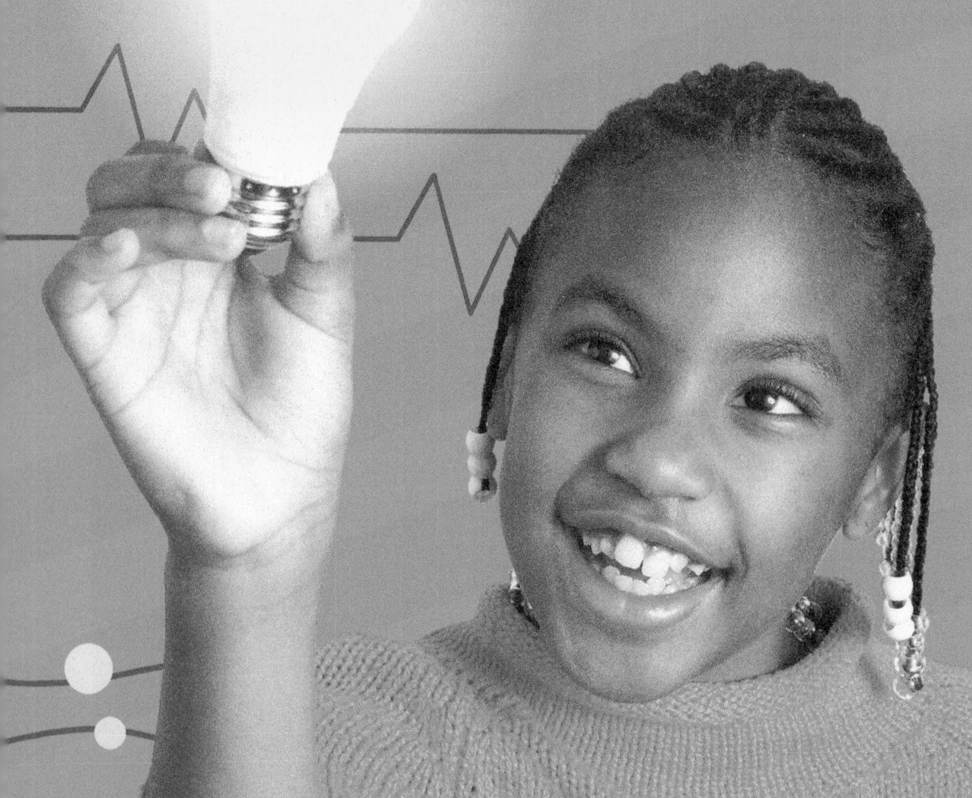

LESSON 1 PE 4-PS3-2, PE 4-PS3-4, 3-5-ETS1-1

Energy Transfer and Transformation

Activity Guide, pages 88–107

Students explore the **anchoring phenomenon** that band members cause different kinds of energy to be transferred and transformed as they play and sing.

SEP Planning and Carrying Out Investigations; Constructing Explanations and Designing Solutions

DCI **PS3.A** Definitions of Energy; **PS3.B** Conservation of Energy and Energy Transfer; **PS3.D** Energy In Chemical Processes and Everyday Life; **ETS1.A** Defining Engineering Problems

CCC Energy and Matter; Systems and System Models; Influence of Engineering, Technology, and Science on Society and the Natural World; Science as a Human Endeavor

LESSON 2 PE 4-PS3-1, PE 4-PS3-3

Collisions

Activity Guide, pages 108–123

Students explore the **anchoring phenomenon** that a wrecking ball uses stored energy to build momentum for a collision with another object.

SEP Asking Questions and Defining Problems; Constructing Explanations and Designing Solutions

DCI **PS3.A** Definitions of Energy; **PS3.B** Conservation of Energy and Energy Transfer; **PS3.C** Relationship Between Energy and Forces

CCC Energy and Matter; Influence of Engineering, Technology, and Science on Society and the Natural World; Science as a Human Endeavor

LESSON 3 PE 4-PS4-1

Waves

Activity Guide, pages 124–141

Students explore the **anchoring phenomenon** that ocean waves cause a surfer to move.

SEP Developing and Using Models; Scientific Knowledge is Based on Empirical Evidence

DCI **PS4.A** Wave Properties

CCC Patterns

LESSON 4 PE 4-PS4-3, 3-5-ETS1-2

Information Transfer

Activity Guide, pages 142–161

Students explore the **anchoring phenomenon** that satellites in outer space can send digitized information from long distances.

SEP Constructing Explanations and Designing Solutions

DCI **PS4.C** Information Technologies and Instrumentation; **ETS1.C** Optimizing the Design Solution

CCC Patterns; Interdependence of Science, Engineering, and Technology

Unit Review Activity Guide, pages 162–165

UNIT 03

AT A GLANCE

Online-Only Resources

Supporting Unit Resources

You Solve It SUPPORTS LESSON 2

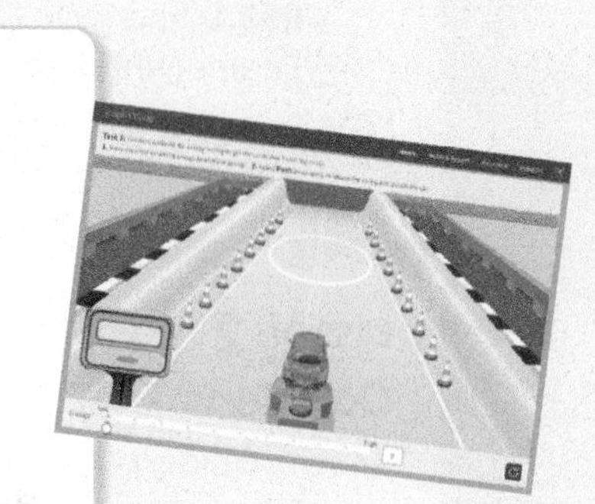

Crash Course is a virtual lab that offers practice in support of **Performance Expectation 4-PS3-3.** Students will predict the changes in energy that occur when objects collide.

- SEP Asking Questions and Defining Problems
- DCI **PS3.A** Definitions of Energy; **PS3.B** Conservation of Energy and Energy Transfer
- CCC Energy and Matter

Unit Project SUPPORTS LESSON 3

60 min

Wave Patterns provides students an opportunity to practice aspects of **Performance Expectation 4-PS4-1.** Students will prepare a multimedia presentation to model different kinds of waves. They will use these models to describe patterns in terms of amplitudes and wavelengths and to provide evidence that waves can cause objects to move.

- SEP Developing and Using Models
- DCI **PS4.A** Wave Properties
- CCC Patterns

Unit Performance Task SUPPORTS LESSONS 1 AND 2

Colliding Objects provides an opportunity for students to practice or be assessed on aspects of **Performance Expectations 4-PS3-3** and **PS3-4.** Students analyze how objects can be set in motion by collisions. They plan experiments, run them, and then collect and analyze data, and they create a multimedia presentation that reports on their procedures and findings.

- SEP Asking Questions and Defining Problems; Planning and Carrying Out Investigations
- DCI **PS3.B** Conservation of Energy and Energy Transfer
- CCC Energy and Matter

Language Development

This worksheet is used as students progress through the unit's lessons. As they come to a highlighted vocabulary term, they should come back to this chart and fill in the blanks with words or phrases.

ONLINE

We've got you covered.

Updates and additional student and teacher resources can be found online. Check back often!

Supporting Lesson Resources

Do the Math!

Lesson 1 Calculate Energy Units; Compare the Speed of Sound
Lesson 2 What Happens to Energy in a Drop
Lesson 3 Compare Earthquake Models
Lesson 4 Code Blue

Language SmArts

Lesson 1 Interpret; Research; Cause and Effect; Recall Relevant Information
Lesson 2 Cause and Effect
Lesson 3 Wave Recall; Connecting Ideas
Lesson 4 Drawing Inferences; Message Mistakes; Engineering the Internet; Understanding Logical Connections

MAKING SENSE OF PHENOMENA

This idea organizer is used to make sense of the following **anchoring phenomena**:
Lesson 1—The band members cause different kinds of energy to be transferred and transformed as they play and sing.
Lesson 2—When the wrecking ball hits the wall, the wall moves.
Lesson 3—Ocean waves cause a surfer to move.
Lesson 4—A satellite sends information from space to Earth.

The idea organizer also connects the investigative phenomena back to the anchoring phenomenon in each lesson.

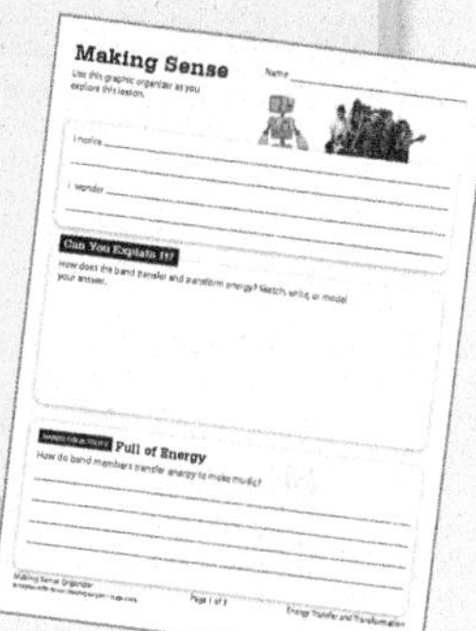

Take It Further

Lesson 1 People in Science & Engineering: Mayra Artiles and Zena Mitchell; Careers in Science & Engineering: Physicist; The Paynes and Fast-Traveling Whale Songs
Lesson 2 People in Science & Engineering: Amanda Steffy; Careers in Science & Engineering: Crash Test Engineer; Collision Game!; Bump!
Lesson 3 People in Science & Engineering: Christian Doppler, Debra Fischer, and Wanda Diaz-Merced; Theater Acoustics; Seismic Waves and Earthquakes
Lesson 4 Elephant Communication; Wave That Flag; People in Science & Engineering: Alexander Graham Bell, Hedy Lamarr, and the Navajo Code Talkers; Careers in Science & Engineering: Graphics Engineer

Assessment

Unit Readiness Check: Are You Ready?
Lesson Quizzes: Can You Apply It?
Unit 3 Test
Performance-Based Assessment
Assessments are available in an editable, printable format or can be administered and auto-graded online.

LESSON

Energy Transfer and Transformation

ANCHORING PHENOMENON

The band members cause different kinds of energy to be transferred and transformed as they play and sing.

ENGAGE **Can You Explain It?**

Students observe and ask questions about how the band uses energy. They answer the Can You Explain It? question to describe how the energy that the band uses while performing is transferred and transformed.

EVALUATE **Lesson Check**

Students gauge their understanding of the anchoring phenomenon.

HANDS-ON ACTIVITY

EXPLORATION 1

Full of Energy

Investigative Phenomenon

Each form of energy can be transferred.

Students connect back to the **anchoring phenomenon** that when the band plays music, energy is transferred.

HANDS-ON ACTIVITY

EXPLORATION 2

Light the Bulb

Investigative Phenomenon

Transformation of energy makes it useful.

Students connect back to the **anchoring phenomenon** that when the band plays, electrical and other forms of energy are transformed to produce sound that is emitted by the speakers.

EXPLORATION 3

Energy is All Around

Investigative Phenomenon

Stored energy can be used later.

Students connect back to the **anchoring phenomenon** that stored energy is used to run the band's equipment.

EXPLORATION 4 **Heat**

Investigative Phenomenon Energy can be transferred as heat.

Students connect back to the **anchoring phenomenon** that small amounts of heat are produced by the equipment.

EXPLORATION 5 **Energy of Sound**

Investigative Phenomenon Sound can transfer energy over a distance.

Students connect back to the **anchoring phenomenon** that when the band plays, energy is transferred and transformed to produce sound, which travels from the speakers to the audience.

Making 3D Connections

The **anchoring phenomenon** in this lesson supports students' understanding of and application of these Next Generation Science Standards.

Building to the Performance Expectations

PE 4-PS3-2 Make observations to provide evidence that energy can be transferred from place to place by sound, light, heat, and electric currents.

PE 4-PS3-4 Apply scientific ideas to design, test, and refine a device that converts energy from one form to another.*

3-5-ETS1-1 Define a simple design problem that includes specified criteria and constraints.

SEP

Planning and Carrying Out Investigations Make observations to produce data. *(Explorations 1, 2, 3)*

Constructing Explanations and Designing Solutions Use evidence to construct an explanation. Apply scientific ideas to solve design problems. *(Explorations 1, 2, 3)*

DCI

PS3.A Definitions of Energy The faster a given object is moving, the more energy it possesses. *(Explorations 1, 2, 3, 4, 5)*

PS3.B Conservation of Energy and Energy Transfer Energy is present whenever there are moving objects, sound, light, or heat. *(Explorations 1, 2, 3, 4, 5)*

PS3.D Energy In Chemical Processes and Everyday Life The expression "produce energy" typically refers to the conversion of stored energy. *(Exploration 3)*

ETS1.A Defining Engineering Problems Possible solutions to a problem are limited by available materials and resources. *(Exploration 2)*

CCC

Energy and Matter Energy can be transferred. *(Explorations 1, 2, 3, 4, 5)*

Systems and System Models A system can be described in terms of its components and their interactions. *(Explorations 1, 2, 3)*

Influence of Engineering, Technology, and Science on Society and the Natural World Engineers improve existing technologies or develop new ones. *(Explorations 1, 2, 3, 4, 5)*

Science as a Human Endeavor Most scientists and engineers work in teams. *(Explorations 1, 2, 3, 4, 5)*

Vocabulary

Word Wall A word wall, anchor chart, or Language Development chart can be used to support vocabulary.

energy the ability to cause change in matter

circuit the closed path or loop that an electric current flows through

electric current the flow of electric charges along a path

energy transfer movement of energy from place to place or from object to object

energy transformation change in energy from one form to another

heat energy that transfers between objects with different temperatures

You may want to include additional academic terms such as *device* and *vibrations* and any other terms students might struggle with.

Language Development
Prompt students to complete the chart when they come to these highlighted terms within the lesson.

Anchor Chart You may want to make a vocabulary-based anchor chart.

LESSON

01 Energy Transfer and Transformation

Activity Guide, pages 88–89

Students can engage in the Can You Explain It? content by observing the photograph or by exploring the corresponding video online.

ONLINE 

View a video related to using energy to make music.

ANCHORING PHENOMENON

The band members cause different kinds of energy to be transferred and transformed as they play and sing.

PHENOMENON EXPLAINED

Energy is needed when the band performs. To use the energy, they must transfer and transform it.

Lesson Objective

Students will plan and carry out investigations to explore how the parts within a system allow for energy to be transferred and transformed. They will use evidence from observations and data collected to construct an argument that energy is present when objects move, make sound, and or heat up.

Support Discovery

The following prompts can be used to guide student-led discovery.

I notice . . .

After observing the photograph or watching the video, students should record what they noticed about the band. If students struggle to record observations, ask them to identify any sources of sound, heat, or light and then describe what the band members are doing.

Sample answers: I notice that the kids are making music. I notice the kids are singing, dancing, and playing instruments.

I wonder . . .

After observing the photograph or watching the video, students should record what they want to find out more about regarding the band playing music.

Sample answer: I wonder how they can make music. I wonder if it is hard to play an instrument.

Can You Explain It?

In the Can You Explain It?, students make an initial claim that explains the **Anchoring Phenomenon.**

Sample answer: Students may draw a model of how energy is transferred and transformed by the children singing and dancing or write a sentence about how energy moves and changes when the children hit the drum, sing, and dance.

Students will gather evidence about how the band transfers and transforms energy. This will enable them to give a more complete explanation of the **Anchoring Phenomenon** at the end of the lesson.

Alternative Phenomenon

Present a different scenario. Point out to students that they can observe energy transfers involving light, sound, and heat all around them every day. Consider a scene at an amusement park, circus, or state fair where there are many forms of energy in the midst of transfer and transformation. If possible, bring a visual of one or more of these scenarios to class so that students can make in-person observations of how energy is transferred and transformed.

SOCIAL EMOTIONAL LEARNING

Have students set a personal goal for this lesson and make a plan for how to achieve the goal. Throughout the lesson, take daily breaks for students to track their progress. If students struggle setting goals for this lesson, share with them some of the following ideas:, participating more during activity/group work or ensuring everyone in the group has a chance to share an idea, or preserving when an activity or topic is difficult.

LESSON 01

FUNomenal READER

Melting Marshmallows

WHEN TO USE

SCIENCE 

- Anchoring Phenomenon / Alternative Phenomenon
- Options for ELA Instruction
- Build on Prior Knowledge
- Preview the Phenomenon
- Read to Learn
- Support Sense Making
- Science Stretch
- Check for Comprehension

Option 1 Use before students begin the lesson in the Activity Guide to provide an engaging model to introduce the lesson's phenomenon.

Option 2 Use after students have completed the Activity Guide to reinforce students' understanding of the lesson phenomenon by exploring a related phenomenon.

ELA 

- Options for ELA Instruction
- Build on Prior Knowledge
- Read to Learn

Option 3 To use during designated ELA Reading time for independent reading, whole-class instruction, or small-group instruction, look for this icon: ELA

Plan

ANCHORING PHENOMENON / ALTERNATIVE PHENOMENON

The anchoring phenomenon in the Activity Guide is *The band members cause different kinds of energy to be transferred and transformed as they play and sing.* The main example is a group of children who are singing and playing musical instruments. The FUNomenal Reader presents a similar phenomenon *(S'mores can be made with an energy source other than fire)*, and the example is a boy who wants to make s'mores. Both present the same science concepts and cover the same standards but with different phenomena. Guide students to draw connections between the two situations and to understand the underlying principle: energy must be transferred and transformed to be used.

Options for ELA Instruction 

Choose one of the following anchor chart options and project it or print copies. Then display and introduce the chart before reading the text. Revisit the chart after reading the text and encourage students to discuss how the skill connects to the text.

Text Features Have students refer to the *Text Features Anchor Chart* to help them identify the various text features in this story. As they page through the story, students should notice diagrams, photos, and illustrations. Guide them to understand that these visual features help explain ideas in the text.

Point of View Use the *Point of View Anchor Chart* as you discuss point of view in the context of this story. Ask students who is telling the story (Cooper). How do they think the story might be different if it were told from his brother Jonah's point of view?

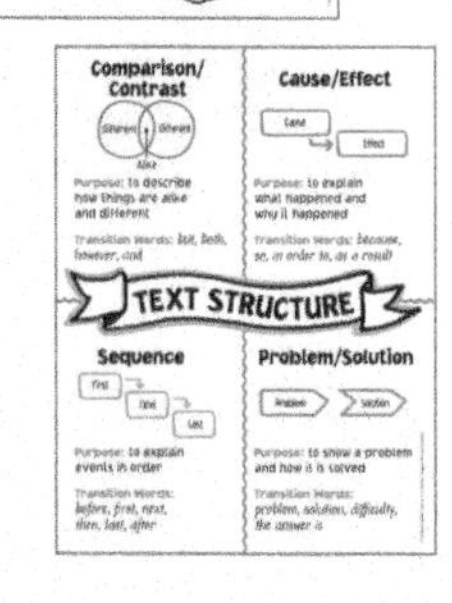

Text Structure Use the *Text Structure Anchor Chart* when discussing types of text structure. Guide students to an understanding of the problem-solution structure of this story. Have them identify the problem and the solution.

Preview

ELA **Build on Prior Knowledge** Ask if any students have used a solar cooker or seen one in a magazine, online, or on TV. Have volunteers share their experiences with the class, including a description of how food was warmed or cooked in the device. Discuss how easy or difficult they think it would be to use a solar cooker for everyday cooking.

Preview the Phenomenon Ask students to study the illustration on the first page of the story (p. 2), which shows a group of kids talking. Photos of activities surround them. Encourage students to record the first questions that come into their minds. Point out that their questions might change as they read through the story. Have them keep their questions handy and periodically check to see if any can be answered

STANDARDS SUPPORTED

SEP

Planning and Carrying Out Investigations

Constructing Explanations and Designing Solutions

DCI

PS3.A Definitions of Energy

PS3.B Conservation of Energy and Energy Transfer

PS3.D Energy in Chemical Processes and Everyday Life

ETS1.A Defining Engineering Problems

CCC

Energy and Matter

Influence of Engineering, Technology, and Science on Society and the Natural World

Science as a Human Endeavor

Melting Marshmallows (continued)

Discover

Read to Learn 

The **Read to Learn** suggestions inside the book's front cover encourage students to interact with the book multiple times for different purposes.

Preview Students look for unfamiliar words and share them with a partner. New terms may include *energy, thermal energy, convection, energy transformation,* and *energy transfer.* Have students look up words they aren't sure about and notice how they are used in the context of the story.

Skim Students skim the photos and illustrations. Have them turn to a partner and share their predictions of what the story will be about.

Read As students read the story, ask them to look for connections to one of the following anchor chart skills. **Text Features, Point of View, Text Structure**

Support Sense Making

Choose one or more of the following:

- Be sure students can identify the phenomenon presented on the opening pages of the story: Cooper wants to make s'mores, but he doesn't have access to a campfire or a kitchen. The story follows Cooper's investigation into how to make s'mores using energy from the sun.
- Engage in a class discussion about energy transfers. Explain that heat can be used to change the structures of foods other than marshmallows and pieces of chocolate. Have pairs of students brainstorm foods that change by being cooked. After partners have been given ample time to brainstorm, call everyone together and have pairs share their ideas with the class.
- On a whiteboard or other surface, project the Engineering Design Process graphic from the Teacher Guide's overview for Unit 1. As a class, detail the steps Cooper follows as he builds a solar cooker and improves on his design. What are the criteria? What are the constraints?
- Interested students can develop a multimedia presentation that is designed to teach others about how to make a solar cooker.

Extend

Science Stretch

The **Science Stretch** suggestions inside the book's back cover help students think about what they read. Students can complete one or more as time allows.

Build and test a solar cooker that can heat a bowl of soup. If possible, provide empty pizza boxes and other supplies for students to use.

Draw a diagram that illustrates how energy is transferred and transformed when a marshmallow melts. Have students refer to the diagrams on pp. 9 and 15 of the story as a reference.

Write a blog post that describes three energy transfers during a school day. Examples might include bodies converting energy in food, light bulbs in ceiling lights, sound energy of a musical instrument.

SOCIAL EMOTIONAL LEARNING

How did Cooper use collaboration in this story? Sample answer: He got his older brother to help him set up a solar cooker.

Check for Comprehension Have students write a short paragraph that describes how energy is transferred and transformed in a solar cooker.

EXPLORATION 1 HANDS-ON ACTIVITY

Full of Energy

Activity Guide, pages 90–93

TIME ESTIMATE

SHORT ON TIME?

Rather than have each group observe and collect data at each of five stations, have five groups visit one station each, then combine observations into the data table as a whole class.

POSSIBLE MATERIALS

- ☐ safety goggles
- ☐ bouncy balls
- ☐ popper or pop-up plastic toys
- ☐ pinwheel
- ☐ wind-up cars
- ☐ tuning forks (different sizes)

PREPARATION

The materials list includes materials for five stations. Prepare each of the stations before class begins, and prepare short explanations of the materials in each station.

INVESTIGATIVE PHENOMENON
Each form of energy can be transferred.

Phenomenon Explained Students explore the **investigative phenomenon** by observing a variety of different energy systems, identifying the forms of energy present and recognizing the occurrence of energy transfer. Students record data about their observations.

Form a Question After observing the photograph, students should form a question about how we use energy to do things. If students struggle to form a question, ask them to name different forms of energy at work in the photograph. **Sample answer:** Where does energy come from? Where does energy go? How do we use energy if we can't see it?

STEP 1 Students discuss examples of energy they've observed throughout the day. **Sample answer:** turning on the lights, taking a shower with warm water, warming up food, eating breakfast, the moving of the school bus, listening to morning announcements, riding my bike

STEP 2 Before moving to a station to begin their observations, students consider what a system is and think about what evidence will determine the presence of energy in a system. **Sample answer:** A system is a group of related things that make up a whole. The whole can carry out different functions than the individual pieces. Something moving, making noise, or lighting up are all evidence of energy being present.

STEP 3 Students rotate among the five stations, noting observations. As they record their observations, remind them to think about where the energy originates and what effect its transfer has on the system.

- **Make a Claim** Claims should indicate an understanding that energy can be used to do things because it can be transferred from object to object and place to place.
- **Evidence** Students should cite as evidence the data from the activity that describes a specific form of energy, an energy transfer, and how that transfer resulted in a type of work.
- **Reasoning** Students should explain their reasoning that energy can be used to do things.

FORMATIVE ASSESSMENT

MAKING SENSE OF PHENOMENA

Students gain understanding of energy transfer as they explore the **investigative phenomenon.** They should connect this to the **anchoring phenomenon** that when the band plays music, energy is transferred. Students should understand that each form of energy—motion, light, sound, mechanical, etc.—can be transferred between places and between objects.

REMEDIATION If students struggle to connect the **investigative phenomenon** back to the **anchoring phenomenon,** have them match types of energy in the band scene with types of energy observed at each station.

MAKING SENSE OF PHENOMENA IDEA ORGANIZER

After completing Exploration 1, students can fill in the **Idea Organizer** to summarize the connection between transferring energy and how the band transfers energy when they make music.

SOCIAL EMOTIONAL LEARNING

Have students reflect on their contribution to the group. The following questions should stimulate self-awareness as well as awareness of group dynamics:

- How much did you share your thoughts with the group?
- How did you encourage quieter members of the group to share their thoughts?
- What would you like to do differently the next time you're in a group?

Activity Outcome

Students should identify forms of energy and types of energy transfer to understand that energy transfer causes a change in matter.

Performance Indicators	
	record observations about forms of energy and energy transfer within a system
	make a claim that connects energy transfer to a specific effect within a system
	support the claim using collected data as evidence

EXPLORATION 2 | HANDS-ON ACTIVITY

Light the Bulb

Activity Guide, pages 94–96

TIME ESTIMATE

SHORT ON TIME?

To eliminate time students spend experimenting with circuit components, consider giving groups the correct plan for a working circuit in advance. Alternatively, this exploration can be completed as a whole class.

POSSIBLE MATERIALS

- ☐ battery (size D) with holder
- ☐ light bulb with holder
- ☐ three lengths of wire
- ☐ switch

PREPARATION

Gather enough materials for each group to have a complete set. Prepare for class by separating the materials for each group into a small container or bag. A wire stripper will be included in the kit in order to strip the ends of the wires.

INVESTIGATIVE PHENOMENON
Transformation of energy makes it useful.

Phenomenon Explained Students explore the **investigative phenomenon** by planning, constructing, and testing a simple circuit. They document how to solve design problems by comparing diagrams of their original plans for the circuit with diagrams of their final working circuits.

Form a Question After observing the photograph, students should form a question about what role a circuit might play in powering the flashlight. If students struggle to form a question, ask them to name the energy input/output of the flashlight. **Sample answer:** What is a circuit? How does a circuit help us? How does energy move through a circuit? What things use a circuit?

STEP 1 and 2 Students develop a plan for constructing a circuit, connect the parts according to their plan, and diagram the circuit. **Sample answer:** 1. Place a battery in the holder. 2. Connect a wire from the battery holder to the light switch. 3. Connect a wire from the light bulb to the switch. 4. Connect a wire from the switch to the battery holder. 5. Test the switch to see if the lightbulb lights up. Students' drawing should show a model of how they connected all the pieces.

STEP 3 Students test and revise their circuits until they light up the bulb, then draw and label a diagram of their working circuit. **Sample answer:** Students should describe any changes they made and how the changes lit up the bulb. Students' drawing should show how their circuit helped to make the lightbulb light up.

- **Make a Claim** Claims should indicate an understanding that electrical energy is transformed into light energy in the circuit.
- **Evidence** Students should cite as evidence a description of their working circuit.
- **Reasoning** Students should explain their reasoning that transformation of energy makes it useful by describing how transforming energy stored in a battery makes the lightbulb useful.

FORMATIVE ASSESSMENT

MAKING SENSE OF PHENOMENA

Students gain understanding of how transformation of energy makes it useful as they explore the **investigative phenomenon.** They should connect this to the **anchoring phenomenon** that when the band plays music, energy is transformed from one form to another. Students should understand, for example, that hitting a drum transforms energy of motion into sound energy.

REMEDIATION If students struggle to connect the **investigative phenomenon** back to the **anchoring phenomenon,** have them find examples of electrical energy in the band scene and ask them how it is transformed.

Activity Outcome

Students should plan, construct, and run tests to develop a working circuit.

Performance Indicators	
	record observations about forms of energy and energy transfer within a system
	make a claim that explains how energy transformation can make energy useful
	support the claim using descriptions of how the working circuit transforms energy

MAKING SENSE OF PHENOMENA IDEA ORGANIZER

After completing Exploration 2, students can fill in the **Idea Organizer** to summarize the connection between transformation of energy and the anchoring phenomenon that the band transforms energy when they make music.

SOCIAL EMOTIONAL LEARNING

Have students complete the following "I" statements as a way to identify and evaluate their role in the technical challenge of creating a circuit.

- I find it easy to identify energy when it is . . .
- I can see the need for energy to transform because . . .
- In my group, I am good at . . .

EXPLORATION 3

Energy Is All Around

Activity Guide, pages 97–100

TIME ESTIMATE

Materials Alert For this exploration, it may prove useful to have a variety of batteries on hand for students to contemplate when discussing the many advantages of stored energy.

INVESTIGATIVE PHENOMENON
Stored energy can be used later.

Phenomenon Explained Students explore the **investigative phenomenon** by gathering evidence about how energy stored in coal and batteries transforms into useful forms of energy—energy to power a flashlight, a cell phone, a remote-control drone, a laptop is all part of a system.

Where Does Our Energy Come From?

Everyday Phenomenon **If a gadget or device does not need to be plugged in, it usually gets its electrical energy from a battery.**

Students should connect the **everyday phenomenon** about the battery supplying energy to the **anchoring phenomenon** that stored energy is used to run the band's equipment.

Help students understand that the chemical energy stored in coal transforms into electric current through a process that involves burning the coal. After the electricity is made, it travels from the power station over wires into houses.

Saving It for Later

Ask students to think about the advantages of being able to store chemical energy in batteries. Initiate a discussion about which size of battery is most common or most useful.

Transfer to Transform

Take a minute to discuss light energy. Remind students that heat energy commonly exists along with light energy, and ask them for an example.

Change Forms of Energy

Emphasize the similarities and differences between energy transfer and energy transformation. When energy transfers, it moves from one object to another or from one place to another. When energy transforms, it changes its form. Encourage students to diagram an energy system that includes both an energy transfer and an energy transformation.

SOCIAL EMOTIONAL LEARNING

Have students complete the following "I" statements as a way to identify and evaluate their role in distinguishing between energy transfer and energy transformation.

- I find it easy to identify energy when it is . . .
- I can see the need for energy to transfer because . . .
- In my group, I am good at . . .

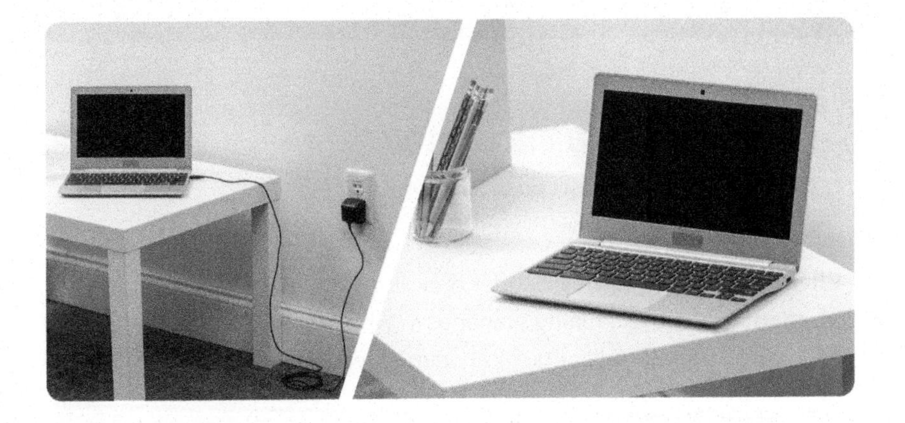

FORMATIVE ASSESSMENT

MAKING SENSE OF PHENOMENA

Students gain understanding of energy transfer as they explore the **investigative phenomenon.** They should connect this to the **anchoring phenomenon** that the energy the band uses to create music originates somewhere else. Some of the instruments get energy from batteries; others use electric current from plugs. While making music, band members transform electrical energy into sound energy.

REMEDIATION If students struggle to connect the **investigative phenomenon** back to the **anchoring phenomenon,** have them point out places where the band seems to be using electricity and ask them to explain where that energy had been previously.

MAKING SENSE OF PHENOMENA IDEA ORGANIZER

After completing Exploration 3, students can fill in the **Idea Organizer** to summarize the connection between energy being transferred and transformed and the anchoring phenomenon that when the band sings, dances, and plays instruments they are transferring and transforming energy.

EXPLORATION 4

Heat

Activity Guide, pages 101–102

TIME ESTIMATE

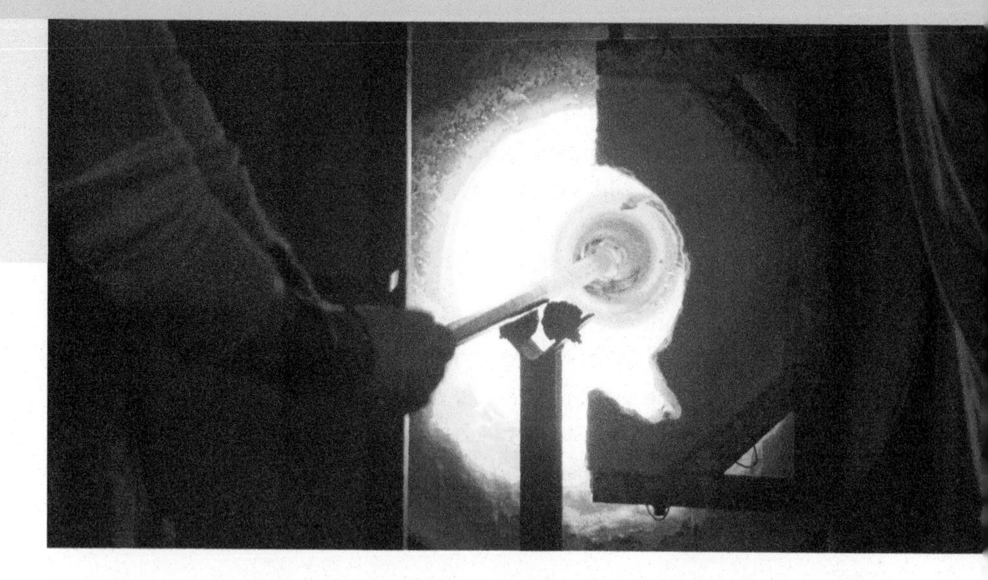

INVESTIGATIVE PHENOMENON
Energy can be transferred as heat.

Phenomenon Explained Students explore the **investigative phenomenon** by examining scenarios in which energy is transferred as heat, with and without contact between objects.

Hot or Not?

Ask students what visual clues they might use to determine whether or not an object is hot. Remind students to look for visual evidence—don't touch!

Hot by Contact

After students contemplate the cooking pancake, ask them to think of another scenario in which heat is transferred by contact, such as snuggling up with a furry pet or taking a hot bath.

Distant Heat

Initiate a discussion about heat from the sun. Ask students how, even from a distance, heat from the sun affects life on Earth.

SOCIAL EMOTIONAL LEARNING

Have students discuss the role of heat transfer in survival stories. Students should define heat stroke and describe ways to help someone suffering from over-heating.

FORMATIVE ASSESSMENT

MAKING SENSE OF PHENOMENA

Students gain understanding of heat as they explore the **investigative phenomenon.** They should connect this to the **anchoring phenomenon** that when the band uses electronic equipment, such as amplifiers, a small amount of heat is released.

REMEDIATION If students struggle to connect the **investigative phenomenon** back to the **anchoring phenomenon,** have them recall other instances in which heat is a byproduct of an energy transfer or transformation.

MAKING SENSE OF PHENOMENA IDEA ORGANIZER

After completing Exploration 4, students can fill in the **Idea Organizer** to summarize the connection between heat and the anchoring phenomenon that when the band uses electronic equipment a small amount of heat is released.

EXPLORATION 5

Energy of Sound

Activity Guide, pages 103–104

TIME ESTIMATE

Materials Alert Access to a stringed instrument and/or a drum and drum stick would enhance student understanding of the relationship between energy level and sound level.

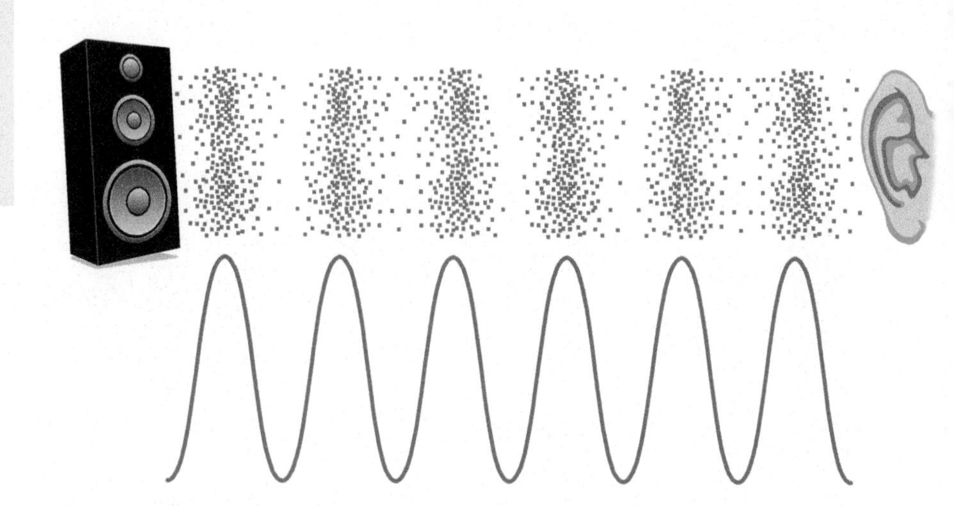

INVESTIGATIVE PHENOMENON
Sound can transfer energy over a distance.

Phenomenon Explained Students explore the **investigative phenomenon** by understanding the relationship between sound waves and vibration. Students identify the source of sound waves and make connections between energy levels and sound intensity.

Sound All Around

Students should understand that sound is the movement of energy through vibrations. Take a moment to compare and contrast the guitarist and the speaker. Have students identify the original energy source of the sound for each photo (motion, electricity).

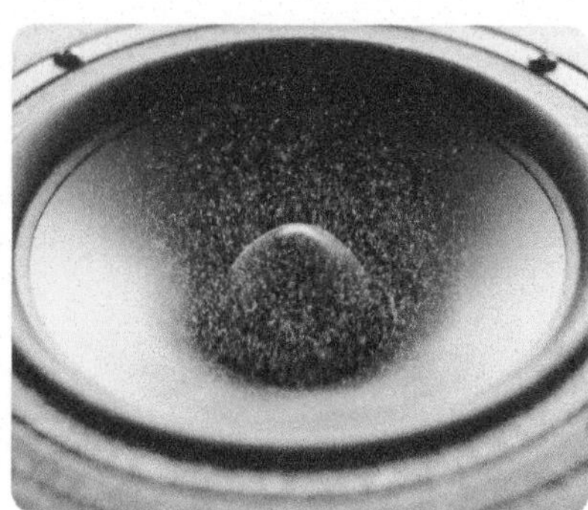

Loud and Soft, High and Low

To help students associate energy levels with sound intensity, pluck a stringed instrument or strike a drum with different degrees of intensity and have students draw a conclusion about the relationship between energy of motion (plucking, striking) and the quality of sound.

SOCIAL EMOTIONAL LEARNING

Have students discuss ways they could support students who are frightened by loud noises. For example, they could explain why the loud noise is happening or sit with them to comfort them.

FORMATIVE ASSESSMENT

MAKING SENSE OF PHENOMENA

Students gain understanding of sound energy as they explore the **investigative phenomenon.** They should connect this to the **anchoring phenomenon** that when the band plays music, energy is transferred and transformed to produce sound, which travels from the speakers to the audience.

REMEDIATION If students struggle to connect the **investigative phenomenon** back to the **anchoring phenomenon**, review the properties of sound energy—that it can travel through air; that it comes from vibrations.

MAKING SENSE OF PHENOMENA IDEA ORGANIZER

After completing Exploration 5, students can fill in the **Idea Organizer** to summarize the connection between sound energy and the anchoring phenomenon that when the band sings, dances, and plays instruments energy is transferred and transformed to produce sound.

LESSON 01

ONLINE-ONLY RESOURCES

Take It Further

Engage • Explore/Explain • Elaborate • Evaluate

TIME ESTIMATE

These Take It Further paths may be completed to enrich and extend students' comprehension of content covered within this lesson.

ONLINE

People in Science & Engineering: Mayra Artiles, Car Engineer; Zena Mitchell, Electrical Engineer

In this feature, students read about engineers Mayra Artiles, a Latin American woman, and Zena Mitchell, an African American woman.

Careers in Science & Engineering: Dr. Michael Alcubierre

Students study the work of Dr. Michael Alcubierre and then write a brief biography about him.

The Paynes and Fast-Traveling Whale Songs

Students learn how whale songs travel through water.

FORMATIVE ASSESSMENT

Lesson Check

Activity Guide, pages 105–107

Engage • Explore/Explain • Elaborate • Evaluate

Can You Explain It?

Now I know or think that . . .

Sample answer: Energy transfer is the movement of energy from place to place. I can tell from the photo that energy is transferred because movement of fingers makes the guitar strings move. Energy is being transformed because some of the instruments are plugged in and they use an electric current to make sound.

After completing the lesson, use the **Making Sense Idea Organizer** to summarize the connections between the **investigative phenomena** and **anchoring phenomenon.**

MAKING CONNECTIONS

After students complete the lesson, they should be able to answer a question about an alternative phenomenon related to when a toaster toasts bread and how the changes that occur are similar to energy transfer and transformation made by the band.

Sample answer: This is similar because the toaster transforms electrical energy into heat and sound (when the bread pops up) as the band does. Heat is also transferred from the glowing coils in the toaster to the bread, just as the band transfers sound energy.

Checkpoints

1. d—electric light
2. a—sound
3. b—an airplane taking off; c—water dripping; d—orchestra playing music; f—kids whispering
4. **Sample answer:** First, I would put in the batteries and turn on the toy. I would then make observations to determine if the toy moves, makes sound, and/or lights up. If so, then I know energy was transferred from the batteries into part of the toy and transformed to make the toy move, make sound, and/or light up.
5. **Sample answer:** The energy came from an electric current. The energy is transformed into microwave and used to warm food. I know heat was involved because the broccoli is warm when it comes out of the microwave.
6. Students' drawing should show a system where energy is being transferred and transformed. The labels should identify the type of energy and how it transfers and transforms. One example could be a circuit or something being plugged into the wall.

SOCIAL EMOTIONAL LEARNING

Have students reflect on the goals they set at the beginning of the lesson. Allow them to discuss how successful they were in meeting their goals.

LESSON

02 Collisions

ANCHORING PHENOMENON

When the wrecking ball hits the wall, the wall moves.

ENGAGE **Can You Explain It?**

Students observe and ask questions about what happens when objects collide. They answer the Can You Explain It? question to describe what happens to the wall when the wrecking ball collides with it.

EVALUATE **Lesson Check**

Students gauge their understanding of the anchoring phenomenon.

HANDS-ON ACTIVITY

EXPLORATION 1 **Test It! Stored Energy in a Rubber Band**

50 min

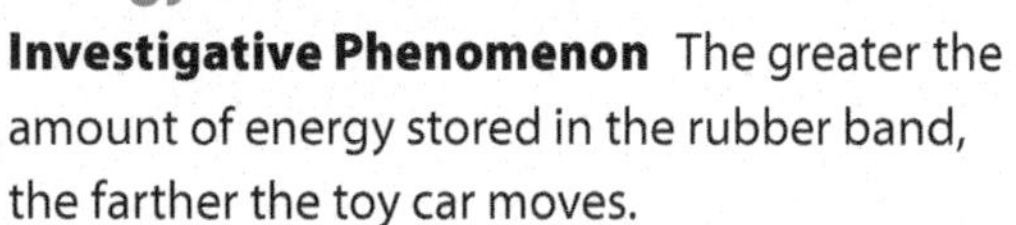

Investigative Phenomenon The greater the amount of energy stored in the rubber band, the farther the toy car moves.

Students should connect back to the **anchoring phenomenon** that the wrecking ball's stored energy of position becomes motion energy that is transferred to the wall during impact.

HANDS-ON ACTIVITY

EXPLORATION 2 **Speed and Energy**

Investigative Phenomenon The faster an object is moving, the greater the energy that can be transferred in a collision.

Students should connect back to the **anchoring phenomenon** that the speed of the wrecking ball affects how much damage is done to the wall.

EXPLORATION 3 **Things That Move Have Energy**

30 min

Investigative Phenomenon Motion energy affects collisions.

Students should connect back to the **anchoring phenomenon** that the speed of the wrecking ball affects how much damage is done to the wall.

EXPLORATION 4 **Collisions**

Investigative Phenomenon Energy is transferred during collisions.

Students should connect back to the **anchoring phenomenon** that when the wrecking ball collides with the wall, energy is transferred, and the wall moves.

Making 3D Connections

The **anchoring phenomenon** in this lesson supports students' understanding of and application of these Next Generation Science Standards.

Building to the Performance Expectations

PE 4-PS3-1 Use evidence to construct an explanation relating the speed of an object to the energy of that object.

PE 4-PS3-3 Ask questions and predict outcomes about the changes in energy that occur when objects collide.

SEP

Asking Questions and Defining Problems Ask questions that can be investigated and predict reasonable outcomes based on patterns such as cause and effect relationships. *(Explorations 1, 3)*

Constructing Explanations and Designing Solutions Use evidence to construct an explanation. Apply scientific ideas to solve design problems. *(Explorations 1)*

DCI

PS3.A Definitions of Energy The faster a given object is moving, the more energy it possesses. *(Explorations 1, 2, 3)*

PS3.B Conservation of Energy and Energy Transfer Energy is present whenever there are moving objects, sound, light, or heat. *(Explorations 1, 3)*

PS3.C Relationship Between Energy and Forces When objects collide, the contact forces transfer energy so as to change the objects' motions. *(Exploration 4)*

CCC

Energy and Matter Energy can be transferred. *(Explorations 2, 3)*

Influence of Engineering, Technology, and Science on Society and the Natural World Engineers improve existing technologies or develop new ones. *(Explorations 3, 4)*

Science as a Human Endeavor Most scientists and engineers work in teams. Science affects everyday life. *(Explorations 3, 4)*

Vocabulary

Word Wall A word wall, anchor chart, or Language Development chart can be used to support vocabulary

collision when two objects bump into each other

You may want to include additional academic terms such as *transform*, *collapse*, *minimize*, and *parallel* and any other terms students might struggle with.

Language Development Prompt students to complete the chart when they come to these highlighted terms within the lesson and to add their own terms as they come across unknown science terms.

Anchor Chart As you progress through the unit, you may want to make a vocabulary-based anchor chart using the Language Development chart as a guide that can be displayed and filled out as a whole group during each lesson.

LESSON

02 Collisions

Activity Guide, pages 108–109

Students can engage in the Can You Explain It? content by observing the photograph or by exploring the corresponding video online.

ONLINE

View a video related to a collision.

ANCHORING PHENOMENON
When the wrecking ball hits the wall, the wall moves.

PHENOMENON EXPLAINED
The wrecking ball uses stored energy to build momentum for a collision with another object.

Lesson Objective

Students can use evidence to recognize the correlation between speed and the amount of energy an object possesses and identify collisions as a form of motion energy.

Support Discovery

The following prompts can be used to guide student-led discovery.

I notice . . .

After observing the photograph or watching the video, students should record what they noticed about the motion of the ball and its effect on the wall. If students struggle to record observations, ask them to describe the wall.

Sample answers: I notice that there is a hole in the wall, maybe made from the wrecking ball.

I wonder . . .

After observing the photograph or watching the video, students should record what they want to understand about the wrecking ball's effect on the wall.

Sample answer: I wonder how the wrecking ball can cause so much damage to the wall.

Can You Explain It?

In the Can You Explain It?, students make an initial claim that explains the **Anchoring Phenomenon.**

Sample answer: The wrecking ball hits the wall so hard that it breaks the wall.

Students will gather evidence about motion energy and energy transfer. This will enable them to give a more complete explanation of the **Anchoring Phenomenon** at the end of the lesson.

Alternative Phenomenon

If students are unfamiliar with large collision objects such as a wrecking ball, remind them of examples of collisions that happen every day, such as bumping into someone in the hallway or walking into a wall while texting. Ask students to describe what happens when two soccer players run very fast toward a ball and they end up colliding. What makes that collision different from simply bumping into each other?

SOCIAL EMOTIONAL LEARNING

Guide students to reflect on their goals from previous lessons and on any feedback they received from their teachers or peers. Then have each student set a personal goal for this lesson and make a plan for how to achieve the goal. Throughout the lesson, take daily breaks for students to track their progress in meeting their goals. As students move from lesson to lesson, they can continue to work towards their initial goals or set new ones. If students struggle setting goals for this lesson, share with them some of the following ideas: identifying how energy is transferred, working with others when not everyone agrees, or preserving when an activity or topic is difficult.

LESSON 02

FUNomenal READER

Course Corrections

WHEN TO USE

SCIENCE 

- Anchoring Phenomenon / Alternative Phenomenon
- Options for ELA Instruction
- Build on Prior Knowledge
- Preview the Phenomenon
- Read to Learn
- Support Sense Making
- Science Stretch
- Check for Comprehension

Option 1 Use before students begin the lesson in the Activity Guide to provide an engaging model to introduce the lesson's phenomenon.

Option 2 Use after students have completed the Activity Guide to reinforce students' understanding of the lesson phenomenon by exploring a related phenomenon.

ELA 20 min

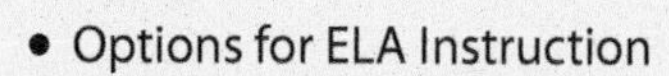

- Options for ELA Instruction
- Build on Prior Knowledge
- Read to Learn

Option 3 To use during designated ELA Reading time for independent reading, whole-class instruction, or small-group instruction, look for this icon: ELA

Plan

ANCHORING PHENOMENON / ALTERNATIVE PHENOMENON

The anchoring phenomenon in the Activity Guide is *When the wrecking ball hits the wall, the wall moves.* The main example is a wrecking ball striking a wall. The FUNomenal Reader presents a similar phenomenon (*Speed affects how much energy is transferred when things collide*), and the example is miniature golf. Both present the same science concepts and cover the same standards but with different phenomena. Guide students to draw connections between the two situations and to understand the underlying principle: energy is transferred when one object collides with another.

Options for ELA Instruction 

Choose one of the following anchor chart options and project it or print copies. Then display and introduce the chart before reading the text. Revisit the chart after reading the text and encourage students to discuss how the skill connects to the text.

Argument Have students consult the online *Science and Engineering Practices Handbook* for more information on the claim-evidence-reasoning format Luciana uses in the story. They can also use the *Parts of an Argument Anchor Chart* as a reference.

Following and Giving Instructions Use the *Following and Giving Instructions Anchor Chart* as you discuss how Luciana learns to improve her miniature golf game by talking with her sister and watching what her sister does. Student pairs can take turns giving and following tips on how to do something.

Respond to Reading After reading, have student pairs use the *3 Big Questions Anchor Chart* to discuss their responses to the story.

Preview

ELA **Build on Prior Knowledge** Students may know that energy is transferred when one object collides with another, but they may not understand how speed relates to the amount of energy transferred. Have student discuss the speed of different colliding objects and how speed affects the motion of the objects.

Preview the Phenomenon Ask students to study the illustration on p. 6 of the story, which shows a girl hitting a miniature golf ball very hard. Encourage students to record the first questions that come into their minds, focusing on the action of the golf swing and the movement of the ball. Point out that their questions might change as they read through the story. Have them keep their questions close by and periodically check to see if any can be answered.

STANDARDS SUPPORTED

SEP

Asking Questions and Defining Problems

Constructing Explanations and Designing Solutions

DCI

PS3.A Definitions of Energy

PS3.B Conservation of Energy and Energy Transfer

PS3.C Relationship Between Energy and Forces

CCC

Energy and Matter

Influence of Engineering, Technology, and Science on Society and the Natural World

Science as a Human Endeavor

Course Corrections (continued)

Discover

Read to Learn 

The **Read to Learn** suggestions inside the book's front cover encourage students to interact with the book multiple times for different purposes.

Preview Students look for unfamiliar words and share them with a partner. New terms may include *collision* and *energy*. Have students look up words they aren't sure about and notice how they are used in the context of the story.

Skim Students skim the illustrations. Have them turn to a partner and share their predictions of what the story will be about.

Read As students read the story, ask them to look for connections to one of the following anchor chart skills. **Argument, Following and Giving Instructions, Respond to Reading**

Support Sense Making

Choose one or more of the following:

- Be sure students can identify the phenomenon presented on the opening pages of the story: speed affects the amount of energy transfer in a collision. Luciana claims that one should hit something as hard as possible to make it go far, as in baseball. The story follows Luciana as she plays miniature golf and realizes that hitting a ball hard is not always the best tactic.
- Have students analyze the claims-evidence-reasoning argument Luciana makes in the story. Is her claim supported by the evidence? In this case, Luciana must adjust her claim based on what she learns during numerous attempts at hitting a ball into a hole. Help students understand that scientists and engineers likewise perform repeated trials and may adjust their hypothesis as they go.
- Discuss the scoring system for miniature golf, in which the winner has the fewest points rather than the most. A player wants to get the ball into the hole with the fewest swings of the club. Ask volunteers to demonstrate how Luciana learned to hit the ball with less force to get a better result. Relate this to the effect of speed on the energy transfer in collisions.

Extend

Science Stretch

The **Science Stretch** suggestions inside the book's back cover help students think about what they read. Students can complete one or more as time allows.

How does speed affect the collision of two balls? **Sample answer:** The more speed an object has, the more motion of energy the object has—and the farther the balls travel.

Design your own mini-golf course. Students can work in pairs to draw a course on paper, or they can use modeling clay or other items you have on hand in the classroom.

When would you want the most energy transfer in a collision? When would you want less? **Sample answer:** I want the most energy transfer when I am kicking a football. I want less when I am hitting a small drum with a drumstick.

SOCIAL EMOTIONAL LEARNING

How can you react when someone doesn't agree with you? **Sample answer:** I can calmly explain my thinking and listen carefully to the other person's ideas.

Check for Comprehension Have students write a short paragraph that describes how energy is transferred during a collision between a golf club and a ball.

EXPLORATION 1 | HANDS-ON ACTIVITY

Test It! Stored Energy in a Rubber Band

Activity Guide, pages 110–113

TIME ESTIMATE

SHORT ON TIME?

This activity can be done as a whole class to save the amount of time individual groups would take to plan and conduct the investigation.

POSSIBLE MATERIALS

- ☐ safety goggles
- ☐ giant rubber band
- ☐ tape
- ☐ chair
- ☐ ruler
- ☐ toy car or truck
- ☐ meterstick
- ☐ index card

PREPARATION

Clear a space on the floor large enough for students to conduct their experiments. Help students choose roles in their groups, such as materials manager, data taker, and cleanup crew. Distribute materials to students prior to starting the activity.

INVESTIGATIVE PHENOMENON

The greater the amount of energy stored in the rubber band, the farther the toy car moves.

Phenomenon Explained Students explore the **investigative phenomenon** by conducting a test to show that the amount of stored energy in the rubber band determines how far the car moves.

Form a Question After observing the photograph, students should form a question about energy stored in the pole as it bends. If students struggle to form a question, remind them of how the band used stored energy to play music. **Sample answers:** How does energy get stored? How can someone use stored energy?

STEP 1 Students establish a way to measure how far the rubber band is pulled to ensure there will be consistency in the amount of stored energy as they conduct the investigation. **Sample answer:** The marks will represent different amounts of energy that the stretched rubber band will store. They are important because this way everyone is pulling back the car the same amount.

STEP 2 and 3 Before students test the device, they review their investigation question. Suggest they make comparisons about the results as they record data about the stored energy of the rubber band.

STEP 4 Their presentation results should show that the car traveled farther when the rubber band was stretched farther back, thus increasing its stored energy.

- **Make a Claim** Claims should indicate that the amount of stored energy changes depending on how far the rubber band is stretched.
- **Evidence** Students should cite as evidence the data from the activity that shows that the toy travels farther when the rubber band is stretched farther.
- **Reasoning** Students should explain their reasoning that more energy is stored the more the rubber band is stretched. That energy is then transferred to the toy, affecting how far it travels.

FORMATIVE ASSESSMENT

MAKING SENSE OF PHENOMENA

As they explore the **investigative phenomenon**, students gain understanding that the stored energy of the rubber band becomes the motion energy that is transferred to the toy. They should connect this to the **anchoring phenomenon** that the wrecking ball's stored energy becomes motion energy that is transferred to the wall during impact. Students should understand that energy can be stored, transformed into motion energy, and transferred.

REMEDIATION If students struggle to connect the **investigative phenomenon** back to the **anchoring phenomenon,** have them compare the rubber band with the wrecking ball and the toy with the wall.

Activity Outcome

Students should design and follow the steps of the test in order to observe that the car went farther when the more the rubber band was stretched.

Performance Indicators	
	measure and record distance the car traveled relative to the distance the rubber band was stretched
	make a claim that the amount of stored energy can change
	support the claim using collected data as evidence

MAKING SENSE OF PHENOMENA IDEA ORGANIZER

After completing Exploration 1, students can fill in the **Idea Organizer** to summarize the connection between stored energy and the anchoring phenomenon that the wrecking ball's stored energy becomes motion energy that is transferred to the wall during impact.

SOCIAL EMOTIONAL LEARNING

Have students discuss how they communicate with friends or family members when they work together in other aspects of their lives. The following promotes effective communication:

- actively listening to everyone
- giving others the opportunity to share their ideas
- having a judgement-free zone
- giving feedback respectfully

EXPLORATION 2 HANDS-ON ACTIVITY

Speed and Energy

Activity Guide, pages 114–116

TIME ESTIMATE

SHORT ON TIME?

This activity can be done as a whole class to save the amount of time individual groups would take to set up and conduct the investigation.

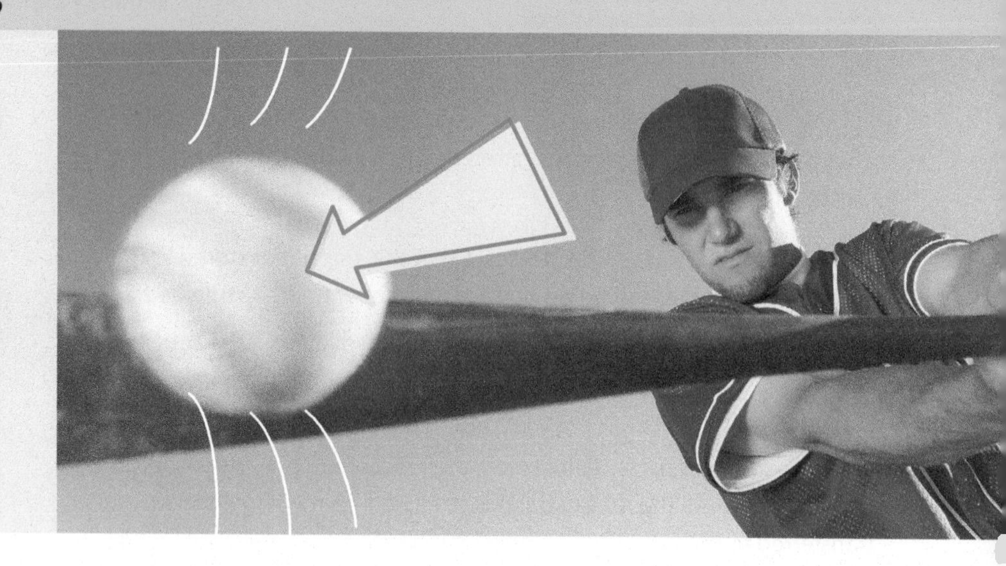

POSSIBLE MATERIALS

- ☐ string
- ☐ large plastic cup
- ☐ medium wooden block
- ☐ masking tape

PREPARATION

Decide if this will be an individual, small-group, or classroom activity, and distribute materials as needed. Consider asking students to measure how far the cup moves or to record their observations. If this is a classroom activity, have someone record observations on the board.

INVESTIGATIVE PHENOMENON

The faster an object is moving, the greater the energy that can be transferred in a collision.

Phenomenon Explained Students explore the **investigative phenomenon** by observing how a block moving at different speeds causes the cup to move. As the block is swung, its stored energy becomes motion energy. Students repeat the act of swinging the block to confirm their observations.

Form a Question After observing the photograph, students should form a question about how the swing of the bat affects the motion of the ball. If students struggle to form a question, ask them to think about how far the ball goes in a home run versus when it's just tossed casually. **Sample answer:** How does an object's energy affect its speed?

STEP 1 Students swing the block only a few centimeters and observe how it moves the cup. A small, slow swing will not move the cup much. **Sample answers:** The cup moved a little. The block knocked into the cup and pushed it.

STEP 2 Students repeat the exercise several more times, each time increasing the swing of the block. They should observe greater movement of the cup as the speed of the block increases with bigger swings. **Sample answer:** The second time the block knocked into the cup, it pushed it farther on the desk. The last time, the cup moved very far across the table.

- **Make a Claim** Claims should indicate that the speed of the block affects how far the cup moves.
- **Evidence** Students should cite as evidence the distance the cup travels in relation to how fast the swing of the block was.
- **Reasoning** Students should explain their reasoning that a faster swing has more energy, so it moves the cup farther when they collide.

FORMATIVE ASSESSMENT

MAKING SENSE OF PHENOMENA

As they explore the **investigative phenomenon**, students gain understanding that speed increases the motion energy that is transferred to the cup. They should connect this to the **anchoring phenomenon** that the wrecking ball's speed will affect the amount of energy that is transferred to the wall during impact. Students should understand that the block had stored energy which increased as speed increased, resulting in greater motion energy.

REMEDIATION If students struggle to connect the **investigative phenomenon** back to the **anchoring phenomenon,** have them compare the block with the wrecking ball and the cup with the wall.

MAKING SENSE OF PHENOMENA IDEA ORGANIZER

After completing Exploration 2, students can fill in the **Idea Organizer** to summarize the connection between how speed increases the motion energy being transferred in a collision and the anchoring phenomenon of how the wrecking ball's speed will affect the amount of energy transferred to the wall during impact.

Activity Outcome

Students should follow the steps of the experiment in order to observe that the cup moved more when the block swung faster.

Performance Indicators	
	follow instructions to conduct the experiment
	remember or take note of observations
	make a claim that the speed of the block's swing affects how much the cup moves
	support the claim using observations as evidence

SOCIAL EMOTIONAL LEARNING

Have students discuss how they make sure they understand a task in other aspects of their life, such as sports or chores. The following are strategies for understanding instructions:

- Read the instructions multiple times, or ask to hear them repeated.
- Form questions to address anything that's unclear.
- Ask the teacher or another student questions.
- Repeat the instructions to ensure accuracy.

EXPLORATION 3

Things That Move Have Energy

Activity Guide, pages 117–118

TIME ESTIMATE

Materials Alert For this exploration have a few medium-sized balls handy so that students can demonstrate motion energy as it relates to stored energy and speed. If you choose to replicate the bowling activity, have three cups on hand to serve as pins.

INVESTIGATIVE PHENOMENON
Motion energy affects collisions.

Phenomenon Explained Students explore the **investigative phenomenon** by examining examples in which stored energy is changed to motion energy. Examples also demonstrate that speed can increase motion energy, which in turn affects collisions.

Falling Objects

Everyday Phenomenon **A falling book transforms stored energy to motion energy.**

Students should connect the **everyday phenomenon** that falling objects transform stored energy into motion energy to the **investigative phenomenon** that stored energy transforming into motion energy can affect collisions.

Have students look at the picture of the dish on the shelf. Explain that the higher up the dish is on the shelf, the more stored energy it has because of the pull of gravity acting on the dish. When it falls, that stored energy becomes motion energy. Have students consider what would happen if the dish fell from a lower shelf.

Let's Go Bowling!

If time allows, have students mimic the bowling activity shown on page 116. Set up three cups (facing up) and hand out a few small balls. Let students try rolling the ball toward the cups at different speeds as the class observes.

FORMATIVE ASSESSMENT

MAKING SENSE OF PHENOMENA

As they explore the **investigative phenomenon**, students gain understanding that motion energy affects objects when they collide. They should connect this to the **anchoring phenomenon** that the speed of the wrecking ball affects how much damage is done to the wall. Students should understand that speed increases motion energy, producing a larger collision.

REMEDIATION If students struggle to connect the **investigative phenomenon** back to the **anchoring phenomenon**, have them predict the motion of the pins when a bowling ball is rolled slowly versus quickly. If you are conducting a classroom activity, demonstrate the result after the students make their predictions. They should assume that the faster ball will move the cups more.

MAKING SENSE OF PHENOMENA IDEA ORGANIZER

After completing Exploration 3, students can fill in the **Idea Organizer** to summarize the connection between how motion energy affects objects when they collide and the anchoring phenomenon that the speed of the wrecking ball affects how much damage is done to the wall.

EXPLORATION 4

Collisions

Activity Guide, pages 119–120

TIME ESTIMATE

Materials Alert For this exploration, have paper and markers handy for students to work in groups or as a class to brainstorm questions about the kinds of equipment needed in crash test dummies.

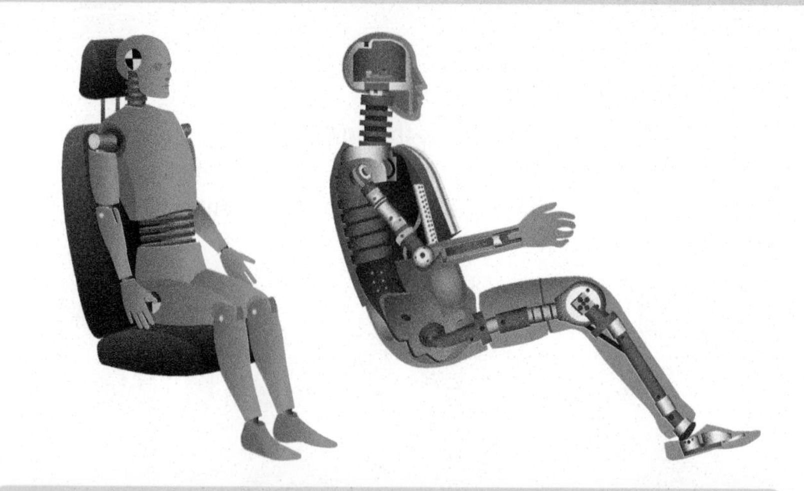

INVESTIGATIVE PHENOMENON
Energy is transferred during collisions.

Phenomenon Explained Students explore the **investigative phenomenon** by examining real-world examples in which energy is transferred during both large and small collisions. In these collisions, some energy is transformed into heat or sound energy.

Crashing Dummies

Everyday Phenomenon **When a baseball bat hits a ball, you can hear the collision, and the ball changes direction.**

Students should understand that a collision affects the object that is hit. Motion energy from the first object is transferred to the second, often with visible signs of impact. Have students compare and describe the two images of the car crashing into the wall. How does the impact look different in each? Students should understand that the speed of the car affects the magnitude of the collision. With this in mind, have students develop questions about what types of sensors and equipment they think should be installed inside a crash test dummy.

Too Hot to Handle!

When objects collide, they don't just transfer energy between them. They also transfer energy into the air around them. The hammer produces a loud noise—sound energy—when it strikes the nail. The head of the hammer and nail become warm because heat is produced as a result of the energy transference. Have students give examples of energy transfers that result in loud sounds or heat. Have students connect back to the band needing a fan when they played music. Heat can be evidence of energy being transferred and or transformed.

SOCIAL EMOTIONAL LEARNING

Have students discuss how they stay safe at school. The following are recommendations for safety:

- Follow school rules.
- Follow safety instructions in class.
- Respect and follow instructions from group members who are acting as safety monitors.

In the classroom, consider inviting students to participate in drafting policies, rules, and procedures.

FORMATIVE ASSESSMENT

MAKING SENSE OF PHENOMENA

As they explore the **investigative phenomenon**, students gain understanding that energy is transferred in collisions. They should connect this to the **anchoring phenomenon** that when the wrecking ball collides with the wall, energy is transferred and the wall moves. Students should understand that some energy is transferred to the wall, causing it to break, and some energy is changed to sound and heat.

REMEDIATION If students struggle to connect the **investigative phenomenon** back to the **anchoring phenomenon,** have them brainstorm collisions they witness every day. They may list more obvious examples of collisions, such as people bumping into each other, or less obvious examples, such as people or animals walking. Prompt them to think about the effects of those collisions on the objects involved.

MAKING SENSE OF PHENOMENA IDEA ORGANIZER

After completing Exploration 4, students can fill in the **Idea Organizer** to summarize the connection between energy being transferred in a collision and how when the wrecking ball collides with the wall, energy is transferred and the wall moves.

LESSON 02

ONLINE-ONLY RESOURCES

Take It Further

Engage • Explore/Explain • Elaborate • Evaluate

TIME ESTIMATE

These Take It Further paths may be completed to enrich and extend students' comprehension of content covered within this lesson.

ONLINE 

People in Science & Engineering: Amanda Steffy

In this feature, students read about NASA engineer Amanda Steffy. She and her team test tires that must handle tough conditions on Mars, such as extremely cold weather and very sharp or loose rocks.

Bump!

Students research how the bumpers of cars have changed over time. (No outside research required.)

Collision Game!

Students design and build a game that uses the stored energy. (Outside research required.)

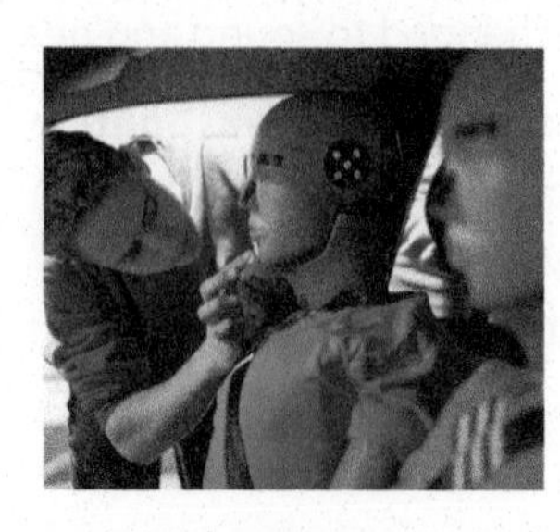

Careers in Science & Engineering: Crash Test Engineer

Students learn about people who are responsible for making sure moving vehicles meet safety standards.

FORMATIVE ASSESSMENT

Lesson Check

Activity Guide, pages 121–123

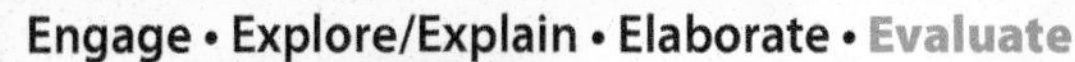

Can You Explain It?

Now I know or think that . . .

Sample answer: When the wrecking ball hit the wall, it caused the wall to move and made a loud sound. Energy moved between the wrecking ball and wall when they collided. The more speed the ball has, the more motion energy it has. When there is more energy, more damage can occur.

After completing the lesson, use the **Making Sense Idea Organizer** to summarize the connections between the **investigative phenomena** and **anchoring phenomenon.**

MAKING CONNECTIONS

After students complete the lesson, they should be able to describe the transfer of energy in collisions as large as a wrecking ball and as small as the falling blocks. This is a cause-and-effect relationship in which stored energy is transformed into motion energy and then transferred to the next block in line.

Sample answer: The falling blocks are similar to the wrecking ball because the energy that a falling block has moves to the next block when they collide. This pattern repeats until all the blocks have fallen over.

Checkpoints

1. a, c, d
2. **Sample answer:** An engineer uses the data the crash test dummy provides to make the car safer and more durable if it crashes. Then, real people in the car will be less hurt in a crash.
3. b—The energy is stored energy.
4. **Sample answer:** The lighter arrow should travel farther when the same amount of energy is used from an equally stretched bow. (Students should know this from the examples they have looked at so far.)
5. **Sample answer:** Energy from the ball moves into the gong, producing a sound and making the gong move. A faster ball strikes the gong with greater force and the sound will be louder.
6. d—It loses some of its energy.
7. **Sample answer:** The balls will collide, and the faster ball will knock the other ball out of the way.
8. **Sample answer:** A hockey player uses a collision because when they hit the puck, the energy is transferred, and the puck moves.

SOCIAL EMOTIONAL LEARNING

Have students reflect on the goals they set at the beginning of the lesson. Ask them to think about whether the goals were accomplished or if there were challenges. Have students share the factors that contributed to their success.

LESSON

03 Waves

ANCHORING PHENOMENON

Ocean waves cause a surfer to move.

ENGAGE **Can You Explain It?**

Students observe and ask questions about how the surfer moves through the water. They answer the Can You Explain It? question to predict how they think water moves a surfer toward the shore.

EVALUATE **Lesson Check**

Students gauge their understanding of the anchoring phenomenon.

HANDS-ON ACTIVITY

EXPLORATION 1 **Let's Make Waves!** 50 min

Investigative Phenomena Waves move through different mediums.

Students should connect back to the **anchoring phenomenon** that waves can occur in the ocean.

HANDS-ON ACTIVITY

EXPLORATION 2 **Bobbing and Waving** 30 min

Investigative Phenomena Waves move a cork up and down.

Students should connect back to the **anchoring phenomenon** that the surfer can ride ocean waves because of the energy waves carry.

EXPLORATION 3 60 min

How Waves Transfer Energy

Investigative Phenomena Waves carry energy.

Students should connect back to the **anchoring phenomenon** that the energy the waves carry can move the surfer.

EXPLORATION 4 **Wave Parts** 30 min

Investigative Phenomena Waves have different parts.

Students should connect back to the **anchoring phenomenon** that because of the different parts of a wave, the surfer is able to stand up on the board and ride an ocean wave.

Making 3D Connections

The **anchoring phenomenon** in this lesson supports students' understanding of and application of these Next Generation Science Standards.

Building to the Performance Expectations

PE 4-PS4-1 Develop a model of waves to describe patterns in terms of amplitude and wavelength and that waves can cause objects to move.

SEP

Developing and Using Models Develop a model using an analogy, example, or abstract representation to describe a scientific principle. *(Explorations 1, 2, 3, 4)*

Scientific Knowledge is Based on Empirical Evidence Science findings are based on recognizing patterns. *(Explorations 1, 2, 3, 4)*

DCI

PS4.A Wave Properties Waves, which are regular patterns of motion, can be made in water by disturbing the surface. When waves move across the surface of deep water, the water goes up and down in place; there is no net motion in the direction of the wave except when the water meets a beach. Waves of the same type can differ in amplitude (height of the wave) and wavelength (spacing between wave peaks). *(Explorations 1, 2, 3, 4)*

CCC

Patterns Similarities and differences in patterns can be used to sort and classify natural phenomena. Similarities and differences in patterns can be used to sort and classify designed products. *(Explorations 1,2, 3, 4)*

Vocabulary

Word Wall

A word wall, anchor chart, or Language Development chart can be used to support vocabulary.

wave a disturbance that carries energy, such as sound or light

crest the highest point on a wave

trough is the lowest point on a wave

wavelength the distance between a point on one wave's crest or trough and the identical point on the next wave

amplitude height of a wave; it is half the distance from the crest to the trough

volume loudness

You may want to include additional academic terms such as *adjacent, compressed disturbance, expand, identical, particles, seismic,* and *vacuum* and any other terms students might struggle with.

Language Development Prompt students to complete the chart when they come to these highlighted terms within the lesson and to add their own terms as they come across unknown science terms.

Anchor Chart As you progress through the unit, you may want to make a vocabulary-based anchor chart using the Language Development chart as a guide that can be displayed and filled out as a whole group during each lesson.

LESSON

03 Waves

Activity Guide, pages 124–125

Students can engage in the Can You Explain It? content by observing the photograph or by exploring the corresponding video online.

ONLINE 

View a video to see how a surfer moves along a wave.

ANCHORING PHENOMENON
Ocean waves cause a surfer to move.

PHENOMENON EXPLAINED
The waves carry energy that moves the surfer on the water.

Lesson Objective

Students will develop a model to explore wave patterns. They will use their model to differentiate between wavelength and amplitude as well as observe how waves interact.

Support Discovery

The following prompts can be used to guide student-led discovery.

I notice . . .

After observing the photograph or watching the video, students should record what they noticed about the surfer or the wave. If students struggle to record observations, ask them to observe any changes and to describe the location of the surfer or characteristics of the wave.

Sample answer: I notice that the surfer moves along the surface of the water.

I wonder . . .

After observing the photograph or watching the video, students should record what they want to learn about how surfing works.

Sample answer: I wonder how the surfer stays on top of the water and keeps moving.

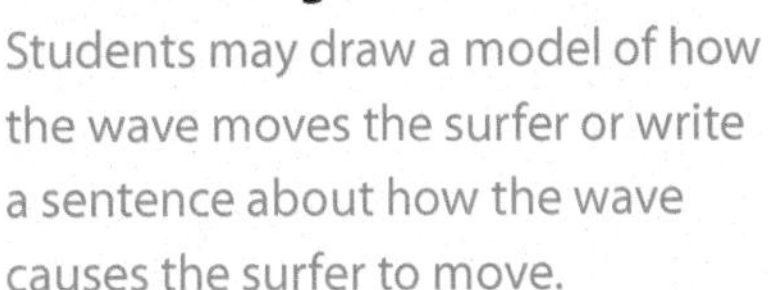

In the Can You Explain It?, students make an initial claim that explains the **Anchoring Phenomenon.** Students may draw a model of how the wave moves the surfer or write a sentence about how the wave causes the surfer to move.

Students will gather evidence about how waves transfer energy. This will enable them to give a more complete explanation of the **Anchoring Phenomenon** at the end of the lesson.

Alternative Phenomenon

If students are unfamiliar with surfing or ocean waves, guide them to think of other examples of water waves, such as ones that move a sponge in a tub of soapy water. You may want to bring a dish tub and sponge to class so that students can make in-person observations of how water waves can make objects move.

SOCIAL EMOTIONAL LEARNING

Guide students to reflect on their goals from previous lessons and on any feedback they received from their teachers or peers. Then have each student set a personal goal for this lesson and make a plan for how to achieve the goal. Throughout the lesson, take daily breaks for students to track their progress in meeting their goals. As students move from lesson to lesson, they can continue to work towards their initial goals or set new ones. If students struggle setting goals for this lesson, share with them some of the following ideas: explaing how waves move, analyzing data, or ensuring everyone in the group has a chance to share.

LESSON 03

FUNomenal READER

Breaking Glass

WHEN TO USE

SCIENCE 

- Anchoring Phenomenon / Alternative Phenomenon
- Options for ELA Instruction
- Build on Prior Knowledge
- Preview the Phenomenon
- Read to Learn
- Support Sense Making
- Science Stretch
- Check for Comprehension

Option 1 Use before students begin the lesson in the Activity Guide to provide an engaging model to introduce the lesson's phenomenon.

Option 2 Use after students have completed the Activity Guide to reinforce students' understanding of the lesson phenomenon by exploring a related phenomenon.

ELA 20 min

- Options for ELA Instruction
- Build on Prior Knowledge
- Read to Learn

Option 3 To use during designated ELA Reading time for independent reading, whole-class instruction, or small-group instruction, look for this icon: ELA

Plan

ANCHORING PHENOMENON / ALTERNATIVE PHENOMENON

The anchoring phenomenon in the Activity Guide is *Ocean waves cause a surfer to move,* and the main example is a person on a surfboard riding a wave. The FUNomenal Reader presents a similar phenomenon (*Sound waves carry energy that can shatter a glass*), and the example is a singer whose voice can shatter glass. Both present the same science concepts and cover the same standards but with different phenomena. Guide students to draw connections between the two situations and to understand the underlying principle: waves create motion through the transfer of energy.

Options for ELA Instruction 

Choose one of the following anchor chart options and project it or print copies. Then display and introduce the chart before reading the text. Revisit the chart after reading the text and encourage students to discuss how the skill connects to the text.

Learning Mindset Have student pairs study the *My Learning Mindset Anchor Chart* and then decide which of the traits describe Terrell, the story's protagonist. Challenge partners to find where in the story he shows these traits. Have them consider if these are good traits for studying science.

Ask and Answer Questions Use the *Ask and Answer Questions Anchor Chart* when introducing, developing, or reviewing those skills in the context of this story. Discuss how Terrell asks questions in the story to find out more about sound waves.

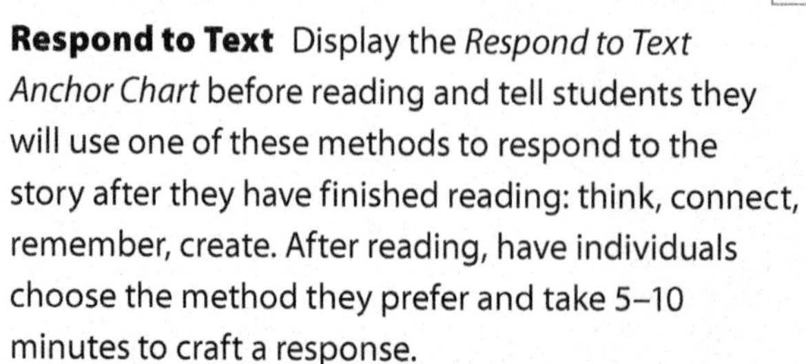

Respond to Text Display the *Respond to Text Anchor Chart* before reading and tell students they will use one of these methods to respond to the story after they have finished reading: think, connect, remember, create. After reading, have individuals choose the method they prefer and take 5–10 minutes to craft a response.

Preview

ELA **Build on Prior Knowledge** Have students discuss where they see waves in everyday life. For example, students may see wavelike motions when they shake sheets or towels when folding laundry. They already know that waves move, but they may not know that there are different kinds of waves.

Preview the Phenomenon Ask students to study the illustration on p. 2 of the story, which shows a boy watching a TV show in which a singer's voice causes windows to break. Encourage students to record the first questions that come into their minds, focusing on what's happening on the TV screen. Point out that their questions might change as they read through the story. Have them keep their questions handy and periodically check to see if any can be answered.

STANDARDS SUPPORTED

SEP

Developing and Using Models

Scientific Knowledge is Based on Empirical Evidence

DCI

PS4.A Wave Properties

CCC

Patterns

Breaking Glass (continued)

Discover

Read to Learn

The **Read to Learn** suggestions inside the book's front cover encourage students to interact with the book multiple times for different purposes.

Preview Students look for unfamiliar words and share them with a partner. New terms may include *wave, crest, trough, amplitude,* and *wavelength.* Have students look up words they aren't sure about and notice how they are used in the context of the story.

Skim Students skim the illustrations and photos. Have them turn to a partner and share their predictions of what the story will be about.

Read As students read the story, ask them to look for connections to one of the following anchor chart skills. **Learning Mindset, Ask and Answer Questions, Respond to Text**

Support Sense Making

Choose one or more of the following:

- Demonstrate for students the sound waves that are produced by a drum. Bring a small drum into the classroom or use a tightly stretched material. Then pass it around the room so each student has a chance to strike the drum and observe how the drum vibrates. If feasible, provide safe and appropriate materials for students to make their own drums.
- Have students consider the term "noise pollution." Invite volunteers to describe noises in the local area that can be irritating or even harmful, including farm machinery, jackhammers, and noise from airplanes. Have partners discuss ways in which people can be protected from harmful noises, especially those with a high decibel level and/or a long duration. Solutions include changing airplane flight paths and adding soundproofing to highways and public transportation.
- Mrs. Abbasi says, "Anything is possible with physics." As a class, discuss what she means by this statement. As Terrell discovers, sound can break glass under unusual and very tightly controlled conditions—but it is not an everyday occurrence.

Extend

Science Stretch

The **Science Stretch** suggestions inside the book's back cover help students think about what they read. Students can complete one or more as time allows.

Suppose you are a sound wave. What happens as you move through an ear? Provide a diagram of the inner ear for students to use as they write their imaginative description.

Research how buildings are designed to have the best acoustics. Present what you learned. Provide appropriate books or a set of links to online sites about acoustics for students to use.

Place two fingers on your upper throat and then hum. What do you notice when you hum loudly and softly? **Sample answer:** When I hum loudly, the vibrations are stronger. When I hum softly, the vibrations are weaker.

SOCIAL EMOTIONAL LEARNING

Draw and label some sound waves and ask a classmate for feedback. Listen respectfully to the classmate's opinions. As needed, model for students how to give and receive feedback.

Check for Comprehension Have students write three things they found out in the story, two things they found interesting, and one question they still have about sound waves.

EXPLORATION 1 HANDS-ON ACTIVITY

Let's Make Waves!

Activity Guide, pages 126–127

TIME ESTIMATE

SHORT ON TIME?

Arrange students into several small groups. Assign each group one of the lab steps. Have groups share what they learned from their part of the activity in class discussion.

POSSIBLE MATERIALS

- ☐ plastic container
- ☐ table tennis ball
- ☐ water
- ☐ puffed rice
- ☐ shoebox
- ☐ speaker or smartphone
- ☐ large, round cloth
- ☐ safety goggles

PREPARATION

Preassemble the materials so that each pair of students can pick up their box of materials and be ready to start the activity.

Some materials in this activity are edible. Before the activity, discuss why it is important not to eat anything in the science lab. Foster good safety practices by prohibiting students from eating the rice.

INVESTIGATIVE PHENOMENON
Waves move through different mediums.

Phenomenon Explained Students explore the **investigative phenomenon** by observing the behavior of water waves, sound waves, and mechanical waves. Students gather evidence about how each wave type interacts with the medium through which it travels.

Form a Question After observing the photograph, students should form a question about waves. **Sample answers:** How are waves formed? How do waves move?

STEP 1 Students generate waves in a pan of water to observe how the waves move a floating ball. **Sample answer:** The ball moved up and down in the water. When I tapped the water, the water made waves that moved the ball.

STEP 2 Students use sound from a speaker or a smartphone to vibrate a shoebox. They observe patterns in the movement of puffed rice on top of the box. **Sample answer:** The rice is bouncing on the box with the music. Louder sounds make the rice move more.

STEP 3 Students observe the motion of a large, round cloth as they use it to produce waves. Ask students to compare how the waves moved in each medium that they tested in Steps 1–3. **Sample answer:** As the water waves moved across the pan, the ball bobbed. The sound waves made the puffed rice bounce. The cloth wave moved across the cloth.

- **Make a Claim** Claims should state that waves can move a medium and objects in contact with a medium.
- **Evidence** Students should provide observations of how each medium moved or caused an object in contact with the medium to move. For example, water waves caused a floating ball to move.
- **Reasoning** Students should explain that the waves provide the energy needed to move a medium or an object. This was seen when the rice bounced on the box with the speaker.

FORMATIVE ASSESSMENT

MAKING SENSE OF PHENOMENA

Students gain understanding that waves travel through a medium and that waves can move objects as they explore the **investigative phenomenon.** They should connect this to the **anchoring phenomenon** that waves can move a surfer on a wave. Students should relate the movement of the wave through the water to the movement of the surfer.

REMEDIATION If students struggle to connect the **investigative phenomenon** back to the **anchoring phenomenon,** have them discuss what would happen to a surfer if waves did not move water.

Activity Outcome

Students should make observations of waves in each medium to determine that all waves carry energy that can move objects.

Performance Indicators	
	record observations about waves and the motion of objects
	make a claim that waves carry energy that can move objects
	support the claim using observations as evidence

MAKING SENSE OF PHENOMENA IDEA ORGANIZER

After completing Exploration 1, students can fill in the **Idea Organizer** to summarize the connection between waves traveling through a medium and that they can move objects and the anchoring phenomenon that the waves can move a surfer.

SOCIAL EMOTIONAL LEARNING

Have students discuss when individuals in a group might have different ideas. Encourage them to compare times when multiple ideas are helpful and when they could be distracting. Discuss why it is important to listen respectfully to all ideas presented in a group, even if they are not accepted in the end or used by the group to explain a phenomenon or design a solution.

EXPLORATION 2 HANDS-ON ACTIVITY

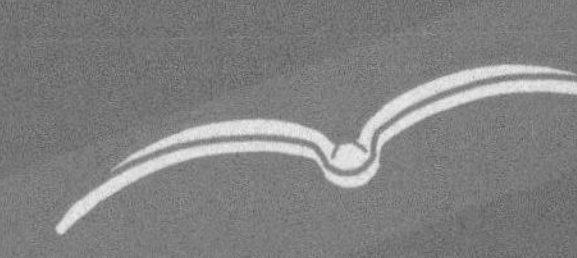

Bobbing and Waving

Activity Guide, pages 129–130

TIME ESTIMATE

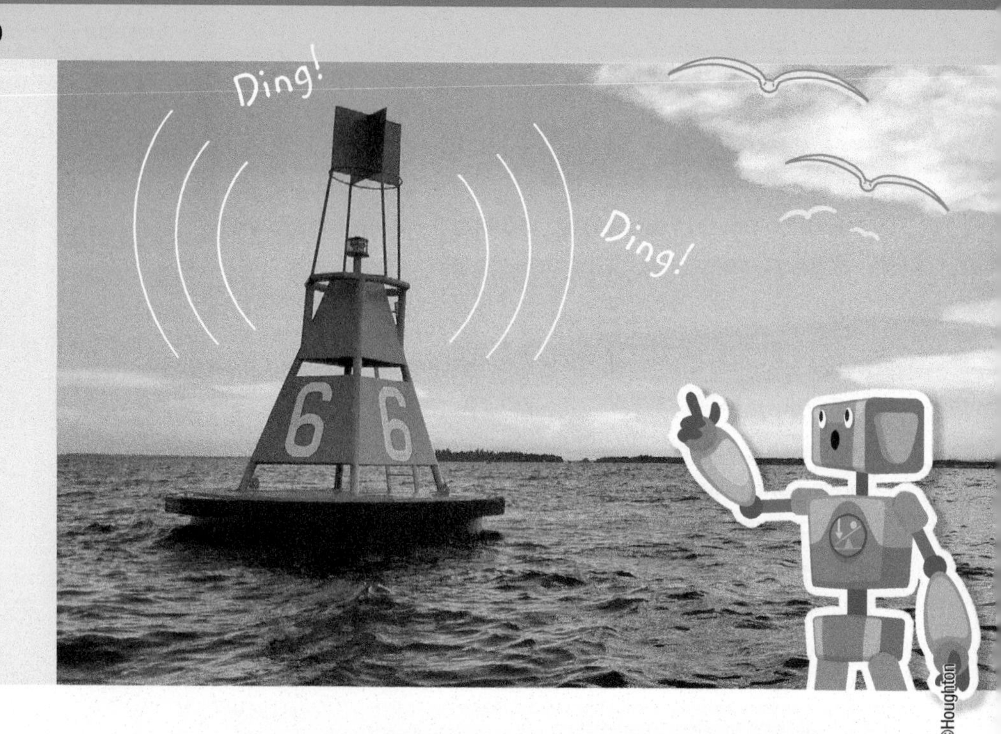

SHORT ON TIME?

This activity also works well as a teacher demonstration.

Encourage students to observe the motion of the waves and the cork from the top and side of the container. Have volunteers share their observations in class discussion.

POSSIBLE MATERIALS

- ☐ plastic container
- ☐ water
- ☐ cork

PREPARATION

This activity can cause splashing, so gather several towels to clean up water that could become a slip/fall hazard. Give students aprons to protect their clothing.

Materials Alert Consider filming the movement of the cork in the container using a smartphone or video camera. Students can use the slow motion feature to observe how the cork moves with the water.

INVESTIGATIVE PHENOMENON

Waves move a cork up and down.

Phenomenon Explained Students explore the **investigative phenomenon** by observing how a cork behaves in water. They gather evidence about how changing the energy of waves in the water affects the movement of the cork.

Form a Question After observing the photograph, students should form a question about how waves affect buoys. Sample answers: Why don't buoys float away?

STEP 1 Students observe what happens when they drop a cork into a container of water. Sample answer: I observe the cork moving up and down. I observe the cork moving slightly in the water.

STEP 2 As they rock the container, students observe how increasing wave energy affects the motion of the cork. Students should record what they see the cork doing as they rock the container. **Sample answer:** The cork moves a greater distance when the waves are stronger.

- **Make a Claim** Claims should state that waves in the container move the cork.
- **Evidence** Students should provide observations of how the cork moved when they rocked the container to provide more wave energy.
- **Reasoning** Students should explain that the cork's motion depends on the energy of waves in the container. When the waves had more energy, the corked moved more.

FORMATIVE ASSESSMENT

MAKING SENSE OF PHENOMENA

Students should gain an understanding that waves move floating objects as they explore the **investigative phenomenon.** Students should also observe that changing the energy of a wave changes the motion it produces. They should connect these observations to the **anchoring phenomenon** by comparing the motion of a cork in the container with the motion of a surfer on a wave.

REMEDIATION If students struggle to connect the **investigative phenomenon** back to the **anchoring phenomenon,** ask them to compare a floating cork to a floating surf board.

MAKING SENSE OF PHENOMENA IDEA ORGANIZER

After completing Exploration 2, students can fill in the **Idea Organizer** to summarize the connection between waves moving floating objects and the anchoring phenomenon that the change in energy of the waves changes the movement of the surfer.

Activity Outcome

Students should observe how waves with different energy move the cork.

Performance Indicators	
	record the observation that a wave moves a floating cork up and down
	explain that adding more energy to the wave will change the motion of the cork

EXPLORATION 3

How Waves Transfer Energy

Activity Guide, pages 131–134

TIME ESTIMATE

Materials Alert Have a jump rope and a stretchy spring available to demonstrate the wave types presented in this Exploration.

INVESTIGATIVE PHENOMENON
Waves carry energy.

Phenomenon Explained Students explore the **investigative phenomenon** by gathering evidence that waves carry energy.

Waves 101

Have students use the image of the ripple waves on p. 129 to identify evidence that the rock that formed the waves was small (*the ripples are small and close together*). Use a drawing task or a quick write activity for students to explain how the ripples in the image would change if the rock were larger.

Ocean Waves and Energy Transfer

Students may use a flow chart model to show each energy transfer involved in ocean waves that crash on the shore. The flow chart should include: wind → water → beach and/or air (as sound).

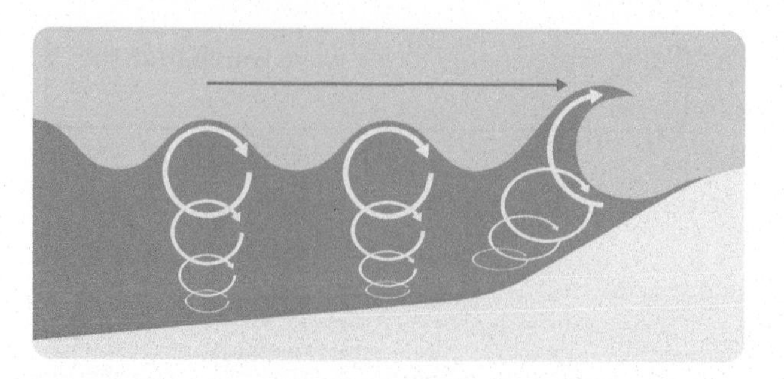

Waves That Move Up and Down

Use a jump rope to demonstrate up and down waves. Ask a student volunteer to hold one end of the jump rope very still at waist height. Send a wave down the rope. Ask students to use one hand to show the direction the rope moves and the direction that the wave travels.

Shake Like a Quake!

Explain that a loud sound results from large waves, then use a think-pair-share activity to have students predict how they could model soft and loud sounds using a stretchy spring. Use the spring to test some of the students' predictions. Guide students to observe that compressing more coils of the spring will lead to a larger wave in the spring.

Have students conduct research to learn more about earthquake waves. They should discover that both wave types described in the Exploration are present in the Earth system during an earthquake.

SOCIAL EMOTIONAL LEARNING

Have volunteers share how music has helped changed their mood. Discuss how some songs make us calm, while others help us feel more energetic. Give students a few minutes to make a list of three of their favorite songs and when they might benefit from listening to each one.

FORMATIVE ASSESSMENT

MAKING SENSE OF PHENOMENA

As they explore the **investigative phenomenon**, students gain the understanding that there are different types of waves, but that all waves carry energy. They should connect this to the **anchoring phenomenon** that a water wave carries energy that can move a surfer toward the shore.

REMEDIATION If students struggle to connect the **investigative phenomenon** back to the **anchoring phenomenon,** ask a student to hold one end of a jump rope while you send a single wave down the rope. Tell students to imagine that the wave in the rope is an ocean wave carrying a surfer towards the shore.

MAKING SENSE OF PHENOMENA IDEA ORGANIZER

After completing Exploration 3, students can fill in the **Idea Organizer** to summarize the connection between the different types of waves and how much energy they carry and the anchoring phenomenon that a water wave carries energy that can move a surfer toward the shore.

EXPLORATION 4

Wave Parts

Activity Guide, pages 135–138

TIME ESTIMATE

Materials Alert Have graph paper and colored pencils available for students to practice drawing waves with different wavelengths and amplitudes.

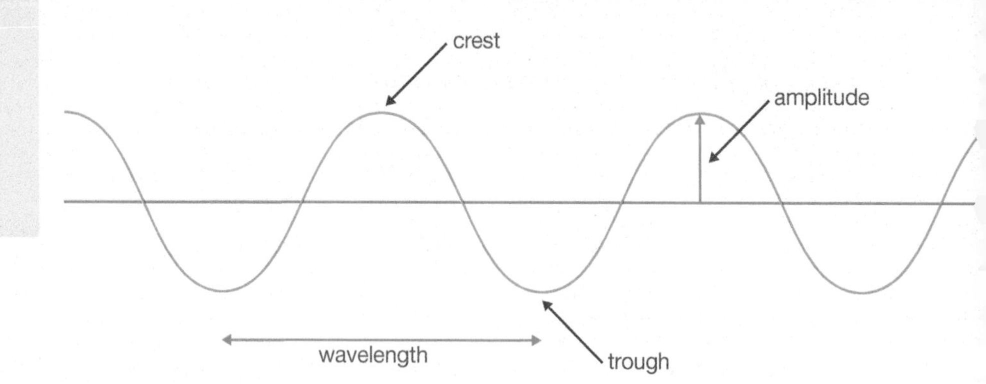

INVESTIGATIVE PHENOMENON
Waves have different parts.

Phenomenon Explained Students explore the **investigative phenomenon** by identifying wave parts on a diagram and by comparing wave characteristics for different sounds.

Can You Hear This?

Draw students' attention to the different artistic representations of sound waves. After they compare the waves, have students form pairs to discuss what they learn from the representations about the relationship between amplitude and the distance between the crest and trough (*The smaller the amplitude, the smaller the distance; the bigger the amplitude, the bigger the distance*).

Everyday Phenomenon **You feel the vibrations on the ground as a large truck drives by.**

Ask students if they have ever felt the vibrations of a large truck traveling along a nearby road. Explain that the truck generates waves that travel through the ground. You feel the waves as they vibrate your feet up and down. You do not feel the waves generated by a person walking on the same road because the waves the person makes have a much smaller amplitude. Help students make connections between the vibrations a truck makes to the vibrations made by the speakers when the band played instruments. Have students also discuss what types of vibrations were made when the wrecking ball hit the building. Compare the amplitude of each of these examples.

SOCIAL EMOTIONAL LEARNING

Have students work in pairs to model waves, then ask volunteers to share their modeling method with the class. **Sample answer:** We could work together by holding hands and moving our arms up and down to make the shape of a wave.

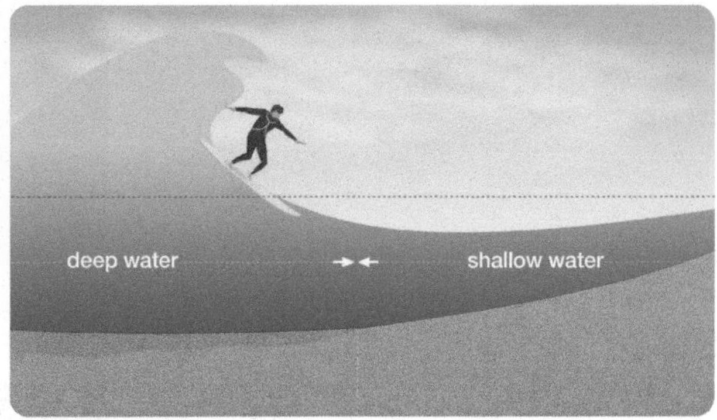

FORMATIVE ASSESSMENT

MAKING SENSE OF PHENOMENA

Students learn about different wave parts as they explore the **investigative phenomenon**. They should connect this to the **anchoring phenomenon** that a surfer is able to stand up on his board and ride an ocean wave because a wave has different parts.

REMEDIATION If students struggle to connect the **investigative phenomenon** back to the **anchoring phenomenon,** have them look at the image of the surfer at the beginning of the lesson. Ask them to identify where the surfer must be located to ride a wave to the shore (*near the crest of the wave*).

MAKING SENSE OF PHENOMENA IDEA ORGANIZER

After completing Exploration 4, students can fill in the **Idea Organizer** to summarize the connection between wave parts and the anchoring phenomenon that the parts of the wave help move the surfer.

LESSON 03

ONLINE-ONLY RESOURCES

Take It Further

Engage • Explore/Explain • Elaborate • Evaluate

TIME ESTIMATE

These Take It Further paths may be completed to enrich and extend students' comprehension of content covered within this lesson.

ONLINE

People in Science & Engineering: Christian Doppler, Debra Fischer, Wanda Diaz-Merced

In this feature, students read about the origins and applications of the Doppler effect. Dr. Debra Fischer, an astrophysicist, applies the Doppler effect to find planets. Dr. Wanda Diaz-Merced, a blind, Latin-American astronomer, uses sound to represent large sets of data. Help students connect the information in this section to their understanding of wave types and parts.

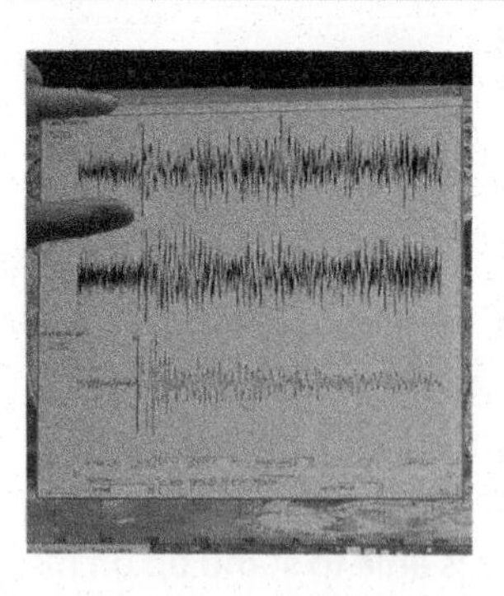

Seismic Waves and Earthquakes

Students explore the definition of seismic waves and learn about how this information is applied to the study of earthquakes. They can learn about the careers of seismologists. (Outside research required.)

Theater Acoustics

Students carry out research about design of acoustics in theaters and how acoustics are used to magnify and increase the range of sound waves. (Outside research required.)

FORMATIVE ASSESSMENT

Lesson Check

Activity Guide, pages 139–141

Engage • Explore/Explain • Elaborate • Evaluate

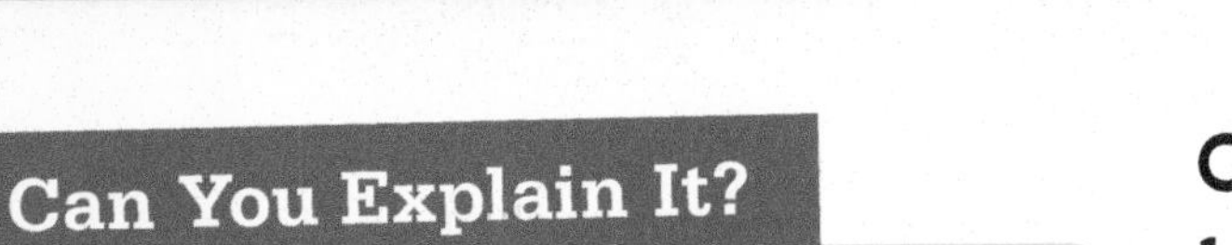

Can You Explain It?

Now I know or think that . . .

Sample answer: Waves carry energy through movement. A surfer wants to be sure to paddle out to the waves through the troughs and jump up onto the board before the waves crest. Surfers need to know about the energy in the waves and need to pay attention to the size (or amplitude) of waves. The spacing between waves (the wavelength) is also important.

After completing the lesson, use the **Making Sense Idea Organizer** to summarize the connections between the **investigative phenomena** and **anchoring phenomenon.**

MAKING CONNECTIONS

After students complete the lesson, they should be able to answer a question about an alternative phenomenon. Here they explain evidence of a wave moving through a medium other than water (parachute cloth is to ball as water is to surfer).

Sample answer: The waves in the parachute are similar to the waves in the ocean because both waves carry energy and, as the waves move, they transfer energy to the ball.

Checkpoints

1. d
2. **Sample answer:** As it passes me, I may bob up and down a little. I would feel the energy of the wave push past me toward shore.
3. The earthquake was very strong. A high amplitude means that the earthquake waves have a lot of energy.
4. Students should label **a** at the top of the wave (crest), **b** at the bottom of the wave (trough), **c** on line with arrows at both ends (wavelength), and **d** (amplitude) is the arrow going from center line (midpoint of wave) to crest.
5. **Sample answer:** The distance from one trough to the next is the same as the distance from one crest to the next. The crest is the top of the wave, and the trough is the bottom. The distance between two crests or troughs is the wavelength.
6. Sound waves with more energy and volume have larger amplitudes. Sound waves with less energy and volume have smaller amplitudes.

SOCIAL EMOTIONAL LEARNING

Have students reflect on the goals they set at the beginning of the lesson. Ask them to think about whether the goals were accomplished or if there were challenges. Have students share the factors that contributed to their success.

LESSON

04 Information Transfer

ANCHORING PHENOMENON

A satellite sends information from space to Earth.

ENGAGE **Can You Explain It?**

Students observe and ask questions about how a satellite transfers information to Earth. They answer the Can You Explain It? question to predict how they think information is transmitted between satellites and Earth.

EVALUATE **Lesson Check**

Students gauge their understanding of the anchoring phenomenon.

HANDS-ON ACTIVITY

EXPLORATION 1 **Engineer It! • Communication Solution**

Investigative Phenomenon You can transmit information across distances.

Students should connect back to the **anchoring phenomenon** that a satellite uses codes to transmit information.

HANDS-ON ACTIVITY

EXPLORATION 2 **Pixels to Pictures**

30 min

Investigative Phenomenon Pixels are put together to send information.

Students should connect back to the **anchoring phenomenon** that the satellite uses digitized codes to transmit information.

EXPLORATION 3 **History of Information Transfer**

Investigative Phenomenon Information can be transferred in many ways.

Students should connect back to the **anchoring phenomenon** that a satellite uses codes to transmit information.

EXPLORATION 4 **Bits and Bytes**

Investigative Phenomenon Digitized information can be transmitted over long distances.

Students should connect back to the **anchoring phenomenon** that digitized information is sent from Earth to satellites in space and back to Earth.

Making 3D Connections

The **anchoring phenomenon** in this lesson supports students' understanding of and application of these Next Generation Science Standards.

Building to the Performance Expectations

PE 4-PS4-3 Generate and compare multiple solutions that use patterns to transfer information.

3-5-ETS1-2 Generate and compare multiple possible solutions to a problem based on how well each is likely to meet the criteria and constraints of the problem.

SEP

Constructing Explanations and Designing Solutions Generate and compare multiple solutions to a problem based on how well they meet the criteria and constraints of the design solution. *(Explorations 1, 3)*

DCI

PS4.C Information Technologies and Instrumentation Digitized information is transmitted over long distances without significant degradation. *(Explorations 1,2, 3, 4)*

ETS1.C Optimizing the Design Solution Different solutions need to be tested in order to determine which of them best solves the problem, given the criteria and the constraints. *(Explorations 1,3)*

CCC

Patterns Similarities and differences in patterns can be used to sort and classify natural phenomena. Similarities and differences in patterns can be used to sort and classify designed products. *(Explorations 1,2, 3)*

Interdependence of Science, Engineering, and Technology Knowledge of relevant scientific concepts and research findings is important in engineering. *(Explorations 1,3)*

Vocabulary

Word Wall A word wall, anchor chart, or Language Development chart can be used to support vocabulary.

pixel a dot that makes a picture

code a system of letters, numbers, or symbols that are used in place of words or letters

You may want to include additional academic terms such as *accurate, beneficial, convert, decode, digital, efficient, encode, exist, magnify, network, pulse, realistic, relay, resolution,* and *universal* and any other terms students might struggle with.

Language Development Prompt students to complete the chart when they come to these highlighted terms within the lesson and to add their own terms as they come across unknown science terms.

Anchor Chart As you progress through the unit, you may want to make a vocabulary-based anchor chart using the Language Development chart as a guide that can be displayed and filled out as a whole group during each lesson.

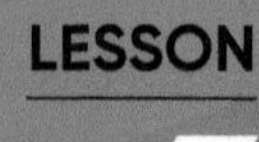

LESSON

04 Information Transfer

Activity Guide, pages 142–143

Students can engage in the Can You Explain It? content by observing the photograph or by exploring the corresponding video online.

ONLINE 

View a video about communication satellites.

ANCHORING PHENOMENON
A satellite sends information from space to Earth.

PHENOMENON EXPLAINED
Satellites are in outer space and can send digitized information from long distances.

Lesson Objective

Students explore and compare patterns in multiple methods of transferring information and transfer information using codes and pixels.

Support Discovery

The following prompts can be used to guide student-led discovery.

I notice . . .

After observing the photograph or watching the video, students should record what they noticed about the satellite. If students struggle to record observations, ask them to identify where the satellite is in relation to Earth.

Sample answer: I notice that the satellite is in space.

I wonder . . .

After observing the photograph or watching the video, students should consider how information might be sent over great distances.

Sample answers: I wonder what the satellite is used for. I wonder how the satellite got into space.

Can You Explain It?

In the Can You Explain It?, students make an initial claim that explains the **Anchoring Phenomenon.** Students may draw a model of how the satellite sends information through waves, or they might write a sentence about how the satellite uses waves to send information through the air.

Students will gather evidence about how information is transferred. This will enable them to give a more complete explanation of the **Anchoring Phenomenon** at the end of the lesson.

Alternative Phenomenon

If students are unfamiliar with satellites and their role in telecommunication, guide them to consider how they communicate, or send and receive information, each day. They listen to the radio, download a podcast, exchange texts or emails, watch a video online, post messages and images to social media accounts, and so on. Then, point out how various means of communication rely on satellites.

SOCIAL EMOTIONAL LEARNING

Guide students to reflect on their goals from previous lessons and on any feedback they received from their teachers or peers. Then have each student set a personal goal for this lesson and make a plan for how to achieve the goal. Throughout the lesson, take daily breaks for students to track their progress in meeting their goals. As students move from lesson to lesson, they can continue to work towards their initial goals or set new ones.

LESSON 04

FUNomenal READER

Talking Drums

WHEN TO USE

SCIENCE 30 min

- Anchoring Phenomenon / Alternative Phenomenon
- Options for ELA Instruction
- Build on Prior Knowledge
- Preview the Phenomenon
- Read to Learn
- Support Sense Making
- Science Stretch
- Check for Comprehension

Option 1 Use before students begin the lesson in the Activity Guide to provide an engaging model to introduce the lesson's phenomenon.

Option 2 Use after students have completed the Activity Guide to reinforce students' understanding of the lesson phenomenon by exploring a related phenomenon.

ELA 20 min

- Options for ELA Instruction
- Build on Prior Knowledge
- Read to Learn

Option 3 To use during designated ELA Reading time for independent reading, whole-class instruction, or small-group instruction, look for this icon: 

Plan

ANCHORING PHENOMENON / ALTERNATIVE PHENOMENON

The anchoring phenomenon in the Activity Guide is *A satellite sends information from space to Earth,* and the main example is a communications satellite in space. The FUNomenal Reader presents a similar phenomenon (*West African cultures used drums to communicate*), and the example is a Nigerian drum called a *dundun.* Both present the same science concepts and cover the same standards but with different phenomena. Guide students to draw connections between the two situations and to understand the underlying principle: information can be transferred from place to place.

Options for ELA Instruction 

Choose one of the following anchor chart options and project it or print copies. Then display and introduce the chart before reading the text.

Text Features Have students refer to the *Text Features Anchor Chart* to help them identify the various text features in this story. As they page through the story, students should notice a map, a diagram, a webpage, and illustrations. Guide them to understand that these visual features help explain ideas in the text.

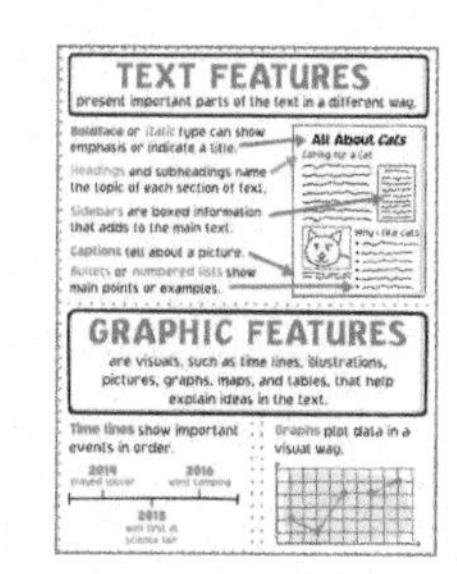

Informational Text Use the *Informational Text Anchor Chart* to discuss the difference between literary and informational text. Help students understand that this story has fictional characters (Oladunni and her father) presenting factual information about a Nigerian method of communicating with drums.

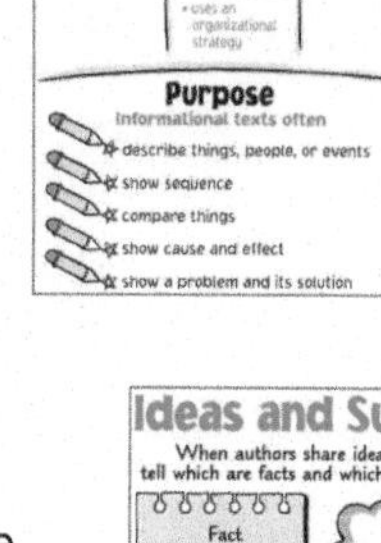

Ideas and Support Use the *Ideas and Support Anchor Chart* to discuss the difference between fact and opinion. Have students determine if these and other statements are fact or opinion: *People have many ways to communicate with one another.* (fact) *Talking drums are the best way to communicate.* (opinion) *Today, talking drums in Nigeria have a ceremonial role.* (fact)

Preview

ELA **Build on Prior Knowledge** Gesture to students to stand. Wait a moment, and gesture for them to sit down. Discuss how you were able to communicate without words. Ask if this would be a good way of communicating with someone who was in another room or another town. Discuss different ways people can send or receive information over a distance.

Preview the Phenomenon Ask students to study the illustration on page 3 of the story, which shows a girl holding a Nigerian drum she has found in a closet. Encourage students to record the first questions that come into their minds, focusing on the drum and what it might be used for. Point out that their questions might change as they read through the story. Have them keep their questions close by and periodically check to see if any can be answered.

STANDARDS SUPPORTED

SEP

Constructing Explanations and Designing Solutions

DCI

PS4.C Information Technologies and Instrumentation

ETS1.C Optimizing the Design Solution

CCC

Patterns

Interdependence of Science, Engineering, and Technology

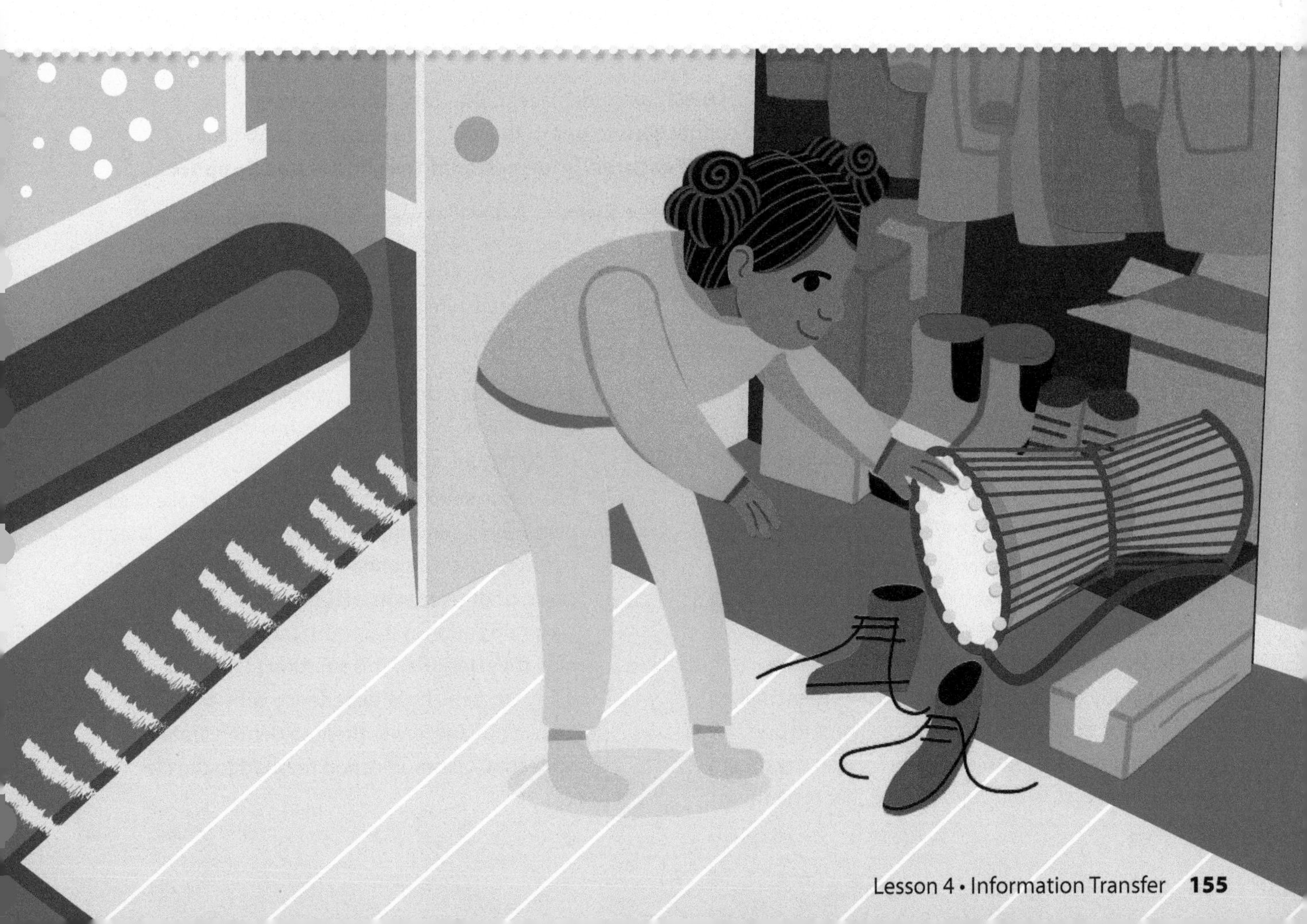

Talking Drums (continued)

Discover

Read to Learn

The **Read to Learn** suggestions inside the book's front cover encourage students to interact with the book multiple times for different purposes.

Preview Students look for unfamiliar words and share them with a partner. New terms may include the Yoruba words *baba, baba agba,* and *kanago.* Have students look up words they aren't sure about and notice how they are used in the context of the story.

Skim Students skim the illustrations and photos. Have them turn to a partner and share their predictions of what the story will be about.

Read As students read the story, ask them to look for connections to one of the following anchor chart skills. **Text Features, Informational Text, Ideas and Support**

Support Sense Making

Choose one or more of the following:

- Be sure students can identify the phenomenon presented on the opening pages of the story: Oladunni finds a Nigerian drum at home and wonders what it is. The story follows her efforts to learn how such drums were once used by Yoruba people as a means of communication.
- Remind students that the definition of *technology* is "something that meets a need or a want." Have students walk around the classroom, jotting down any technology they see. Have them make a T-chart to show the technology items in one column and the problems they solve in the other column. Be sure they understand that something as simple as a drum or a pencil can be considered to be technology. Discuss technology as it is used for communication purposes.
- Challenge small groups of students to make their own way of communicating without words. They might use a series of hand taps, whistles, picture cards, or other means. Have groups share their communication system with the class and explain how they designed this solution to a problem. If any students have experience with American Sign Language, invite them to demonstrate this nonverbal communication method to the class.

Extend

Science Stretch

The **Science Stretch** suggestions inside the book's back cover help students think about what they read. Students can complete one or more as time allows.

Develop a coded message to send using the rhythmic patterns made by a drum. Have students refer to the description in the story of how a talking drum is used and then develop their own method.

Research and make a model of one of the drums in the story. Provide appropriate books or a set of links to online sites about Nigeria for students to use as a reference.

What are the pros and cons of communicating with a drum? **Sample answer:** The drum works best in the morning and evening, and the person on the other end has to understand the drum tones. A cell phone works at any time of day, but its battery can run down.

SOCIAL EMOTIONAL LEARNING

What did you learn about communication from this story? Share your ideas with a classmate. Make sure students listen respectfully to their partner's opinions without interrupting.

Check for Comprehension Ask: *How has the way the Yoruba people communicate over long distances changed over the years?* **Sample answer:** The Yoruba people once used drums and other instruments for communicating over long distances, but now they can use cell phones and email.

EXPLORATION 1 HANDS-ON ACTIVITY

Engineer It! • Communication Solution

Activity Guide, pages 144–146

TIME ESTIMATE

SHORT ON TIME?

This activity can be done as a whole class to save the amount of time individual groups would take to plan and conduct the investigation.

POSSIBLE MATERIALS

- ☐ cardboard
- ☐ cardboard tubes
- ☐ cups
- ☐ glue
- ☐ paper
- ☐ scissors
- ☐ string

PREPARATION

Distribute materials to students prior to starting the activity.

INVESTIGATIVE PHENOMENON
You can transmit information across distances.

Phenomenon Explained Students explore the **investigative phenomenon** by modeling a means to communicate that uses patterns to transfer information. Students test their design solution and record their observations.

Form a Question After observing the photograph, students should form a question about ways to communicate across distances. If students struggle to form a question, ask them to consider what they would do if they wanted to send an important message to someone far away. **Sample answer:** How can you send a message across long distances?

STEP 1 Students explore ways to use patterns to transfer information and then draw a model of their communication solution. Students' drawing should show a model of their solution.

STEP 2 Students make and test their design solution and record their observations. Students should record their observations about how well their communication solution worked. They may even add notes to the model drawn in STEP 1.

STEP 3 As groups compare their work, remind them to focus on how to improve their designs by testing and retesting and to record all results as evidence that they can use to support claims about their design.

- **Make a Claim** Claims should indicate how using patterns relates to transferring information.
- **Evidence** Students should cite as evidence the results from testing and improving their designs for a communication solution.
- **Reasoning** Students should explain how useful patterns are for communicating across long distances.

FORMATIVE ASSESSMENT

MAKING SENSE OF PHENOMENA

Students gain an understanding of how patterns can encode information to be transmitted as they explore the **investigative phenomenon.** They should connect this to the **anchoring phenomenon** that a satellite uses codes to transmit information. Students should understand that patterns and codes are used to transfer information, or communicate, across distances.

REMEDIATION If students struggle to connect the **investigative phenomenon** back to the **anchoring phenomenon,** have them discuss what they have learned so far about satellites (they send information back and forth to Earth).

Activity Outcome

Students should test and retest their communication solutions and determine if their design solves the problem.

Performance Indicators	
	record observations about transferring information
	make a claim that patterns help to transfer information across distances
	support the claim using collected data as evidence

MAKING SENSE OF PHENOMENA IDEA ORGANIZER

After completing Exploration 1, students can fill in the **Idea Organizer** to summarize the connection between using patterns to communicate over long distances and the anchoring phenomenon that the satellite encodes information and then sends it long distances to be decoded.

SOCIAL EMOTIONAL LEARNING

Before students share their communication solutions, discuss the interplay of competition and collaboration in science. *Ask, Why is it important to communicate your results to others?*

Discuss the importance of:

- giving others the opportunity to share their ideas
- building on the ideas of each other
- giving others credit, or acknowledgment, for their ideas
- listening and observing

EXPLORATION 2 HANDS-ON ACTIVITY

Pixels to Pictures

Activity Guide, pages 147–149

TIME ESTIMATE

SHORT ON TIME?

This activity can be done as a whole class to save the amount of time individual groups would take to plan and conduct the investigation.

POSSIBLE MATERIALS

- ☐ colored pencils
- ☐ metric ruler
- ☐ paper

PREPARATION

Distribute materials to students prior to starting the activity.

INVESTIGATIVE PHENOMENON
Pixels are put together to send information.

Phenomenon Explained Students explore the **investigative phenomenon** by using grids as models to demonstrate how they can use pixels and the binary code to send and receive images and messages.

Form a Question After observing the photograph, students should form a question about how pixels transfer information. If students struggle to form a question, help them relate pixels to pieces of a puzzle, and ask what they see once they complete a puzzle (a picture). Sample answer: How can pixels be used to send pictures?

STEP 1 and 2 Students color in the 1s in a grid of 1s and 0s (binary code) to find a message. Hi

STEP 3 Students draw a 10×10 grid. Each box on the grid represents one pixel.

STEP 4 Students fill in the grid with 1s and 0s (binary code) to write a message or represent an image. Boxes with 1s reveal the information.

- **Make a Claim** Claims should indicate that an image made of many smaller pixels is clearer than an image with fewer, larger pixels.
- **Evidence** Students should cite as evidence the appearance of the colored pixels in their grids.
- **Reasoning** Students should realize how they were able to put pixels together by using binary code (1s and 0s) to send information or represent an image.

FORMATIVE ASSESSMENT

MAKING SENSE OF PHENOMENA

Students gain an understanding of how multiple pixels can be used to send information as they explore the **investigative phenomenon.** They should connect this to the **anchoring phenomenon** that a satellite uses digitized codes to transmit information. Students should understand that pixels are used to transfer information across distances.

REMEDIATION If students struggle to connect the **investigative phenomenon** back to the **anchoring phenomenon,** have them discuss how they used pixels and code to make or find a message or image, and then relate that experience to how satellites might transfer information.

Activity Outcome

Students should have another student use their grid to find the message or image being transmitted by pixels.

	Performance Indicators
	complete a grid with boxes representing pixels that use code (1s and 0s) to send information
	make a claim that pixels can be used to send information
	support the claim using the color-coded grid as evidence

MAKING SENSE OF PHENOMENA IDEA ORGANIZER

After completing Exploration 2, students can fill in the **Idea Organizer** to summarize the connection using pixels to digitize information and the anchoring phenomenon that a satellite uses digitized codes to transmit information.

SOCIAL EMOTIONAL LEARNING

Have students discuss how they communicate with friends or family members and how they use teamwork in other aspects of their lives. The following promote effective communication and teamwork:

- actively listening to everyone
- giving others the opportunity to share their ideas
- having a judgement-free zone
- not one person dominating/ doing all of the work
- building on the ideas of others

EXPLORATION 3

History of Information Transfer

Activity Guide, pages 150–153

TIME ESTIMATE

INVESTIGATIVE PHENOMENON
Information can be transferred in many ways.

Phenomenon Explained Students explore the **investigative phenomenon** by reading about the history of information transfer to understand how the methods and devices that humans use to communicate over long distances have changed over time.

The Old Ways

Everyday Phenomenon **Throughout history, humans have used codes and signals to transfer information.**

Students should understand that throughout history humans have used codes and signals to transfer information long before digitized information existed. To help students understand this, turn off the lights and, using a flashlight, make long and short bursts of light. Describe how the light is a coded message that someone would decode in order to understand the message.

Newer Ways

Guide students to connect the discovery of electricity to advances in communication technology and how such advances continue today.

Telegraphs

When an operator tapped out a message in Morse code, it sounded like a series of beeps, with a dash sounding slightly longer than a dot. Operators could also flash lights to send messages in Morse code across a valley or from ship to shore and ship to ship.

Codes

Shorthand is method of rapid writing that uses symbols and abbreviations. When you *encode* a message, it looks like scrambled nonsense; the person who *decodes* the message must use the same code to unscramble it. Some people can "crack the code."

FORMATIVE ASSESSMENT

MAKING SENSE OF PHENOMENA

Students gain understanding of the different ways codes have been used to transfer information as they explore the **investigative phenomenon.** They should connect this to the **anchoring phenomenon** that the satellite uses codes to transmit information. Students should understand that information can be encoded and transferred in many ways.

REMEDIATION If students struggle to connect the **investigative phenomenon** back to the **anchoring phenomenon,** have them work with a partner to discuss the purpose of a spy satellite. Then, have them devise their own code to send secret messages.

MAKING SENSE OF PHENOMENA IDEA ORGANIZER

After completing Exploration 3, students can fill in the **Idea Organizer** to summarize the connection between the different way codes have been used to transfer information and the anchoring phenomenon that a satellite uses codes to transmit information.

EXPLORATION 4

Bits and Bytes

Activity Guide, pages 154–158

TIME ESTIMATE

Materials Alert For this Exploration, have a hand lens available so students can look at the binary code.

INVESTIGATIVE PHENOMENON
Digitized information can be transmitted over long distances.

Phenomenon Explained Students explore the **investigative phenomenon** by reading about how binary code is used to transmit information across global networks and how high-tech devices (cell phones, computers) can receive and decode information by converting it from digitized form (binary code) to voice—and vice versa.

Bits of Code

Refer students to the word *digital* in the first sentence. Write the word on the board and underline the root *digit*. Explain that it comes from the Latin *digitus*, meaning "finger," but it also refers to counting, as when people count on their digits, or fingers. We use *digital* to refer to numbers used in computer technology.

Connecting the World Codes, Computers, and Networks

Discuss examples of wireless technology, pointing out that the radio used to be called *the wireless*. Ask students what their lives would be like without satellites: We would not have the type of worldwide information transfer that we know today.

How Computers Help Us Communicate

Clarify that a modem is an electronic hardware device engineered to convert signals from one computer into signals that another computer can read.

How Cell Phones Help Us Communicate

Some students may think that telephone wires transmit sound waves. Clarify that landline telephone wires carry electrical impulses with coded information. Cell phone signals are radio waves that send coded information. The code is decoded at the other end of the call and reproduced as sound.

Bits of Color

Students can relate to high-definition television, or HDTV. Point out that each pixel is a very tiny lit area on a display screen. The higher the resolution, the more pixels there are each square unit, hence the high degree of detail. HD also gives depth and dimension to images.

SOCIAL EMOTIONAL LEARNING

Before students answer the question at the bottom of page 156, have a class discussion about how to take turns in a conversation.

Discuss the importance of:

- asking questions
- listening to give the other person an opportunity to talk
- taking time to pause and reflect on what someone tells you
- encouraging the other person to share and explore their ideas by talking, drawing, or using models
- recognizing that silent moments happen in conversations

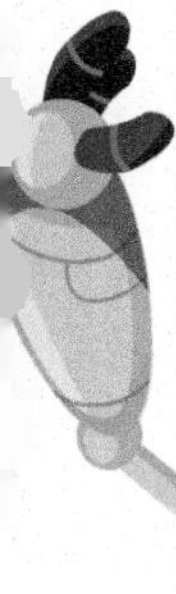

FORMATIVE ASSESSMENT

MAKING SENSE OF PHENOMENA

Students gain understanding of how digitized information is transmitted as they explore the **investigative phenomenon.** They should connect this to the **anchoring phenomenon** that digitized information is sent from Earth to satellites in space and back to Earth. Students should understand that digitized information can be transmitted over long distances.

REMEDIATION If students struggle to connect the **investigative phenomenon** back to the **anchoring phenomenon,** have them work with a partner to discuss the discuss the importance of digital devices and the use binary code to transmit signals. Then, have them compare a pixelated image on HDTV to the grid activity in Exploration 2, Pixels to Picture.

MAKING SENSE OF PHENOMENA IDEA ORGANIZER

After completing Exploration 4, students can fill in the **Idea Organizer** to summarize the connection between digitized information is transmitted and the anchoring phenomenon that digitized information is sent from Earth to a satellite in space and back to Earth.

LESSON 04

ONLINE-ONLY RESOURCES

Take It Further

Engage • Explore/Explain • **Elaborate** • Evaluate

TIME ESTIMATE

These Take It Further paths may be completed to enrich and extend students' comprehension of content covered within this lesson.

ONLINE

Elephant Communication: Elephant Stomp Sounds

In this feature, students learn that animals depend on behavioral or sound patterns to survive.

People in Science & Engineering: Alexander Graham Bell and Hedy Lamarr

Students learn how both Alexander Graham Bell and Hedy Lamarr helped to change communication technology.

Wave That Flag

Students discover how semaphore is used by a lifeguard at the beach to inform people and keep them safe. (No outside research required.)

Careers in Science & Engineering: Graphics Engineer

Graphics engineers use computers to make designs from models and sketches. Students meet Eddie Del Rio, a graphic engineer who works in the film industry. (No outside research required.)

FORMATIVE ASSESSMENT

Lesson Check

Activity Guide, pages 159–161

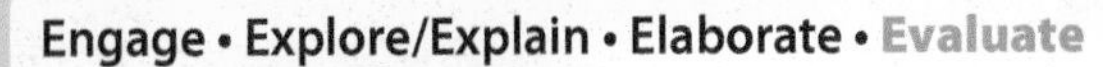

Can You Explain It?

Now I know or think that . . .

Sample answer: Information can be transferred by using different types of patterns such as signals or using zeros and ones. Satellites can encode messages digitally and send them long distances. The messages are then decoded and understood by the receiver.

After completing the lesson, use the **Making Sense Idea Organizer** to summarize the connections between the **investigative phenomena** and **anchoring phenomenon.**

MAKING CONNECTIONS

After students complete the lesson, they should be able to answer a question about an alternative phenomenon to explain how energy is transferred to enable communication. Here they compare the use of a video app to help to a satellite.

Sample answer: A video call is similar to a satellite because it can transfer information digitally in order to communicate or share information.

Checkpoints

1. a, c, d
2. **Sample answer:** If the operator encodes a letter wrong or the second operator decodes a letter wrong, the message could be miscommunicated.
3. 1—your cell phone; 2—tower close to your cell phone; 3—relay; 4—tower near your friend's relay; 5—friend's cell phone.
4. I LEARNED MANY THINGS ABOUT SIGNALS
5. a—Morse code, b—flags, c—scytale, d—texts to a friend using your phone
6. c— They go from sender to tower to relay to tower to receiver.
7. coded: Morse code, talking on the phone, scytale, text messages; uncoded: talking on the phone, text message, talking face-to-face.
8. a—They do not depend on understanding a language. c—They can be encoded and decoded digitally and sent by waves.

SOCIAL EMOTIONAL LEARNING

Have students reflect on the goals they set at the beginning of the lesson. Ask them to think about whether the goals were accomplished or if there were challenges. Have students share the factors that contributed to their success.

UNIT

03 Review

Activity Guide, pages 162–164

The Unit review items enable you to assess student comprehension of core ideas, as well as cross cutting concepts and science and engineering practices.

1. **DOK 1** **a.** motion

   If students choose b or c, have them focus on the image of the marbles to describe what the marbles are doing (they are moving). Then ask them if what the picture shows applies to any of the other answer choices (wind, spring). If students chose d (heat), ask them to describe an image they would use to demonstrate heat.

2. **DOK 2** **a.** It changes direction, **d.** It loses some of its energy.

   If students choose b or c, remind them of their Explorations in Lesson 2. If they still have difficulties, remind them about the video of the wrecking ball and have them describe what happens to the ball and the wall in the collision.

3. **DOK 3** **Sample answer:** I could put a blinking light on the tower. Two criteria are that the battery doesn't need to be replaced all the time, and the light must be visible on all sides of the tower. One constraint is that the light must be visible from far enough away that the planes see it in order to avoid the tower.

   If students struggle, have them review Lesson 1, Exploration 3. Discuss how batteries store energy.

4. **DOK 2** **a.** electrical energy into light and heat

   If students struggle to answer the question, have them focus on the image and describe what they see. If necessary, have students review what they learned in Lesson 1 about how energy is transformed and transferred.

5. **DOK 3** **Sample answer:** A system of energy transfer is created by the heat being transferred from the flame to the water inside the bowl.

   If students struggle to answer the question, have them focus on the image and describe what they see. Point out that a system has multiple parts that work together. The flame produces heat that is then transferred through the bowl to heat up the water.

6. **DOK 3** **a.** light waves, **c.** sound waves

   If students choose b or d, have them define or describe water waves and seismic waves and then observe the image again. Make sure they understand the scenario depicted, and have them imagine being at a concert. Point out that it would have to be quite a rock concert to produce a seismic wave (earthquake!).

7. **DOK 3** **Sample answer:** A faster swing has more energy, so it causes the ball to move faster and farther. A slower swing has less energy, so the ball doesn't go as fast.

   If students struggle, have them review in Lesson 2, Exploration 2, Speed and Energy and Exploration 3, Things That Move Have Energy.

8. **DOK 2** Energy waves are moving through the water toward the shore. The water only moves up and down because of the energy.

   If students struggle to answer the question, have them review Lesson 3, Exploration 1, Let's Make Waves, and Exploration 3, How Waves Transfer Energy. Have them focus on the images on Activity Guide page 129 and describe what they see.

9. **DOK 2** **Sample answer:** They both can communicate over long distances. They are different because one uses digitized coding and the other uses natural-made sounds.

   If students struggle to answer the question, have them review the Take It Further for Lesson 4 about Elephant Stomp Sounds. Ask students if they can hear the transmission of messages from their cell phones. They can't hear the radio signals, just as they can't hear the elephants' signals.

10. **DOK 2** They used smoke to create patterns that let soldiers know information.

    If students struggle to answer the question, have them review Activity Guide, pages 148–151, Lesson 4, The History of Information Transfer.

3D Item Analysis	1	2	3	4	5	6	7	8	9	10
SEP Developing and Using Models	•	•		•	•	•	•	•		
SEP Constructing Explanations and Designing Solutions			•							•
DCI PS3.A Definitions of Energy	•		•	•	•	•	•	•		
DCI PS3.B Conservation of Energy and Energy Transfer		•	•	•	•	•	•			
DCI PS4.C Information Technologies and Instrumentation									•	•
DCI PS3.D Energy In Chemical Processes and Everyday Life					•					
DCI PS4.4 Wave Properties								•		
ETS1.A Defining Engineering Problems			•							
CCC Energy and Matter	•	•	•	•	•	•	•	•		
CCC Patterns									•	•
CCC Systems and System Models			•	•	•					

UNIT

04 Shaping Landforms

Activity Guide, page 165

Unit Storyline

In Unit 3, students explored the concept of energy and the relationship between energy transfer, energy transformation, and communication. In this Unit, students explore how landscapes change. They use models to examine the factors and processes that transform land over time, and then construct explanations based on their findings. By observing the patterns that occur in their explorations, students can determine the causes of land changes.

LESSON 1 PE 4-ESS2-1

Factors That Shape Earth's Surface

Activity Guide, pages 166–181

Students explore the **anchoring phenomenon** that a canyon formed in the middle of flat land.

- SEP Planning and Carrying Out Investigations
- DCI **ESS2.A** Earth Materials and Systems
- DCI **ESS2.E** Biogeology
- CCC Cause and Effect
- CCC Scientific Knowledge Assumes an Order and Consistency in Natural Systems

LESSON 2 PE 4-ESS2-1

Fast and Slow Changes

Activity Guide, pages 182–197

Students explore the **anchoring phenomenon** that different factors can cause quick or slow changes on Earth's surface.

- SEP Planning and Carrying Out Investigations
- DCI **ESS2.A** Earth Materials and Systems
- DCI **ESS2.E** Biogeology
- CCC Cause and Effect

LESSON 3 PE 4-ESS1-1

Rock Layers Record Landform Changes

Activity Guide, pages 198–217

Students explore the **anchoring phenomenon** that these are real footprints in a vertical wall of solid rock.

- SEP Constructing Explanations and Designing Solutions
- DCI **ESS1.C** The History of Planet Earth
- CCC Patterns
- CCC Scientific Knowledge Assumes an Order and Consistency in Natural Systems

Unit Review Activity Guide, pages 218–220

UNIT 04

AT A GLANCE

Online-Only Resources

Supporting Unit Resources

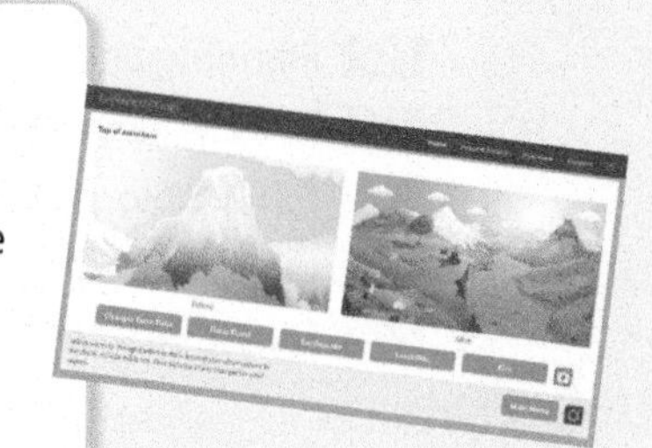

You Solve It SUPPORTS LESSONS 1 AND 2

Evidence of Change is a virtual lab that offers practice in support of **Performance Expectations 4-ESS2-1 and 4-ESS2-2.** Students will determine the forces that cause changes to Earth's surface.

- SEP Planning and Carrying Out Investigations
- DCI **ESS2.A** Earth Materials and Systems
- CCC Cause and Effect

Unit Project SUPPORTS LESSONS 1 AND 2

90 min

Nearby Weathering provides students an opportunity to practice aspects of **Performance Expectation 4-ESS2-2.** Students will identify the differences between weathering and erosion, understand how weathering can affect property, and design solutions to lessen, end, or reverse the effects of weathering.

- SEP Planning and Carrying out Investigations
- DCI **ESS2.A** Earth Materials and Systems, **ESS2.E** Biogeology
- CCC Cause and Effect

Unit Performance Task SUPPORTS LESSONS 1 AND 2

Model It, Map It provides an opportunity for students to practice or be assessed on aspects of **Performance Expectation 4-ESS2-1.** Students develop models and plan and carry out an investigation to demonstrate the effects of how a land feature is changed by wind or water.

- SEP Planning and Carrying Out Investigations, Developing and Using Models
- DCI **ESS1.C** The History of Planet Earth
- CCC Cause and Effect**,** Systems and System Models

Language Development

This worksheet is used as students progress through the unit's lessons. As they come to a highlighted vocabulary term, they should come back to this chart and fill in the blanks with words or phrases.

We've got you covered.

Updates and additional student and teacher resources can be found online. Check back often!

Supporting Lesson Resources

Do the Math!

Lesson 1 Calculating Changes
Lesson 2 A Waterfall Over Time
Lesson 3 Canyon Clues

Language SmArts

Lesson 1 Close Reading, Summarizing Landforms, Understand Cause and Effect
Lesson 2 Summarizing, Categorizing Information
Lesson 3 Conducting Research, Summarize, Close Reading

Take It Further

Lesson 1 People in Science and Engineering: Anjali Fernandes; Careers in Science and Engineering: Environmental Geologist; Deposition Rate!
Lesson 2 People in Science and Engineering: Kerry Sieh; The Science of Slopes; Careers in Science and Engineering: Geophysicist
Lesson 3 People in Science and Engineering: Edward Cope; Changes in Environments; Careers in Science and Engineering: Museum Director

MAKING SENSE OF PHENOMENA

This idea organizer is used to make sense of the following **anchoring phenomena**:
Lesson 1—This canyon formed in the middle of flat land.
Lesson 2—Different factors can cause quick or slow changes on Earth's surface.
Lesson 3—These are real footprints in a vertical wall of solid rock.

It also connects the investigative phenomena back to the anchoring phenomenon in each lesson.

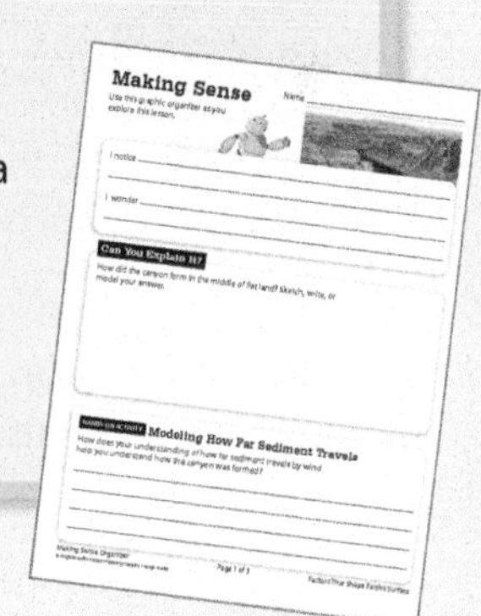

Assessment

Unit Readiness Check: Are You Ready?
Lesson Quizzes: Can You Apply It?
Unit 4 Test
Performance-Based Assessment

Assessments are available in an editable, printable format or can be administered and auto-graded online.

LESSON

01 Factors That Shape Earth's Surface

ANCHORING PHENOMENON

The canyon formed in the middle of flat land.

ENGAGE **Can You Explain It?**

Students observe and ask questions about a canyon.

They answer the Can You Explain It? question to consider how such a canyon could have formed in the middle of flat land.

EVALUATE **Lesson Check**

Students gauge their understanding of the anchoring phenomenon.

HANDS-ON ACTIVITY

EXPLORATION 1 **Modeling How Far Sediment Travels**

Investigative Phenomenon Many factors on Earth affect how far sediment travels.

Students should connect back to the **anchoring phenomenon** that moving water weathered the rock and carried away the resulting sediment, causing the canyon to become deeper over time.

HANDS-ON ACTIVITY

EXPLORATION 2 **A Sweet Test**

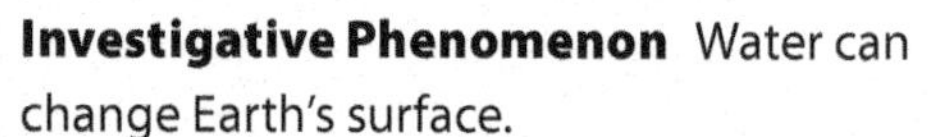

30 min

Investigative Phenomenon Water can change Earth's surface.

Students should connect back to the **anchoring phenomenon** by modeling processes that change Earth's surface.

EXPLORATION 3 **Earth's Surface**

Investigative Phenomenon Agents of change on Earth's surface constantly sculpt and shape rocks.

Students should connect back to the **anchoring phenomenon** by understanding that the canyon was formed because of moving water, wind, and ice.

Making 3D Connections

The **anchoring phenomenon** in this lesson supports students' understanding of and application of these Next Generation Science Standards.

Building to the Performance Expectations

PE 4-ESS2-1 Make observations and/or measurements to provide evidence of the effects of weathering or the rate of erosion by water, ice, wind, or vegetation.

SEP

Planning and Carrying Out Investigations Make observations and measurements to produce data to serve as the basis for evidence for an explanation of a phenomenon. *(Explorations 1, 2)*

DCI

ESS2.A Earth Materials and Systems Rainfall helps to shape the land and affects the types of living things found in a region. Water, ice, wind, living organisms, and gravity break rocks, soils, and sediments into smaller particles and move them around. *(Explorations 1, 2, 3)*

ESS2.E Biogeology Living things affect the physical characteristics of their regions. *(Exploration 3)*

CCC

Cause and Effect Cause and effect relationships are routinely identified, tested, and used to explain change. *(Explorations 1, 2, 3)*

Scientific Knowledge Assumes an Order and Consistency in Natural Systems Science assumes consistent patterns in natural systems. *(Explorations 1, 2, 3)*

Vocabulary

Word Wall A word wall, anchor chart, or Language Development chart can be used to support vocabulary

weathering the breaking down of rocks on Earth's surface into smaller pieces

erosion the process of moving weathered rock and soil from one place to another

deposition another process that changes Earth's surface, it occurs when water, or wind, slows down and drops (deposits) the rocks and sediment it carries

environment all the living and nonliving things that surround and affect an organism

You may want to include additional academic terms such as *factors, sediment, keystone, debris, small-scale, slightest, eroding, organism,* and any other terms students might struggle with.

Language Development Prompt students to complete the chart when they come to these highlighted terms within the lesson and to add their own terms as they come across unknown science terms.

Anchor Chart As you progress through the unit, you may want to use the Language Development chart as a guide to make a vocabulary-based anchor chart that can be displayed and filled out as a whole group during each lesson.

LESSON

01 Factors That Shape Earth's Surface

Activity Guide, pages 166–167

Students can engage in the Can You Explain It? content by observing the photograph or by exploring the corresponding video online.

ONLINE 

View a video of a river flowing through a canyon.

ANCHORING PHENOMENON
The canyon formed in the middle of flat land.

PHENOMENON EXPLAINED
The canyon wasn't always there. Over time the land was weathered and eroded, primarily by flowing water. The canyon is the result of various processes that change Earth's surface.

Lesson Objective

Students will identify, explain, and record evidence about how water and wind shape Earth's surface, and then describe ways in which these factors cause weathering, erosion, and deposition to occur.

Support Discovery

The following prompts can be used to guide student-led discovery.

I notice . . .

After observing the photograph or watching the video, students should record what they observe about the canyon.

Sample answer: I notice there is a river at the bottom of the canyon.

I wonder . . .

After observing the photograph or watching the video, students should record what they want to find out about how the canyon formed.

Sample answers: I wonder how the river got to the bottom of the canyon. I wonder what caused the different layers of rock.

Alternative Phenomenon

If students are unfamiliar with canyons, show them photographs of other geologic landforms shaped by water, such as V-shaped valleys formed by glaciers, arches in rock cliffs eroded by waves, or small streams cutting through a pasture. Pair students, and have them discuss how water is a sculptor of the land. Circulate to gauge students' prior knowledge about the ways in which flowing water has an effect on the landforms of Earth's surface. Call on students to share a one-sentence summary of the impact of water over time.

Can You Explain It?

In Can You Explain It?, students make an initial claim that explains the **Anchoring Phenomenon.**

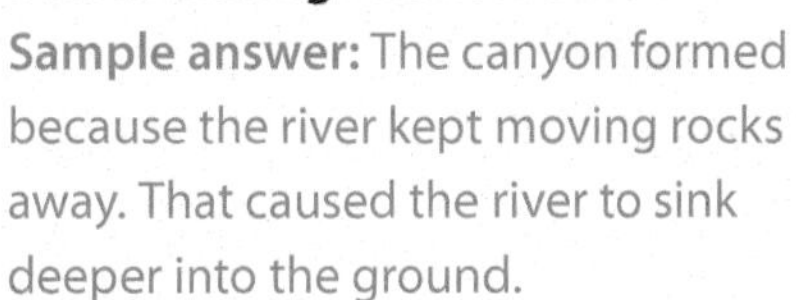

Sample answer: The canyon formed because the river kept moving rocks away. That caused the river to sink deeper into the ground.

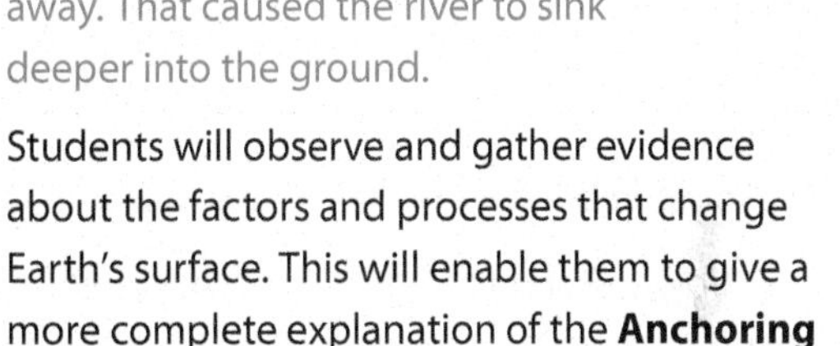

Students will observe and gather evidence about the factors and processes that change Earth's surface. This will enable them to give a more complete explanation of the **Anchoring Phenomenon** at the end of the lesson.

SOCIAL EMOTIONAL LEARNING

Guide students to reflect on their goals from previous lessons and on any feedback they received from their teachers or peers. Then have each student set a personal goal for this lesson and make a plan for how to achieve the goal. Throughout the lesson, take daily breaks for students to track their progress in meeting their goals. As students move from lesson to lesson, they can continue to work towards their initial goals or set new ones. If students struggle to set goals for this lesson, share with them some of the following ideas: comparing Earth's features, working in groups, or sharing ideas when you're scared to.

LESSON 01

FUNomenal READER

Disappearing Land

WHEN TO USE

SCIENCE 

- Anchoring Phenomenon / Alternative Phenomenon
- Options for ELA Instruction
- Build on Prior Knowledge
- Preview the Phenomenon
- Read to Learn
- Support Sense Making
- Science Stretch
- Check for Comprehension

Option 1 Use before students begin the lesson in the Activity Guide to provide an engaging model to introduce the lesson's phenomenon.

Option 2 Use after students have completed the Activity Guide to reinforce students' understanding of the lesson phenomenon by exploring a related phenomenon.

ELA 

- Options for ELA Instruction
- Build on Prior Knowledge
- Read to Learn

Option 3 To use during designated ELA Reading time for independent reading, whole-class instruction, or small-group instruction, look for this icon: ELA

Plan

ANCHORING PHENOMENON / ALTERNATIVE PHENOMENON

The anchoring phenomenon in the Activity Guide is *This canyon formed in the middle of flat land,* and the main example is a river flowing through the bottom of a canyon. The FUNomenal Reader presents a similar phenomenon *(The Birling Gap coastline has changed significantly over time),* and the example is the eroded coastline of Birling Gap in England. Both present the same science concepts and cover the same standards but with different phenomena. Guide students to draw connections between the two situations and to understand the underlying principle: wind and water shape Earth's surface.

Options for ELA Instruction 

Choose one of the following anchor chart options and project it or print copies. Then display and introduce the chart before reading the text. Revisit the chart after reading the text and encourage students to discuss how the skill connects to the text.

Author's Purpose Use the *Author's Purpose Anchor Chart* to discuss why the author wrote this story. Was it mainly to persuade, to inform, or to entertain?

Informational Text Display the *Informational Text Anchor Chart* as you discuss this nonfiction reader. Have students identify the topic, facts about that topic, and graphic features such as maps that give more information about the topic.

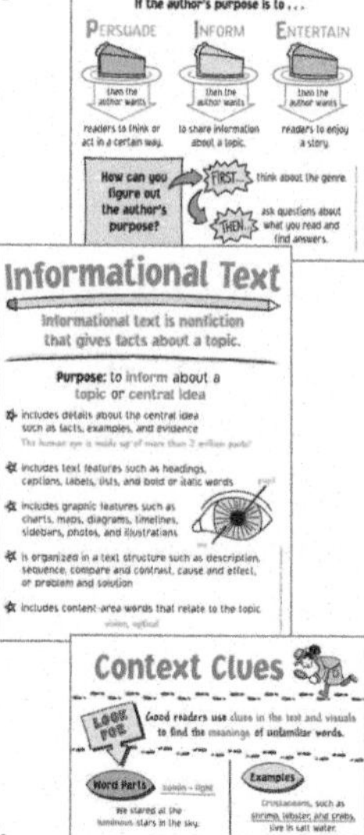

Context Clues Use the *Context Clues Anchor Chart* if students struggle to understand the meaning of some words in the story. Remind them to look for clues in the text and visuals. For example, in the sentence *The coastline of a country is a vulnerable place because it can easily be attacked from the ocean,* the text after *because* gives a clue to the meaning of *vulnerable.*

Preview

ELA **Build on Prior Knowledge** Show students photos of geologic landforms that have been shaped by water. Discuss how water is a sculptor of the land. Gauge students' prior knowledge about the ways in which flowing water and waves have an effect on the landforms of Earth's surface over time.

Preview the Phenomenon Ask students to study the photo on pages 2 and 3 of the story, which shows a panoramic view of the Birling Gap coastline and cottages in England. Encourage students to record the first questions that come into their minds about the landforms and buildings they see. Point out that their questions might change as they read through the story. Have them keep their questions on hand and periodically check to see if any can be answered.

STANDARDS SUPPORTED

SEP

Planning and Carrying Out Investigations

DCI

ESS2.A Earth Materials and Systems

ESS2.E Biogeology

CCC

Cause and Effect

Scientific Knowledge Assumes an Order and Consistency in Natural Systems

Disappearing Land (continued)

Discover

Read to Learn 

The **Read to Learn** suggestions inside the book's front cover encourage students to interact with the book multiple times for different purposes.

Preview Students look for unfamiliar words and share them with a partner. New terms may include *deposition, erosion, fossil,* and *weathering.* Have students look up words they aren't sure about and notice how they are used in the context of the story.

Skim Students skim the photos. Have them turn to a partner and share their predictions of what the story will be about.

Read As students read the story, ask them to look for connections to one of the following anchor chart skills.
Author's Purpose, Informational Text, Context Clues

Support Sense Making

Choose one or more of the following:

- Be sure students can identify the phenomenon presented on the opening pages of the reader: the coastline of Birling Gap has changed considerably over time. The remaining pages describe what the coastline was like many years ago and how and why it has changed—and continues to change.
- Have students describe what they have observed after a strong storm. Help them understand that changes they have seen in human-made buildings and in natural structures such as bushes and trees also affect landforms. Relate these changes to what has happened to the Birling Gap cottages and coastline.
- Encourage a student-led discussion of the changes at Birling Gap in terms of energy transfer. Gravitational potential energy and motion energy of wind and water are changed into landform movement that results in a reshaping of landforms.
- Remind students that natural systems proceed through cycles regardless of human intervention. Discuss how people at Birling Gap and Cape Hatteras moved buildings farther from shore and restored beaches by bringing in more sand but have been unable to reduce the weathering and erosion taking place on the coastline.

Extend

Science Stretch

The **Science Stretch** suggestions inside the book's back cover help students think about what they read. Students can complete one or more as time allows.

Draw a model of places around your school where weathering, erosion, and deposition have occurred. If feasible, take students on a walk around your school's grounds or the surrounding neighborhood and have them record their observations.

Conduct an investigation to identify factors that influence the rate of weathering. Provide materials students might need, such as water, vinegar, and limestone.

Research how people have reduced the impact of weathering, erosion, and deposition. Construct a model of a solution. **Sample answer:** My model shows how planting trees with deep roots on hillsides can help stop soil erosion.

SOCIAL EMOTIONAL LEARNING

Identify ways you can reduce your frustration when investigating something that happens slowly. **Sample answer:** I remind myself that scientists often have to observe something over a long period of time to see changes.

Check for Comprehension Have students write a paragraph explaining why they think tourists visit Birling Gap to see the effects of weathering and erosion there. Be sure they use details from the text to support their claims.

EXPLORATION 1 | HANDS-ON ACTIVITY

Modeling How Far Sediment Travels

Activity Guide, pages 168–170

TIME ESTIMATE

SHORT ON TIME?

As a class, brainstorm questions, choose one to investigate, and develop a plan that individual groups can conduct.

POSSIBLE MATERIALS

- ☐ fan
- ☐ butcher paper, 1.5 m per team
- ☐ masking tape
- ☐ 200 mL beaker of silt
- ☐ sand
- ☐ gravel
- ☐ meterstick
- ☐ stopwatch
- ☐ safety goggles

Materials Alert You may wish to use something to cover the classroom work area. If the fan isn't powerful enough, use paper plates to fan the materials.

PREPARATION

Make sure pairs can work without bumping into one another. Or, have students move outside, but make sure you choose an area that is protected. This will ensure that wind does not affect outcomes of the investigation.

INVESTIGATIVE PHENOMENON
Many factors on Earth affect how far sediment travels.

Phenomenon Explained Students explore the **investigative phenomenon** by developing a plan using a model and testing the factors that affect how far sediment travels.

Form a Question After students read about how wind affects landforms, they should form a question about how wind affects the motion of sediment. If students struggle to form a question, ask them to reflect on a windy day and what they observed moving in the wind. **Sample answer:** How does wind move pieces of sand if they are heavy?

STEPS 1 and 2 Students make a plan to investigate their question about wind, then carry out their plan. Make sure students explain how they will test how far sediment travels and what question they will address. Students should provide evidence and reasons for adding the materials. **Sample answer:** Students' plans should show how they will investigate how wind moves sediment. Possible steps could be using the fan to blow on the sand and gravel to see what happens.

STEP 3 Students organize their data for presentation. Encourage students to choose a method for sharing their data that makes it easy for their classmates to understand their results.

- **Make a Claim** Claims should indicate that the longer and faster the wind blows, the farther sediment travels.
- **Evidence** Students should cite as evidence the data from the activity that shows that the longer and faster the fan blew, the farther the sediment traveled.
- **Reasoning** Students should explain that the greatest distances measured indicate the farthest the sediment traveled, and these distances occurred during the longest times blowing the fan or when the fastest fan speed was used.

FORMATIVE ASSESSMENT

MAKING SENSE OF PHENOMENA

Students gain understanding that many factors on Earth affect how far sediment travels as they explore the **investigative phenomenon.** They should connect this to the **anchoring phenomenon** that the canyon formed in the middle of flat land. Students should understand that if wind can move so much sand that far, water would be able to move a lot more sand a lot farther. They should infer that wind and water together might help make a big canyon.

REMEDIATION If students struggle to connect the **investigative phenomenon** back to the **anchoring phenomenon,** have them think of the land where the canyon formed as being made up partly of sediment from crumbling rock. Discuss what might happen to that sediment if the wind blew fast or for a long time over the land.

Activity Outcome

Students should develop a plan and conduct a test using a model of wind erosion in order to infer that how far sediment travels.

Performance Indicators	
	develop and conduct a plan using a model of wind erosion
	make a claim about how wind moves sediment
	support the claim using collected data as evidence

MAKING SENSE OF PHENOMENA IDEA ORGANIZER

After completing Exploration 1, students can fill in the **Idea Organizer** to summarize the connection between the many factors on Earth affecting how far sediment travels and the anchoring phenomenon that moving water weathered the rock and carried away the resulting sediment, causing the canyon to become deeper over time.

SOCIAL EMOTIONAL LEARNING

Encourage students to think about a situation in which they were nervous, whether or not it involved public speaking. Invite them to share how they coped with the situation or what they wished they had done to stay calm. Suggest that they role-play some situations and strategies their group discusses.

EXPLORATION 2 HANDS-ON ACTIVITY

A Sweet Test

Activity Guide, pages 171–172

TIME ESTIMATE

SHORT ON TIME?

This activity can be done as a teacher demonstration to save time. Students can observe and record observations individually or with a partner.

POSSIBLE MATERIALS

- [ ] small lidded container
- [ ] 2 sugar cubes
- [ ] water
- [ ] pipet

PREPARATION

Before students begin, have them read the Exploration and predict what will happen to the sugar cube.

INVESTIGATIVE PHENOMENON

Water can change Earth's surface.

Phenomenon Explained Students explore the **investigative phenomenon** by modeling processes that change Earth's surface.

Form a Question After they read about how landforms change, students should form a question about how water can cause changes to Earth's surface. If students struggle to form a question, ask them to consider how different bodies or sources of water (such as rivers, lakes, oceans, groundwater, etc.) might cause changes. **Sample answer:** How does water change Earth's surface?

STEP 1 Students weather the sugar cube without water and record what they observe. **Sample answer:** The sugar cube broke into smaller pieces. There are small pieces of sugar cube at the bottom of the container.

STEP 2 Students weather the sugar cube in water and record what they observe. If students do not see much change, they can add a couple more drops of water and repeat the step. **Sample answer:** The sugar cube has "melted" a little. Small pieces of the sugar cube broke off and there are small pieces on the bottom of the container. The water mixed with the small pieces of sugar cube.

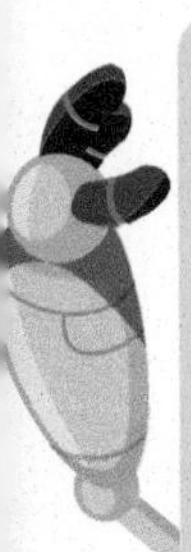

FORMATIVE ASSESSMENT

MAKING SENSE OF PHENOMENA

Students gain understanding that water can change Earth's surface as they explore the **investigative phenomenon.** They should connect this to the **anchoring phenomenon** that the canyon formed in the middle of flat land. Student should understant that they are modeling processes that change Earth's surface: the rocks making up landforms, like the canyon, can be broken apart and changed by water in a similar way as the sugar cubed was changed.

REMEDIATION If students struggle to connect the **investigative phenomenon** back to the **anchoring phenomenon,** have a class discussion about the model students made and the how the sugar cube is like rocks that make up canyons and other landforms. Explain that rocks can dissolve like the sugar cube, though much more slowly.

MAKING SENSE OF PHENOMENA IDEA ORGANIZER

After completing Exploration 2, students can fill in the **Idea Organizer** to summarize the connection between how water can change Earth's surface and the anchoring phenomenon that a canyon is the result of various processes that change Earth's surface.

Activity Outcome

Students should model weathering processes and record observations in order to explain how these processes change Earth's surface.

Performance Indicators	
	model weathering
	make and record observations
	explain how this weathering changes Earth's surface

EXPLORATION 3

Earth's Surface

Activity Guide, pages 173–178

TIME ESTIMATE

INVESTIGATIVE PHENOMENON
Agents of change on Earth's surface constantly sculpt and shape rocks.

Phenomenon Explained Students explore the **investigative phenomenon** by exploring how Earth's surface changes are caused by moving water, wind and ice. They study and describe the causes and effects of weathering, erosion, and deposition.

Changes You Can See

Everyday Phenomenon **Weathering changes structures made of rock.**

Have students describe an **everyday phenomenon** that they have observed in the weathering of buildings and other structures made of rock. Help students recognize the cause-and-effect relationships among changes they can observe and what has caused them. Then help them connect their observations to the **anchoring phenomenon** that the canyon formed in the middle of flat land.

Ask: How does a decaying building compare to the wall of a canyon? **Sample answer:** Both are affected by weathering. Without maintenance, they will change shape.

Earth's Changing Surface

Discuss the processes of weathering, erosion, and deposition, and have students compare and contrast them. Remind them of this mnemonic: weathering breaks, erosion takes, deposition drops. **Ask:** Which process did you model in the previous Exploration? weathering How do you know? The sugar cubes broke apart into smaller pieces. Make sure students understand that in the previous Exploration they modeled two ways that weathering of rocks occurs: by rocks bumping against one another (or water crashing into rocks) and by water dissolving rocks.

Water Weathering

After students read the text and examine the photographs, ask them to identify the different forms of water described or pictured. Explain that rainwater that falls to Earth and flows over the surface is known as runoff. This flowing water, along with rivers and waves, can cause weathering, erosion, or deposition.

Ask: How do erosion and deposition occur in a river? Sample answer: The flowing river water picks up and moves sediment. Some sediment gets deposited where the water stops or at the river's mouth.

EXPLORATION 3

Earth's Surface (continued)

Activity Guide, pages 173–178, *cont.*

TIME ESTIMATE

Moving Water

Students observe cliff images and circle where change is occurring. Remind them to draw a circle on each of the three images. Then review the cause-and-effect relationships between water and weathering, erosion, and deposition and how these three natural processes affect the environment.

Ask: How do erosion and deposition occur in a river? **Sample answer:** The flowing river water picks up and moves sediment. Some sediment gets deposited where the water stops or at the river's mouth.

Relate the content to the previous Exploration. Discuss how the sugar cubes dissolved but did not go away. Have students relate this investigation to what happens to rocks when they are mixed with water in rivers and ocean waves.

Cold as Ice

Students' labeled drawing should predict the next step in the process of freezing and thawing. **Sample answer:** Part of the rock breaks off.

Everyday Phenomenon **As water turns to ice, it expands, increases in size.**

To connect the **everyday phenomenon** to processes that can change Earth's surface, refer students to image number 5 on Activity Guide page 175. Reinforce that each time water freezes (cause), the crack in the rock gets bigger (effect). Then explain how water turning to ice under a road can push up the surface, creating a bulge in the asphalt called a frost heave. As the cycle of freezing and thawing continues, it creates a pothole, a sunken section in a road. **Ask:** During the cold winter, what will happen to the water that has seeped underground? **Sample answer:** It will freeze and expand. Help students connect this freezing and thawing process to the **anchoring phenomenon** that the canyon formed in the middle of flat land.

Windy Forces

Students research, draw, and write a caption for an example of weathering by wind in their state. Then they identify an example of erosion. Have students work in pairs to do research online or in the library. Students' drawings should include an example of weathering by wind that is local and a caption. Invite them to share their drawings.

Water World

Review the definition of *environment,* and make a class list of different environments, or ecosystems (desert, rainforest, tundra, forest, grassland, freshwater, ocean). Have students generate questions about how the living things in each environment might affect Earth's landforms. Encourage students to look for answers as they read.

Living Things Change Their Environments and Organism Cause and Effect

Before students explore changes caused by organisms and describe the effects caused by these changes, make a class list of phenomena students have observed that show how organisms change Earth's surface, such as grass growing in sidewalk crevices or woodpecker holes in trees. Discuss how these organisms combined with the forces of erosion, deposition, and weathering can reshape Earth's landforms. **Sample answer:** Termites move soil from one location to another, making large structures.

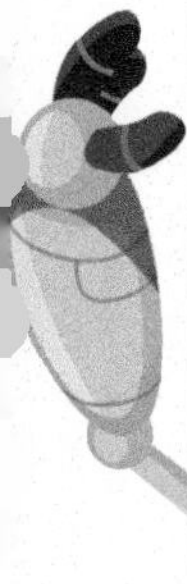

FORMATIVE ASSESSMENT

MAKING SENSE OF PHENOMENA

As they explore the **investigative phenomenon,** students gain understanding that agents of change on Earth's surface constantly sculpt and shape rocks. They should connect this to the **anchoring phenomenon** that the canyon formed in the middle of flat land. Students should understand that, over time, the canyon formed as water in the river caused weathering and erosion of rock and sediment.

REMEDIATION If students struggle to connect the **investigative phenomenon** back to the **anchoring phenomenon,** have them look again at the photograph of the canyon and discuss with a partner the roles that weathering and erosion may have played in the canyon's formation.

MAKING SENSE OF PHENOMENA IDEA ORGANIZER

After completing Exploration 3, students can fill in the **Idea Organizer** to summarize the connection between how agents of change on Earth's surface constantly sculpt and shape rocks and the anchoring phenomenon that the canyon was formed in the middle of flat land.

LESSON 01

ONLINE-ONLY RESOURCE

Take It Further

Engage • Explore/Explain • Elaborate • Evaluate

TIME ESTIMATE

These Take It Further paths may be completed to enrich and extend students' comprehension of content covered within this lesson.

ONLINE

People in Science & Engineering: Anjali Fernandes

Anjali Fernandes, PhD, is an Indian female geologist who does field research. Point out that geoscientists might conduct field research to understand Earth's processes and materials, or to study Earth's history to learn about plants and animals that lived long ago, as well as what the past climates of Earth were like and how they have changed over time.

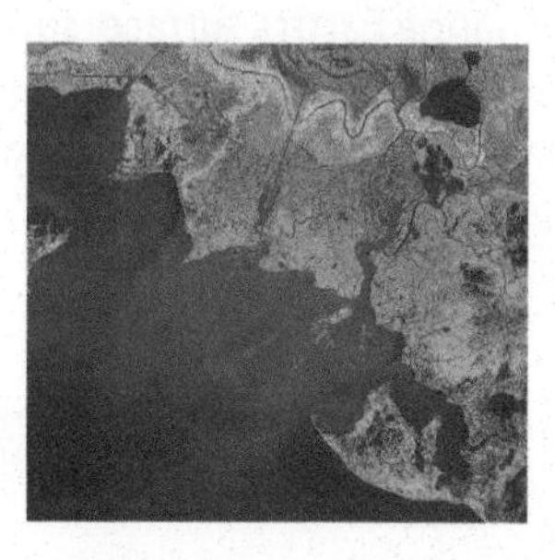

Deposition Rate!

Students will analyze the rate of deposition in the Mississippi River.

Careers in Science & Engineering: Environmental Geologist

Students will learn about a career in which people study the effects of different activities on rocks and structures in an environment.

FORMATIVE ASSESSMENT

Lesson Check

Activity Guide, pages 179–181

Engage • Explore/Explain • Elaborate • Evaluate

Can You Explain It?

Now I know or think that. . .

Sample answer: Now I know that the river changed the canyon by washing over or through Earth's surface. Wind and water weathered and eroded the land over time, causing the canyon to get deeper. Plant roots can crack the rock in the canyon and cause it to break away. Animals can carve into structures or burrow in the sand.

After completing the lesson, use the **Making Sense Idea Organizer** to summarize the connections between the **investigative phenomena** and **anchoring phenomenon.**

MAKING CONNECTIONS

After students complete the lesson, they should be able to answer a question about an alternative phenomenon to compare and contrast the rock bridge and canyon. **Sample answer:** This rock bridge is similar because water moved across the rock and broke it into small pieces that moved. The canyon was formed the same way by the moving river. The rock bridge is different because the movement of water created a hole in the rock, instead of forming a canyon.

Checkpoints

1. a—They are the result of wind deposition.
2. a—Ocean waves move sand from one beach to another.
3. **Sample answer:** When rocks and soil are pushed up out of the ground by a chipmunk digging a den, this is evidence of how animals change landforms.
4. **Sample answer:** Rain or melting snow can get into cracks in rocks. When the water freezes, it expands. Over time, this pattern of melting and freezing can break rocks apart.
5. c—A hiker finds small, flat rocks stacked at the peak of a mountain.
6. **Sample answer:** Moving water and ice can break apart rock and move it to a new location. When wind hits the side of a land structure, it can break the land apart and move it to a new location. The roots of plants can cause weathering by growing into the side causing cracks.
7. a—Measure the height of a mountain and monitor the height over time.
8. b—It can erode loose pieces of sand.

SOCIAL EMOTIONAL LEARNING

Have students reflect on the goals they set at the beginning of the lesson. If the goals were not achieved, talk about what students can do to help them achieve the goals.

LESSON

02 Fast and Slow Changes

ANCHORING PHENOMENON

Different factors can cause quick or slow changes on Earth's surface.

ENGAGE Can You Explain It?
Students observe and ask questions about what affects the speed at which Earth's surface changes. They answer the Can You Explain It? question to determine what affects the speed at which Earth's surface changes.

EVALUATE Lesson Check
Students gauge their understanding of the anchoring phenomenon.

HANDS-ON ACTIVITY

EXPLORATION 1 The Rate of Change

Investigative Phenomenon Slope affects the rate of erosion.

Students should connect back to the **anchoring phenomenon** that the slope of an area can affect how quickly or slowly the changes occur on Earth's surface.

HANDS-ON ACTIVITY

EXPLORATION 2 Glaciers on the Move 60 min

Investigative Phenomenon Frozen water can shape Earth's surface slowly.

Students should connect back to the **anchoring phenomenon** that water—whether it is frozen or liquid—can change Earth's surface quickly or slowly.

EXPLORATION 3 Fast Changes 30 min

Investigative Phenomenon Changes to Earth's surface can happen quickly.

Students should connect back to the **anchoring phenomenon** that flash flooding can happen quickly.

EXPLORATION 4 Slow Changes

Investigative Phenomenon Changes to Earth's surface can happen slowly.

Students should connect back to the **anchoring phenomenon** that even though flooding is a fast change, similar changes can happen slowly.

Making 3D Connections

The **anchoring phenomenon** in this lesson supports students' understanding of and application of these Next Generation Science Standards.

Building to the Performance Expectations

PE 4-ESS2-1 Make observations and/or measurements to provide evidence of the effects of weathering or the rate of erosion by water, ice, wind, or vegetation.

SEP

Planning and Carrying Out Investigations Make observations and measurements to produce data to serve as the basis for evidence for an explanation of a phenomenon. *(Explorations 1, 2)*

DCI

ESS2.A Earth Materials and Systems Rainfall helps to shape the land and affects the types of living things found in a region. Water, ice, wind, living organisms, and gravity break rocks, soils, and sediments into smaller particles and move them around. *(Explorations 1, 2, 3, 4)*

ESS2.E Biogeology Living things affect the physical characteristics of their regions. *(Exploration 3, 4)*

CCC

Cause and Effect Cause and effect relationships are routinely identified, tested, and used to explain change. *(Explorations 1, 2, 3, 4)*

Vocabulary

Word Wall A word wall, anchor chart, or Language Development chart can be used to support vocabulary.

You may want to include additional academic terms such as *rate of change, gradual, slope, incline, decline, structural, wedge*, and any other terms students might struggle with.

Language Development Prompt students to complete the chart when they come to these highlighted terms within the lesson and to add their own terms as they come across unknown science terms.

Anchor Chart As you progress through the unit, you may want to use the Language Development chart as a guide to make a vocabulary-based anchor chart that can be displayed and filled out as a whole group during each lesson.

LESSON

02 Fast and Slow Changes

Activity Guide, pages 182–183

Students can engage in the Can You Explain It? content by observing the photograph or by exploring the corresponding video online.

ONLINE

View a video of a landscapes changed by water.

ANCHORING PHENOMENON

Different factors can cause quick or slow changes on Earth's surface.

PHENOMENON EXPLAINED

Earth's surface changes quickly because of different forces. Sometimes heavy rains or winds can cause quick changes, while other times they can carve the surface of Earth slowly.

Lesson Objective

Students will make observations and collect data to use as evidence to explain how rainfall, living organisms, wind, ice and gravity affect Earth's surface.

Support Discovery

The following prompts can be used to guide student-led discovery.

I notice . . .

After observing the photograph or watching the video, students should record what they observe about the two different landscapes.

Sample answers: I notice there is a lot of water covering the land in the flooded area. I notice the canyon has a river at the bottom.

I wonder . . .

After observing the photograph or watching the video, students should record what they want to find out about how these two different landscapes changed.

Sample answers: I wonder how water changed the land. I wonder how constant flooding in flat areas will change the land.

Can You Explain It?

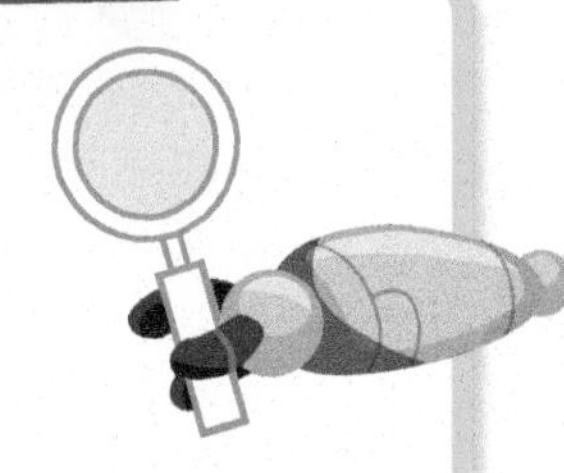

In Can You Explain It?, students make an initial claim that explains the **Anchoring Phenomenon.**

Sample answer: Earth's surface changes quicker if there is a large amount of water or wind.

Students will observe and gather evidence to determine what affects the speed at which Earth's surface changes. This will enable them to give a more complete explanation of the **Anchoring Phenomenon** at the end of the lesson.

Alternative Phenomenon

Encourage students to make observations about how physical change happens in their immediate environments. They know that weather elements such as rain and snow can alter Earth's surface, but they may not know that even plants and animals can change the environment. Discuss the kinds of changes they notice in the local landscape after a significant rainstorm, such washed out roads (fast moving rivers) or boulders and mounds of soil on a highway (landslides). If they notice sidewalks covered in dirt and sand, or small channels appearing in a sloping field or lawn, ask them what they think caused such changes.

SOCIAL EMOTIONAL LEARNING

Guide students to reflect on their goals from previous lessons and on any feedback they received from their teachers or peers. Then have each student set a personal goal for this lesson and make a plan for how to achieve the goal. Throughout the lesson, take daily breaks for students to track their progress in meeting their goals. As students move from lesson to lesson, they can continue to work towards their initial goals or set new ones.

LESSON 02

FUNomenal READER

Fast (and Slow) Field Trip

WHEN TO USE

SCIENCE 

- Anchoring Phenomenon / Alternative Phenomenon
- Options for ELA Instruction
- Build on Prior Knowledge
- Preview the Phenomenon
- Read to Learn
- Support Sense Making
- Science Stretch
- Check for Comprehension

Option 1 Use before students begin the lesson in the Activity Guide to provide an engaging model to introduce the lesson's phenomenon.

Option 2 Use after students have completed the Activity Guide to reinforce students' understanding of the lesson phenomenon by exploring a related phenomenon.

- Options for ELA Instruction
- Build on Prior Knowledge
- Read to Learn

Option 3 To use during designated ELA Reading time for independent reading, whole-class instruction, or small-group instruction, look for this icon: ELA

Plan

ANCHORING PHENOMENON / ALTERNATIVE PHENOMENON

The anchoring phenomenon in the Activity Guide is *Different factors can cause quick or slow changes on Earth's surface.* The main examples are an area with recent flooding and a canyon formed by a river. The FUNomenal Reader presents a similar phenomenon (*Different factors can cause quick or slow changes to natural and human-made monuments*), and the main example is weathering of the Sphinx in Egypt. Both present the same science concepts and cover the same standards but with different phenomena. Guide students to draw connections between the two situations and to understand the underlying principle: rainfall, organisms, wind, ice, gravity, and other factors can shape human-made objects and Earth's surface.

Options for ELA Instruction 

Choose one of the following anchor chart options and project it or print copies. Then display and introduce the chart before reading the text.

Research In the story, Bodie does online research to learn more about human-made monuments around the world and how they have changed over time. Have students refer to the *Research Anchor Chart* as a reminder of good sources to use when doing their own research.

Ideas and Support Use the *Ideas and Support Anchor Chart* to help students determine if these and other statements are fact or opinion: *Different materials can weather monuments slowly or quickly.* (fact) *There is no place in the world cooler than Venice.* (opinion) *Soot from factories and fires has damaged the Taj Mahal.* (fact)

Publishing Options Display the *Publishing Options Anchor Chart* to discuss the format of the story. The first line of the story indicates that this is a travel blog, a way for Bodie to share his thoughts, research, and photos online. Have students suggest other ways that Bodie could have shared his writing.

Preview

ELA **Build on Prior Knowledge** Students should already know that wind, water, and severe weather can affect Earth's surface and some human-made objects. They may not know that plants and animals also can change the environment. Hold a discussion about changes to Earth's surface they see in their community or at school. Examples may include ivy growing on a brick wall, tree roots causing a sidewalk to buckle, and an iron fence that has changed color.

Preview the Phenomenon Ask students to study the illustration and photo on page 2 of the story, which show a boy and the Sphinx. Tell students that this story is the boy's blog about various landmarks around the world, and how those landmarks are changed by forces like landslides, wind and ice. Encourage them to record any questions they have about what they think will be the focus of the blog. Point out that their questions might change as they read through the story. Have them keep their questions nearby and periodically check to see if any can be answered.

STANDARDS SUPPORTED

SEP

Planning and Carrying Out Investigations

DCI

ESS2.A Earth Materials and Systems

ESS2.E Biogeology

CCC

Cause and Effect

Fast (and Slow) Field Trip (continued)

Discover

Read to Learn 

The **Read to Learn** suggestions inside the book's front cover encourage students to interact with the book multiple times for different purposes.

Preview Students look for unfamiliar words and share them with a partner. New terms may include *weathering, erosion,* and *pollution.* Have students look up words they aren't sure about and notice how they are used in the context of the story.

Skim Students skim the illustrations and photos in the story. Have them turn to a partner and share their predictions of what the story will be about.

Read As students read the story, ask them to look for connections to one of the following anchor chart skills. **Research, Ideas and Support, Publishing Options**

Support Sense Making

Choose one or more of the following:

- Be sure students can identify the phenomenon presented on the opening pages of the story: Bodie wonders how much the Sphinx in Egypt has changed since it was built in ancient times. The story follows his efforts to learn more about how human-made monuments have been affected by weathering, erosion, and other factors.
- Provide materials so students can perform one or all of the investigations Bodie does in the story. Have students present their results and discuss if their conclusions match Bodie's.
- Have students work in small groups to choose one monument or place from the story and do more research to learn about it. Have them focus on how the place has changed over time—and why. Groups can report to the class on efforts that are being made to slow the processes.
- If feasible, take the class on a walk around the school or the neighborhood to look for signs of erosion or other changes. Are there any changes due to a recent heavy rain, a windstorm, or an ice storm? Have students note what they see in their science journal or notebook. You may want to have students share their findings with a class of younger students in your school.

Extend

Science Stretch

The **Science Stretch** suggestions inside the book's back cover help students think about what they read. Students can complete one or more as time allows.

Write a short blog post about a fast or slow change you have noticed. If students have trouble thinking of a topic, provide photos of fast and slow changes (moss growing on rocks, upended trees, etc.) they can write about.

Fill out a cause-and-effect chart to show what has caused the monuments in the stories to change over time. Remind students to look back through the text for causes and effects.

Make a travel poster that encourages people to visit one of the monuments in the story. Students may want to do research to find out more about the site they choose.

SOCIAL EMOTIONAL LEARNING

If Bodie asked you to read his blog, what kind of feedback would you give him?

Sample answer: I would tell him that it is well written and has good pictures.

Check for Comprehension Have students pause to think about what they read and then respond to the following prompts: *I became more aware of . . ., I didn't realize that . . ., I still don't understand . . .* Ask volunteers to share their responses with the class.

EXPLORATION 1 HANDS-ON ACTIVITY

The Rate of Change

Activity Guide, pages 184–187

TIME ESTIMATE

SHORT ON TIME?

Encourage students to take on specific roles throughout the activity, such as who will carry out the investigation and who will record the observations. Or, consider having them switch roles when they change the slope.

POSSIBLE MATERIALS

- ☐ paper cup
- ☐ sharpened pencil
- ☐ plastic drinking straw
- ☐ scissors
- ☐ small piece of modeling clay
- ☐ piece of cardboard 31 cm square
- ☐ soil
- ☐ ruler
- ☐ large bottle filled with water (approximately 2L)

Materials Alert You can reuse flattened cereal or packing boxes to create sloped surfaces.

PREPARATION

Choose a location outdoors or in another area of the classroom to conduct the activity, as students will be working with soil and water.

INVESTIGATIVE PHENOMENON
Slope affects the rate of erosion.

Phenomenon Explained Students explore the **investigative phenomenon** by planning and conducting an investigation to model and observe how slope affects the rate of erosion. Students make a claim and use their data to support it.

Form a Question While modeling various slopes with your hand (steep versus level), tell students that *slope* refers to the angle or steepness of a surface. Then have students form a question about how slope affects how Earth's surface changes. If students struggle to form a question, suggest that they generate a question about the Exploration title. **Sample question:** Does a steep slope causes changes to happen quickly or slowly?

STEPS 1, 2, and 3 Review students' investigation plans to make sure they are practical and test only the effect of slope on erosion rate. Remind students they are collecting evidence and to record their observations and data in the space provided.

STEP 4 Before students organize their data to describe the effect of changing the slope on soil erosion, prompt them to look for cause-and-effect relationships in their data. **Sample answer:** When the slope increased, the speed of the erosion increased. When the slope wasn't as steep, erosion happened more slowly.

STEP 5 As groups prepare their data to draw conclusions, remind them to look for patterns. When they compare their data with other groups, have them identify similarities and differences in the data. **Sample answer:** Our data were similar in that when the slope increased, the erosion happened quicker.

- **Make a Claim** Claims should indicate that the rate of erosion increases with slope.
- **Evidence** Students should cite as evidence their data showing that soil moved faster down the steeper slope.
- **Reasoning** Students should explain that when the slope was steepest, the water moved fastest and moved the most soil downhill.

FORMATIVE ASSESSMENT

MAKING SENSE OF PHENOMENA

Students gain understanding that slope affects the rate of erosion as they explore the **investigative phenomenon.** They should connect this to the **anchoring phenomenon** that different factors can cause quick or slow changes on Earth's surface. Students should understand that the speed at which Earth's surface changes varies in part because the slope of the surface varies, causing the rate of erosion to vary.

REMEDIATION If students struggle to connect the **investigative phenomenon** back to the **anchoring phenomenon,** ask groups to share their investigation plans and their results. Have a class discussion about the collective results and what they mean.

MAKING SENSE OF PHENOMENA IDEA ORGANIZER

After completing Exploration 1, students can fill in the **Idea Organizer** to summarize the connection between how slope affects the rate of erosion and the anchoring phenomenon that different factors can cause quick or slow changes to Earth's surface.

Activity Outcome

Students plan and conduct an investigation to observe the effect of slope on the erosion of Earth's surface. They use collected data to the claim that the rate of erosion increases with slope.

Performance Indicators	
	plan and conduct an investigation
	make a claim about how slope affects the rate of erosion
	support the claim using collected data as evidence

SOCIAL EMOTIONAL LEARNING

Explain to students that navigating conflicts about differing ideas can be challenging to anyone of any age. Discuss how learning navigational strategies now can help students later in life. Then discuss why feeling heard is important when different ideas are being voiced.

EXPLORATION 2 HANDS-ON ACTIVITY

Glaciers on the Move

Activity Guide, pages 188–189

TIME ESTIMATE

SHORT ON TIME?

Conduct steps 1 and 2 as a teacher demonstration. Have students individually observe, record what they see, and answer the questions.

POSSIBLE MATERIALS

- ☐ clear plastic cup
- ☐ spoonful of sand
- ☐ spoonful of gravel
- ☐ spoonful of soil
- ☐ water
- ☐ piece of cardboard
- ☐ large ball of clay
- ☐ wooden block

PREPARATION

A day in advance, fill the plastic cups with water and put them in a freezer overnight. Distribute the cups of ice and other materials to students prior to starting the activity.

INVESTIGATIVE PHENOMENON
Frozen water can shape Earth's surface slowly.

Phenomenon Explained Students explore the **investigative phenomenon** by making and observing a model glacier to infer how frozen water affects the rate of change to Earth's surface.

Form a Question After viewing the image of a glacier, students should form a question about glaciers. If students struggle to form a question, ask them to consider different forms of ice with which they are familiar. Sample questions: How do glaciers form? How do glaciers move?

STEP 1 Students make a model of a glacier and Earth's surface over which it moves.

STEP 2 Students observe the effect of moving the model glacier over the surface and record their observations. Then they repeat this step twice.

Explain that glaciers typically move downhill over very long periods of time, shaping rock formations over Earth's surface. When glaciers shape rock formations, it's almost like they leave behind clues. Deep grooves in rock and deposits of sediment can show how far a glacier moved and in which direction. Ask students to describe how they might tell the direction that another group's model glacier moved.

- **Make a Claim** Claims should indicate that a glacier can change Earth's surface slowly by scraping the surface and moving rocks and soil in its path.
- **Evidence** Students should cite as evidence their observations that when the ice was pushed down the slope, a dent was created in the clay and sand was moved.
- **Reasoning** Students should explain their reasoning, such as that, since they used a model of a glacier moving, similar changes to what they observed must occur when a real glacier moves slowly over Earth's surface.

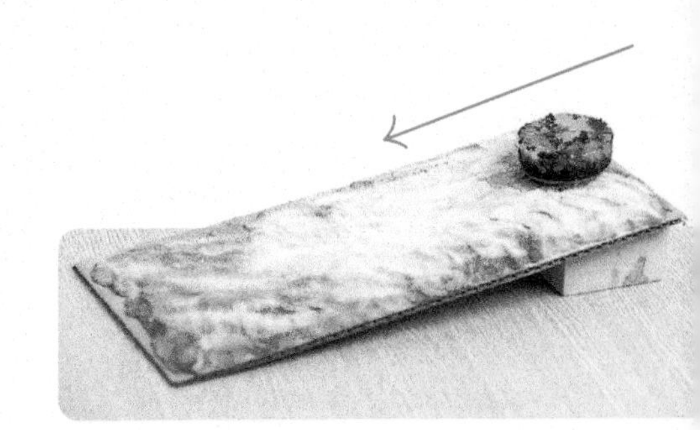

FORMATIVE ASSESSMENT

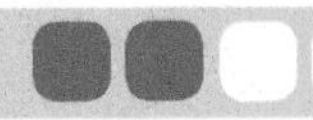

MAKING SENSE OF PHENOMENA

Students gain understanding that frozen water can shape Earth's surface slowly as they explore the **investigative phenomenon.** They should connect this to the **anchoring phenomenon** that different factors can cause quick or slow changes on Earth's surface. Students should understand that a slow-moving glacier can cause Earth's surface to change slowly, and thus the rate of change on Earth's surface can happen slowly or quickly.

REMEDIATION If students struggle to connect the **investigative phenomenon** back to the **anchoring phenomenon,** have them go online to observe pictures of landforms changed by glaciers and discuss them with a partner.

MAKING SENSE OF PHENOMENA IDEA ORGANIZER

After completing Exploration 2, students can fill in the **Idea Organizer** to summarize the connection between how frozen water can shape Earth's surface slowly and the anchoring phenomenon that different factors can cause quick or slow changes to Earth's surface.

Activity Outcome

Students should make and observe a model glacier in order to infer how frozen water affects the rate of change to Earth's surface. They use observations to support a claim that glaciers slowly change Earth's surface.

Performance Indicators	
	make and observe a model glacier
	make a claim that glaciers slowly change Earth's surface
	support the claim using observations as evidence

EXPLORATION 3

Fast Changes

Activity Guide, pages 190–191

TIME ESTIMATE

Preconception Alert After exploring fast changes related to weather, some students might get the impression that all types of weather have negative consequences on Earth. There is a difference between normal weather and natural disasters or natural hazards. Remind students of the difference, and explain that sometimes extreme weather conditions, such as rainstorms, can have positive effects for the environment. For example, the monsoons in Arizona bring much-needed rainwater to plants and animals that live in the desert.

INVESTIGATIVE PHENOMENON
Changes to Earth's surface can happen quickly.

Phenomenon Explained Students explore the **investigative phenomenon** by exploring different factors that cause fast changes on Earth's surface.

Everyday Phenomenon **There are examples of changes to Earth's surface all around us.**

Have students discuss the **everyday phenomenon** of how Earth's surface is constantly changing, even if we do not see those changes with the naked eye. Allow students to generate questions they have about the changes they see in the images of this Exploration. Then use their questions to help them connect the concept of constant change to the **anchoring phenomenon** that flash flooding and events such as those pictured can happen quickly.

Use images to discuss different processes that can make fast changes to Earth's surface. Tell students that these changes can be dangerous. **Ask:** Are all factors that cause fast changes to Earth's surface dangerous? Explain, and give an example. Sample answer: All factors that cause fast changes to Earth's surface can be dangerous, but this does not mean that they will always harm people, animals, or the environment. For instance, some earthquakes can be deadly and cause a great deal of damage, while others are harmless.

After students read all the text and captions and examine the photos, remind them to answer the question. Explain that they should identify all examples of fast changes to Earth's surface listed.

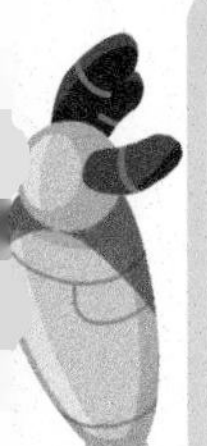

FORMATIVE ASSESSMENT

MAKING SENSE OF PHENOMENA

Students gain understanding that changes to Earth's surface can happen quickly as they explore the **investigative phenomenon.** They should connect this to the **anchoring phenomenon** that flash flooding can happen quickly. Students should understand that Earth's surface can be changed quickly by fast moving water, as well as other processes such as gravity, volcanic eruptions, and earthquakes.

REMEDIATION If students struggle to connect the **investigative phenomenon** back to the **anchoring phenomenon,** have them review the photos and reread the captions in the Exploration.

MAKING SENSE OF PHENOMENA IDEA ORGANIZER

After completing Exploration 3, students can fill in the **Idea Organizer** to summarize the connection between how changes to Earth's surface can happen quickly and the anchoring phenomenon that flash flooding can happen quickly.

EXPLORATION 4

Slow Changes

Activity Guide, pages 192–194

TIME ESTIMATE

INVESTIGATIVE PHENOMENON
Changes to Earth's surface can happen slowly.

Phenomenon Explained Students explore the **investigative phenomenon** by exploring different factors that cause slow changes on Earth's surface.

Slow and Steady and Pushing Through

Students can work in pairs to thoroughly examine the images and captions. Have them identify a cause-and-effect relationship related to plants. **Sample answer:** Rainfall causes plant roots to grow; growing plant roots spread through soil and wedge it apart to change the land. Then, ask students to classify the images showing how glaciers cause changes to Earth's surface (weathering, erosion, or deposition).

Water Processes

Everyday Phenomenon **Rocks downstream are smaller and rounder than those upstream.**

Tell students that small round pebbles could once have been part of a mountain cliff. Refer students to the images and suppose out loud that the flowing the stream comes from the waterfall.

Have student pairs discuss whether or not they agree with this statement: "Sometimes, weathering can happen slowly, but erosion and deposition can happen quickly." **Sample answer:** I agree, because it can take a long time for weathering to break apart the rock under a waterfall, but once it does, water could quickly move it and drop the rock piece somewhere else.

Sand and Time

Everyday Phenomenon **Wind can work like a sandblaster.**

While *abrasion* is too high-level for your students, they still need to understand the eroding power of windblown sand. Refer them to the before-and-after images of the boulder. Point out that the wider sections of boulder were mostly likely made of a harder rock material. Have students form pairs to examine the images and identify factors involved in each change pictured. Have them discuss similar weathering and erosion patterns they may have observed.

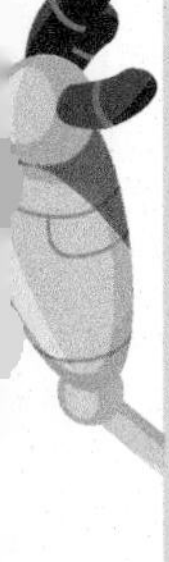

FORMATIVE ASSESSMENT

MAKING SENSE OF PHENOMENA

Students gain understanding that changes to Earth's surface can happen slowly as they explore the **investigative phenomenon.** They should connect this to the **anchoring phenomenon** that even though flooding is a fast change, similar changes can happen slowly. Students should understand that it can take time for water, wind, ice, and plants to affect the shape Earth's surface.

REMEDIATION If students struggle to connect the **investigative phenomenon** back to the **anchoring phenomenon,** have them look for and identify specific examples of weathering, erosion, and deposition in this Exploration's images.

SOCIAL EMOTIONAL LEARNING

Whenever possible, facilitate students in intentionally using collaborative work groups. Reinforce the importance of working together to solve problems such as being unsure and to achieve goals such as answering questions. Invite students to share a positive experience they had in solving a problem or achieving a goal by working with other students.

MAKING SENSE OF PHENOMENA IDEA ORGANIZER

After completing Exploration 4, students can fill in the **Idea Organizer** to summarize the connection between how changes to Earth's surface can happen slowly and the anchoring phenomenon that even though flooding is a fast change, similar changes can happen slowly.

LESSON 02

ONLINE-ONLY RESOURCE

Take It Further

Engage • Explore/Explain • **Elaborate** • Evaluate

TIME ESTIMATE

These Take It Further paths may be completed to enrich and extend students' comprehension of content covered within this lesson.

ONLINE

People in Science & Engineering: Kerry Sieh

Kerry Sieh, PhD, is a geologist and seismologist who studies the Sunda megathrust, a fault on the convergent plate boundary where the Eurasian plate overrides the subducting Indo-Australian plate in the Indian Ocean. As member of the LGBTQ+ community, Sieh identifies as gay.

The Science of Slopes

Students learn about the last ice age and how it changed Earth's surface.

Careers in Science & Engineering: Geophysicist

Students explore the career of a geophysicist.

FORMATIVE ASSESSMENT

Lesson Check

Activity Guide, pages 195–197

Engage • Explore/Explain • Elaborate • Evaluate

Can You Explain It?

Now I know or think that . . .

Sample answer: Now I know or think that things such as heavy rains, high winds, earthquakes, and volcanoes can cause Earth's surface to erode and weather quickly. Slow moving water, wind, glaciers and plant roots can cause Earth's surface to weather and erode slowly. Like in the pictures, flooded areas can change quickly while the river at the bottom of the canyon took a long time to carve the land.

After completing the lesson, use the **Making Sense Idea Organizer** to summarize the connections between the **investigative phenomena** and **anchoring phenomenon.**

MAKING CONNECTIONS

After students complete the lesson, they should be able to answer a question about an alternative phenomenon to explain how a waterfall is like the flooded area and river in the Grand Canyon.

Sample answer: The waterfall is similar to the flooded area and canyon because it is moving water that changes Earth's surface. The water weathers and erodes the land and deposits small pieces of rock as it moves.

Checkpoints

1. c
2. a—Sand was deposited by wind.
3. **Sample answer:** Lots of water on a steep slope can cause a landslide to occur. It loosens the soil and gravity causes the soil to move quickly. Small bits of rock and the slope are my evidence.
4. c—glacier; **Sample answer:** A glacier weathered and eroded the land as it moved. My evidence is the ice in the picture as well as the location and shape of the land.
5. **Sample answer:** Vegetation and glaciers can cause Earth's surface to change slowly. My evidence is that it can take years for glaciers to move.
6. **Sample answer:** More rainfall can cause plant roots to grow faster and thicker, which can cause Earth's surface to change more quickly. The lack of water can cause plant roots to grow slowly or not at all which means they won't change Earth's surface much.

SOCIAL EMOTIONAL LEARNING

Have students reflect on the goals they set at the beginning of the lesson. Ask them to think about whether the goals were accomplished or if there were challenges. Have students share the factors that contributed to their success.

LESSON

03 Rock Layers Record Landform Changes

ANCHORING PHENOMENON

These are real footprints in a vertical wall of solid rock.

ENGAGE Can You Explain It?

Students observe and ask questions about footprints in a rock wall. They answer the Can You Explain It? question to determine what the rock wall can tell them about the past environment.

EVALUATE Lesson Check

Students gauge their understanding of the anchoring phenomenon.

HANDS-ON ACTIVITY

EXPLORATION 1 Layered Landforms 50 min

Investigative Phenomenon There are many layers that make up Earth's surface.

Students should connect back to the **anchoring phenomenon** that the exposed rock layer with the dinosaur footprints is only one of the layers present.

HANDS-ON ACTIVITY

EXPLORATION 2 Layer by Layer 60 min

Investigative Phenomenon Identifying organisms can help determine what type of environment existed.

Students should connect back to the **anchoring phenomenon** that the footprints on the rock were made by a dinosaurs walking on horizontal land.

EXPLORATION 3 Layers of Rock 30 min

Investigative Phenomenon Patterns in rock layers can tell us about past and present environments.

Students should connect back to the **anchoring phenomenon** that Earth is made of many rock layers.

EXPLORATION 4 Evidence of Environments 60 min

Investigative Phenomenon Fossils can be evidence of environmental changes.

Students should connect back to the **anchoring phenomenon** that the fossils on the rock were left there when that layer was horizontal mud. Over time it became rock and the layers became steeper.

Making 3D Connections

The **anchoring phenomenon** in this lesson supports students' understanding of and application of these Next Generation Science Standards.

Building to the Performance Expectations

PE 4-ESS1-1 Identify evidence from patterns in rock formations and fossils in rock layers to support an explanation for changes in a landscape over time.

SEP

Constructing Explanations and Designing Solutions Identify the evidence that supports particular points in an explanation. *(Explorations 1, 2, 3, 4)*

DCI

ESS1.C The History of Planet Earth Local, regional, and global patterns of rock formations reveal changes over time due to earth forces, such as earthquakes. The presence and location of certain fossil types indicate the order in which rock layers were formed. *(Explorations 1, 2, 3, 4)*

CCC

Patterns Patterns can be used as evidence to support an explanation. *(Explorations 1, 2, 3, 4)*

Scientific Knowledge Assumes an Order and Consistency in Natural Systems Science assumes consistent patterns in natural systems. *(Explorations 1, 2, 3, 4)*

Vocabulary

Word Wall A word wall, anchor chart, or Language Development chart can be used to support vocabulary.

relative age the age of one thing compared to another

fossils the preserved remains or traces of an organism, such as a plant or animal

You may want to include additional academic terms such as *aquatic, climate, composition, humid, plateau, subtropical, terrestrial, vertical,* and any other terms students might struggle with.

Language Development Prompt students to complete the chart when they come to these highlighted terms within the lesson and to add their own terms as they come across unknown science terms.

Anchor Chart As you progress through the unit, you may want use the Language Development chart as a guide to make a vocabulary-based anchor chart that can be displayed and filled out as a whole group during each lesson.

LESSON

03 Rock Layers Record Landform Changes

Activity Guide, pages 198–199

Students can engage in the Can You Explain It? content by observing the photograph or by exploring the corresponding video online.

ANCHORING PHENOMENON

These are real footprints in a vertical wall of solid rock.

PHENOMENON EXPLAINED

These dinosaur prints are evidence that the environment has changed over time in many different ways.

Lesson Objective

Students will use reasoning to connect the evidence to explain how patterns found within rock layers can be used to identify changes that have occurred in an environment over time.

Support Discovery

The following prompts can be used to guide student-led discovery.

I notice . . .

After observing the photograph or watching the video, students should record what they observe about the rock wall.

Sample answer: I notice that the rock wall is vertical and that there are footprints on it.

I wonder . . .

After observing the photograph or watching the video, students should record what they want to find out about the footprints on the rock wall.

Sample answers: I wonder what made the prints. I wonder how the rock wall got to be so steep.

Alternative Phenomenon

If students are unfamiliar with fossils, ask them if they've ever seen the imprint of a fallen leaf or a dog's paw prints in sidewalk concrete. Then guide them to consider how their physical environment has changed over time. What changes have they observed? It could be changes in the skyline (new buildings, bridges, or bleachers) or landscape (empty lot turned into a garden, old landfill turned into a hilltop park). Then have them think about the ways that the surface of Earth has changed over time. Tell students to make a list with a partner. Ask them to share their answers with other groups.

Can You Explain It?

In Can You Explain It?, students make an initial claim that explains the **Anchoring Phenomenon.**

Sample answer: This rock wall tells me that this area used to be flat and an animal walked on it.

Students will observe and gather evidence about rock layers to determine what the footprints in the rock wall can tell them about the past environment. This will enable them to give a more complete explanation of the **Anchoring Phenomenon** at the end of the lesson.

SOCIAL EMOTIONAL LEARNING

Guide students to reflect on their goals from previous lessons and on any feedback they received from their teachers or peers. Then have each student set a personal goal for this lesson and make a plan for how to achieve the goal. Throughout the lesson, take daily breaks for students to track their progress in meeting their goals. As students move from lesson to lesson, they can continue to work towards their initial goals or set new ones. If students struggle to set goals for this lesson, share with them some of the following ideas: how Earth's surface changes over time, how fossils help provide evidence of changes on Earth's surface, or working through challenging tasks.

LESSON 03

FUNomenal READER

Uncovering a Story

WHEN TO USE

SCIENCE 

- Anchoring Phenomenon / Alternative Phenomenon
- Options for ELA Instruction
- Build on Prior Knowledge
- Preview the Phenomenon
- Read to Learn
- Support Sense Making
- Science Stretch
- Check for Comprehension

Option 1 Use before students begin the lesson in the Activity Guide to provide an engaging model to introduce the lesson's phenomenon.

Option 2 Use after students have completed the Activity Guide to reinforce students' understanding of the lesson phenomenon by exploring a related phenomenon.

ELA 

- Options for ELA Instruction
- Build on Prior Knowledge
- Read to Learn

Option 3 To use during designated ELA Reading time for independent reading, whole-class instruction, or small-group instruction, look for this icon: ELA

Plan

ANCHORING PHENOMENON / ALTERNATIVE PHENOMENON

The anchoring phenomenon in the Activity Guide is *These are real footprints in a vertical wall of solid rock*, and the main example is dinosaur prints in a rock wall. The FUNomenal Reader presents a similar phenomenon (*This fossil of an oyster shell was found in a local creek bed*), and the example is fossils found by students who are cleaning up a creek bed after a heavy storm. Both present the same science concepts and cover the same standards but with different phenomena. Guide students to draw connections between the two situations and to understand the underlying principle: fossils can help us understand what past environments were like, how they have changed over time, and how changes to Earth's surface have affected them.

Options for ELA Instruction 

Choose one of the following anchor chart options and project it or print copies. Then display and introduce the chart before reading the text.

Ask and Answer Questions Use the *Ask and Answer Questions Anchor Chart* when introducing, developing, or reviewing those skills in the context of this story. Discuss how Dani's questions at the creek bed lead to a class discussion and a visit to a natural history museum.

Context Clues Use the *Context Clues Anchor Chart* to help students understand the meaning of some words in the story. Remind them to look for clues in the text. For *sedimentary* on page 7, students can find the definition in the next sentence: *These rocks form in layers when sand and clay and mud come out of the water and form layers.*

Text Features Have students refer to the *Text Features Anchor Chart* to help them identify the various text features in this story. As they page through the story, students should notice illustrations, photos, diagrams, and a map. Guide them to understand that these visual features help explain ideas in the text.

TEXT FEATURES

GRAPHIC FEATURES

Preview

ELA **Build on Prior Knowledge** Ask students to think about things they have seen that have changed over time. Do they know of any buildings that have been torn down or new ones that have been built? Trees that have been cut down or new ones that have grown? Discuss changes they have observed over time to gauge students' prior knowledge. Then have them think about the ways that the surface of Earth has changed over time. Have partners make a list and then share their answers with other pairs.

Preview the Phenomenon Ask students to study the illustration on page 2 of the story, which shows people picking up something from a creek bed. An accompanying photo shows a fossil. Encourage students to record any questions they have about what might be happening. Point out that their questions might change as they read through the story. Have them keep their questions close by and periodically check to see if any can be answered.

STANDARDS SUPPORTED

SEP

Constructing Explanations and Designing Solutions

DCI

ESS1.C The History of Planet Earth

CCC

Patterns

Scientific Knowledge Assumes an Order and Consistency in Natural Systems

Uncovering a Story (continued)

Discover

Read to Learn 

The **Read to Learn** suggestions inside the book's front cover encourage students to interact with the book multiple times for different purposes.

Preview Students look for unfamiliar words and share them with a partner. New terms may include *fossil, paleontologist,* and *layering up.* Have students look up words they aren't sure about and notice how they are used in the context of the story.

Skim Students skim the illustrations and photos in the story. Have them turn to a partner and share their predictions of what the story will be about.

Read As students read the story, ask them to look for connections to one of the following anchor chart skills. **Ask and Answer Questions, Context Clues, Text Features**

Support Sense Making

Choose one or more of the following:

- Be sure students can identify the phenomenon presented on the opening pages of the story: Dani finds a fossil while cleaning up a creek bed after a heavy storm and wonders how old the fossil is, how it got there, and how it formed. The story is about Dani and his classmates' efforts to answer those questions about fossils.
- Encourage a student-led discussion about why it is important to study fossils. Students can refer to Dani's conversation with the paleontologist and his teacher on pages 12 and 13. Discussion points might include what Ms. Achebe says about most living things dying and leaving no remains at all. How do scientists draw conclusions about the past without a complete fossil record?
- If possible, bring a fossil to class and have students pass it around carefully. Have them call out descriptive phrases as they observe the fossil, while you write those phrases on the board. As a class, determine what organism likely left those fossilized remains. Interested students might want to do online research to find out more and then share their findings with the class.

Extend

Science Stretch

The **Science Stretch** suggestions inside the book's back cover help students think about what they read. Students can complete one or more as time allows.

How could you make a model of fossil formation to demonstrate the process to someone else? **Sample answer:** I could make a comic strip that shows the stages of fossil formation, as on pages 12 and 13 of the story.

Write what fossils can tell us about the way Earth's surface has changed. **Sample answer:** Fossils found in rock layers give clues about the age of the rock and the environment at that time. For example, you can tell if the area was once dry land and then became covered by water.

Make a plan for starting a fossil collection at your school. Students' ideas might include sending a formal request to the principal and finding out how other schools have started a fossil collection.

SOCIAL EMOTIONAL LEARNING

In a small group, discuss how Earth's surface can change over time. Guide students to take turns talking and listen respectfully to others' opinions.

Check for Comprehension Have students write a paragraph that addresses one of Dani's questions: *How can rock layers far away from the ocean include marine fossils?* Encourage them to use details from the story to support their ideas.

EXPLORATION 1 HANDS-ON ACTIVITY

Layered Landforms

Activity Guide, pages 200–201

TIME ESTIMATE

SHORT ON TIME?

This activity can be done as a whole class activity or teacher demonstration to save time and materials.

POSSIBLE MATERIALS

- ☐ large clear container
- ☐ small containers filled with different colored sand

Materials Alert If possible, provide students with four different colors of sand and a stopwatch for measuring pouring time.

PREPARATION

In advance, you may want to premeasure the materials into the small containers for each group.

INVESTIGATIVE PHENOMENON

There are many layers that make up Earth's surface.

Phenomenon Explained Students explore the **investigative phenomenon** by making a model of how different layers of rock form. They use their observations to relate layer thickness and formation time.

Form a Question After reading about rock layers, students should form a question about them. If students struggle to form a question, ask them what they notice about the picture of a canyon wall. **Sample questions:** How do the rock layers form? What causes the rock layers to have different colors?

STEPS 1 and 2 Make sure students choose one color of sand for each layer and that they pour the sand into the jar at a steady rate.

STEP 3 As students repeat pouring sand into the jar three more times, suggest that one group member do all the pouring of the sand to help keep the rate consistent.

Provide rulers and have students measure the layers of sand that they poured. **Ask:** How did the length of time you poured the sand affect the depth, or thickness, of the layer? **Sample answer:** The longer the sand was poured, the deeper, or thicker, the layer was that formed.

- **Make a Claim** Claim should explain that the top layer is the youngest and the bottom layer is the oldest.
- **Evidence** Students should cite as evidence their data showing that the first layer was poured first, which makes it the oldest.
- **Reasoning** Students should explain that pouring the sand for different lengths of time created different thicknesses. Also the first layer poured is the oldest and the top layer is the youngest.

FORMATIVE ASSESSMENT

MAKING SENSE OF PHENOMENA

Students gain understanding that there are many layers that make up Earth's surface as they explore the **investigative phenomenon.** They should connect this to the **anchoring phenomenon** that there are real footprints on a vertical wall of solid rock. Students should understand that pouring the material for different amounts of time made layers of different thicknesses. Thus, their models represent rock layers of varying thicknesses that formed in different amounts of time.

REMEDIATION If students struggle to connect the **investigative phenomenon** back to the **anchoring phenomenon,** have them write a short paragraph explaining why they do or do not think the exposed rock layer with dinosaur footprints is the only layer present.

MAKING SENSE OF PHENOMENA IDEA ORGANIZER

After completing Exploration 1, students can fill in the **Idea Organizer** to summarize the connection between there being many layers that make up Earth's surface and the anchoring phenomenon that there are real footprints on a vertical wall of solid rock.

Activity Outcome

Students should make a model of rock layers in order to observe how layers of different thicknesses form. Students use their observations to infer that rock layer thickness varies with the formation time.

Performance Indicators	
	make a model of different rock layers
	observe how layers of different thicknesses form
	relate layer thickness to formation time

EXPLORATION 2 HANDS-ON ACTIVITY

Layer by Layer

Activity Guide, pages 202–205

TIME ESTIMATE

SHORT ON TIME?

Encourage students to choose a group leader and divide up the activity tasks.

POSSIBLE MATERIALS

- ☐ nature magazines
- ☐ scissors
- ☐ construction paper
- ☐ glue

Materials Alert As an alternative to nature magazines, find and print out environment images online.

PREPARATION

Before you separate students into groups, have materials prepared for each group and an area for the groups to work together.

INVESTIGATIVE PHENOMENON
Identifying organisms can help determine what type of environment existed.

Phenomenon Explained Students explore the **investigative phenomenon** by developing and using a model of rock layers to infer what fossil evidence can reveal about past environments.

Form a Question After they learn about relative age, students should form a question about environments changing over time. **Sample question:** How can I figure out if an environment has changed over time?

STEPS 1, 2, and 3 Encourage students to choose both plants and animals when they select their organisms.

STEPS 4 and 5 Students stack the paper layers they created and exchange stacks with another group.

Ask: What are you modeling when you layer the different pictures on top of one another? What does the stack represent? **Sample answer:** layers of rock that form over time and contain fossils

STEPS 6, 7, and 8 Students examine the layers of their traded stack, use evidence to classify the types of environments, analyze the order of the environments, and record their observations and inferences.

- **Make a Claim** Claims should indicate that fossils give us incomplete glimpses into what an environment was like a long time ago.
- **Evidence** Students should cite as evidence their observations from the activity, such as that the model they created is just like the fossil record, and it provides evidence of how incomplete that glimpse is.
- **Reasoning** Students should explain their reasoning such as that, since their model layers only included some organisms in an environment, the layers are incomplete.

FORMATIVE ASSESSMENT

MAKING SENSE OF PHENOMENA

As they explore the **investigative phenomenon,** students gain understanding that identifying organisms can help determine what type of environment existed. They should connect this to the **anchoring phenomenon** that there are real footprints on a vertical wall of solid rock. Students should understand that land can be changed by various factors and those changes can cause the land to change shape and size. Therefore, the rock wall could have been horizontal long ago, which made it possible for the organism to walk on it and make the footprints.

REMEDIATION If students struggle to connect the **investigative phenomenon** back to the **anchoring phenomenon,** that there are real footprints on a vertical wall of solid rock.

MAKING SENSE OF PHENOMENA IDEA ORGANIZER

After completing Exploration 2, students can fill in the **Idea Organizer** to summarize the connection between how identifying organisms can help determine what type of environment existed and the anchoring phenomenon that there are real footprints on a vertical wall of solid rock.

Activity Outcome

Students should develop and use a model of rock layers containing fossils in order to infer the types and order of past environments.

Performance Indicators	
	develop and use model rock layers with fossils
	make a claim that fossils provide an incomplete record of the past
	support the claim using collected evidence

SOCIAL EMOTIONAL LEARNING

Use this opportunity to encourage students to routinely evaluate how well they worked together in their group. Ask questions such as: How well did you help another student taking longer to complete a task? How well did you suggest strategies or contribute information to the learning situation? This process holds children accountable for improving their part in a group-learning situation.

EXPLORATION 3

Layers of Rock

Activity Guide, pages 206–207

TIME ESTIMATE

30 min

INVESTIGATIVE PHENOMENON
Patterns in rock layers can tell us about past and present environments.

Phenomenon Explained Students explore the **investigative phenomenon** by observing the different patterns in rock layers and inferring what they tell us about past environments.

As you discuss the text and photos, remind students that many processes change and shape Earth. Have them identify what can change the planet's surface. **Sample answers:** rivers, rain, wind, glaciers, gravity, earthquakes, volcanic eruptions, and so on

A Long, Long Story!

Students trace the boundaries of rock layers in a photo and number them from oldest to youngest.

If students have difficulty distinguishing the top and bottom of each layer, draw their attention to the different colors of the rocks in photograph. **Ask:** Why do the layers in the rock have different colors? **Sample answer:** The rock layers may have formed from different types of sediments. Students identify where the oldest rock layer is in the photo. **Sample answer:** at the bottom of the rock

Students explain what the rock layers' thicknesses indicate. **Sample answer:** A thinner layer might have formed over less time than a thicker layer.

Explain to students that there may be many reasons for some rock layers being thicker than others. Ask students to offer explanations for why some layers are thicker or thinner than others. For example, one layer may have had part of it scraped away by Earth processes before another layer settled on top of it, or it may have become rock over a shorter or longer period than another layer.

Students explain the meaning of patterns in the rocks. **Sample answer:** They mean that rocks were made out of different materials at different times.

FORMATIVE ASSESSMENT

MAKING SENSE OF PHENOMENA

As they explore the **investigative phenomenon,** students gain understanding that patterns in rock layers can tell us about past and present environments. They should connect this to the **anchoring phenomenon**that there are real footprints on a vertical wall of solid rock.

REMEDIATION If students struggle to connect the **investigative phenomenon** back to the **anchoring phenomenon,** have them compare the photos in this Exploration with the photo of the rock wall with dinosaur footprints.

MAKING SENSE OF PHENOMENA IDEA ORGANIZER

After completing Exploration 3, students can fill in the **Idea Organizer** to summarize the connection between how patterns in rock layers can tell us about past and present environments and the anchoring phenomenonthat there are real footprints on a vertical wall of solid rock.

EXPLORATION 4

Evidence of Environments

Activity Guide, pages 208–214

TIME ESTIMATE

Materials Alert If possible, obtain and show students rock samples containing fossils from both land and water environments.

Preconception Alert The location of fossils in a rock layer can sometimes be deceptive. Some species of organisms, such as turtles and snakes, might live on land while others might live in water. Sometimes wind, a flash flood, or scavenging animals might move an organism from one environment to another, where parts of it might then fossilize. For these reasons, we have to look for additional evidence about a rock layer's former environment.

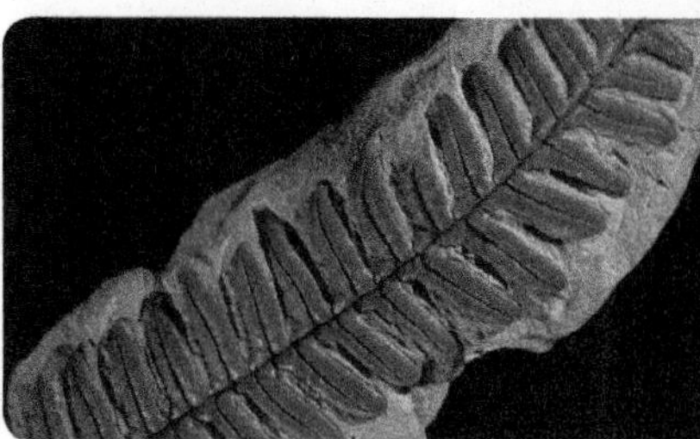

INVESTIGATIVE PHENOMENON
Fossils can be evidence of environmental changes.

Phenomenon Explained Students explore the **investigative phenomenon** by exploring how rock layers and fossils can be used as evidence that environmental changes occurred.

Fossils and Environments

Students observe and read about fossils, then classify them as being from a land or water environment. **Sample answers:** ammonites, water; ferns, land; fish, water; snails, water or land

Seeing History

Everyday Phenomenon **Fossils are forming today as they did in the past.**

Fossils are forming today as they did in the past. Have students think about the **everyday phenomenon** of fossil formation and connect it to the **anchoring phenomenon** that the fossils on the rock were left there when that layer was horizontal mud, and over time it became rock and the layers became steeper. Ask students what they think is fossilizing today, and where fossil formation is occurring.

Layering Up

Students observe rock formations and their fossils at different locations, then correlate and number the layers. Have students choose a partner with which to discuss and explain their reasoning.

As students examine the layers of rock in the images, ask them which layers they think took the longest to form. Most students will answer, "the thick layers." Tell students that rock layers do not form at a consistent rate. Some thick layers may have formed very quickly, while thinner layers may have taken longer to form.

SOCIAL EMOTIONAL LEARNING

Use sentence frames to help children verbalize their thoughts about ways in which people they know record events of the past and why recording the past is important. Write one or more relevant sentence frames on the board, such as, "My friend/family member _____ to remember things that happened long ago." Have students complete the frames individually and then share them with a classmate.

Rock Forms and Forces

Point out to students the displacement of the rock layers along the faults in the images, and discuss why patterns in rock are sometimes disturbed. Invite students to offer reasons based on what they've learned so far. Disturbances can include layers that are in the wrong order (maybe they're upside down or tilted on their sides) as well as layers that are missing (erosion!). For example, an earthquake or volcanic eruption disrupted the layers, moved them, or destroyed them. Then have students explain how moving water can change the patterns in rock layers. Students should understand that water can wear down rock and carry it away from where it formed.

FORMATIVE ASSESSMENT

MAKING SENSE OF PHENOMENA

As they explore the **investigative phenomenon,** students gain understanding that fossils can be evidence of environmental changes. They should connect this to the **anchoring phenomenon** that there are real footprints on a vertical wall of solid rock.

REMEDIATION If students struggle to connect the **investigative phenomenon** back to the **anchoring phenomenon,** have them think about and discuss what evidence about the past fossils of dinosaur footprints might provide.

MAKING SENSE OF PHENOMENA IDEA ORGANIZER

After completing Exploration 4, students can fill in the **Idea Organizer** to summarize the connection between how fossils can be evidence of environmental changes and the anchoring phenomenon that there are real footprints on a vertical wall of solid rock.

LESSON 03 ONLINE-ONLY RESOURCE

Take It Further

Engage • Explore/Explain • **Elaborate** • Evaluate

TIME ESTIMATE

These Take It Further paths may be completed to enrich and extend students' comprehension of content covered within this lesson.

ONLINE 

People in Science & Engineering: Edward Cope

Students learn about the work of a paleontologist who lived in the 1800s and discovered the fossils of more than 1,000 species of extinct animals. Many students may believe that a paleontologist studies only dinosaurs. Point out that paleontologists study all ancient life, from single-celled organisms to more recent extinct mammals.

Changes in Environments

Students learn about fossils from Antarctica and how the environment there has changed over millions of years.

Careers in Science & Engineering: Museum Director

Students read an interview with a museum director and then ask questions of their own.

FORMATIVE ASSESSMENT

Lesson Check

Activity Guide, pages 215–217

Engage • Explore/Explain • Elaborate • Evaluate

Can You Explain It?

Now I know or think that . . .

Sample answer: Now I know that the footprints on the rock wall show that at one time the ground was wet enough for the prints to be made. The wall also was at one time flat enough for the organism to walk on. This is all evidence of a change because the wall can not be walked on in its current state and the mud hardened into rock over time so now it cannot be imprinted.

After completing the lesson, use the **Making Sense Idea Organizer** to summarize the connections between the **investigative phenomena** and **anchoring phenomenon.**

MAKING CONNECTIONS

After students complete the lesson, they should be able to answer a question about an alternative phenomenon to explain how a whale fossil found in the dessert is similar to the dinosaur footprints on the rock wall. **Sample answer:** This whale fossil is similar to the footprints on the rock wall because it shows that long ago this environment might have been an aquatic one.

Checkpoints

1. a—They are found in similar rock layers.
2. **Sample answer:** Fossils tell us what kinds of organisms lived in the past. Knowing the kinds of organisms that existed in the past can tell us about the environments of the past as well.
3. b, d, e
4. **Sample answer:** The fish fossil is the oldest because it is in the bottom layer.
5. a, b, e
6. **Sample answer:** Rock layers form when sediments accumulate over time. These materials may form different layers that you can see when you look at a rock formation. Different materials are sometimes shown as different colors or textures in the rock. The layers also show when changes occurred, such as with earthquakes because parts of the rock formation will have breaks or bends.

SOCIAL EMOTIONAL LEARNING

Have students reflect on the goals they set at the beginning of the lesson. Ask them to think about whether the goals were accomplished or if there were challenges. Have students share the factors that contributed to their success. If the goals were not achieved, talk about what students can do to help them achieve the goals.

UNIT

04 Review

Activity Guide, pages 218–220

The Unit review items enable you to assess student comprehension of core ideas, as well as cross cutting concepts and science and engineering practices.

1. **DOK 2** **Sample answer:** I could take a brick and rub it with sandpaper. The pieces of rock that come off would be evidence of weathering. And the change in how the rock looks and feels would also be effects of weathering.

   Students must be able to recall facts about weathering to answer this question correctly.

2. **DOK 2** **Sample answers:** The cycle of water freezing and thawing in cracks in rocks is one pattern that causes changes to Earth's surface. This pattern can break apart giant rocks and move them, resulting in changes to Earth's surface. Wind blowing sand across rock surfaces can wear down the rock, another example of changing Earth's surface.

   Students who struggle to answer this question may not understand what's being asked of them. First ask them to identify factors that cause weathering and erosion, such as water and wind. Then, guide them to consider the patterns that involve water and wind.

3. **DOK 1** a. earthquakes, landslides

   If students struggle to choose the correct answer choices, rephrase the question. Ask them to identify which answer choices would cause a sudden change to Earth's surface.

4. **DOK 2** The tree roots that are growing have caused the sidewalk to break apart. My evidence is that the bricks are lifted up and the ground isn't flat where the tree root appears to burst out of the ground.

   Students can answer this question by differentiating between weathering and erosion.

5. **DOK 2** Stronger and faster winds will cause quicker changes to Earth's surface. Weaker slower winds take longer to cause the same amount of changes.

   If students are unable to describe the relationship between speed and strength of the wind, encourage them to think about fast and slow changes to Earth's surface.

6. **DOK 1** a. deposition

   If students struggle with this question, have them describe the landscape they see in the picture. For instance, there are many large mounds of sand (dunes). Ask: *How did the sand get there?*

7. **DOK 3** I know the environment has changed because of the different colored layers. My evidence is that a shrimp lives in water, but a snake lives on land, and a fish lives in water. This means the environment changed.

   If students are unable to identify how the environment has changed, identify each organism and compare the environments they live in.

8. **DOK 3** Sample answer: I could model the relationship by drawing a mountain with a stream flowing down it. The moving water in the stream weathers the side of the mountain, erosion moves rock and soil down the stream, and then the stream deposits the broken pieces of rock and soil at the mouth of a river.

   If students struggle to answer this question, suggest they break it down into parts and ask themselves: How can I model weathering? What would be a good way to model erosion? How could I model deposition? It may also help student pairs to work on this together.

9. **DOK 3** Each layer in the rock formed under different conditions. My evidence is different thickness shows that the layering formation process changed in duration.

   If students are unable to make a correct claim, review their model made of different colored sand and compare the layers and what affected their thickness.

10. **DOK 2** a. erosion, d. deposition, e. weathering

    Students should be able to synthesize what they've learned in this unit to answer this question.

3D Item Analysis	1	2	3	4	5	6	7	8	9	10
SEP Constructing Explanations and Designing Solutions	•	•	•			•	•	•	•	•
SEP Planning and Carrying Out Investigations	•							•		
DCI ESS1.C The History of Planet Earth							•		•	
DCI ESS2.A Earth Materials and Systems	•		•			•	•	•	•	•
DCI ESS2.E Biogeology							•		•	
CCC Cause and Effect	•	•	•	•	•	•	•	•	•	•
CCC Patterns		•	•			•		•	•	•
CCC Scientific Knowledge Assumes an Order and Consistency in Natural Systems							•	•	•	

UNIT

05 Earth's Features and Resources

Activity Guide, page 221

Unit Storyline

In Unit 4, students explored the factors and processes that shape and change Earth's surface over time. They examined fossils and other evidence, such as patterns in rock layers, to learn about environmental changes on Earth. In this Unit, students take a closer look at Earth's land and water features by using maps to identify patterns in the locations of where natural hazards, such as earthquakes and volcanoes, occur. Then, they explore ways to reduce the impact of those natural hazards. Finally, students explore and learn how advances in technology are altering the ways we use Earth's natural resources to supply our modern needs.

After completing Unit 5, you may want to administer the End-of-Year Test found online. A Modified End-of-Year Test is also available.

LESSON 1 **PE 4-ESS2-2**

Patterns on Earth

Activity Guide, pages 222–237

Students explore the **anchoring phenomenon** that maps are models that can help us see patterns that may not be visible at Earth's surface.

SEP Analyzing and Interpreting Data; Asking Questions and Defining Problems

DCI **ESS2.B** Plate Tectonics and Large-Scale System Interactions

CCC Patterns

LESSON 2 **PE 4-ESS3-2, 3-5-ETS1-2**

Reducing the Impacts of Natural Hazards

Activity Guide, pages 238–255

Students explore the **anchoring phenomenon** that people who live in areas prone to natural hazards take special precautions to keep themselves safe.

SEP Constructing Explanations and Designing Solutions

DCI **ESS3.B** Natural Hazards; **ETS1.B** Designing Solutions to Engineering Problems

CCC Cause and Effect; Influence of Science, Engineering, and Technology on Society and the Natural World

LESSON 3 **PE 4-ESS3-1; 4-PS3-4; 3-5-ETS1-2**

Resources

Activity Guide, pages 256–277

Students explore the **anchoring phenomenon** that the two cars run off of batteries.

SEP Obtaining, Evaluating, and Communicating Information

DCI **ESS3.A** Natural Resources; **PS3.D** Energy in Chemical Processes and Everyday Life; **ETS1.B** Developing Possible Solutions

CCC Cause and Effect; Interdependence of Science, Engineering, and Technology; Influence of Science, Engineering, and Technology on Society and the Natural World

Unit Review Activity Guide, pages 278–280

Online-Only Resources

Supporting Unit Resources

You Solve It SUPPORTS LESSONS 2 AND 3

Developing Renewable Energy Guidelines is a virtual lab that offers practice in support of **Performance Expectations 4-ESS3-1** and **4-ESS3-2.** Students will work with an engineer and a project manager to make environmentally sound decisions for a town and its residents.

SEP Constructing Explanations and Designing Solutions

DCI **ESS2.A** Natural Resources; **PS3.D** Energy in Chemical Processes and Everyday Life

CCC Cause and Effect; Interdependence of Science, Engineering, and Technology

Unit Project SUPPORTS LESSON 3

Natural Resources Report Card provides students an opportunity to practice aspects of **Performance Expectations 4-ESS3-1** and **4-ESS3-2.** Students will prepare a report card and visual aids to score renewable and nonrenewable energy sources.

SEP Analyzing and Interpreting Data; Engaging in Argument from Evidence

DCI **ESS2.A** Natural Resources; **PS3.D** Energy in Chemical Processes and Everyday Life

CCC Influence of Engineering, Technology, and Science on Society and the Natural World

Unit Performance Task SUPPORTS LESSON 2

Withstanding Water provides an opportunity for students to practice or be assessed on aspects of **Performance Expectation 4-ESS3-2.** Students analyze data to look for patterns to discover how engineers design flood resistent buildings.

SEP Asking Questions and Defining Problems; Developing and Using Models; Constructing Explanations and Designing Solutions

DCI **ESS3.B** Natural Hazards; **ETS1.A** Defining and Delimiting Engineering Problems

CCC Structure and Function; Influence of Science, Engineering, and Technology on Society and the Natural World

Language Development

This worksheet is used as students progress through the unit's lessons. As they come to a highlighted vocabulary term, they should come back to this chart and fill in the blanks with words or phrases.

We've got you covered.

Updates and additional student and teacher resources can be found online. Check back often!

Supporting Lesson Resources

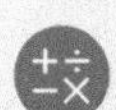

Do the Math!

Lesson 1 California Quake Plot
Lesson 2 Richter Scale
Lesson 3 Calculate Energy Units; Bright Savings

Language SmArts

Lesson 1 Compare and Contrast; Understand Graphics
Lesson 2 Drawing Examples from Text; Gather Information; Summarizing Information
Lesson 3 Compare and Contrast; Summarize; Making Connections; Write a Paper, Cause and Effect

Take It Further

Lesson 1 People in Science & Engineering: Lewis, Clark, and Sacagawea; Volcano Formation; Volcanic Islands; People in Science & Engineering: Carol Reiss
Lesson 2 People in Science & Engineering: Waverly Person; Hawaii Island Lava Hazard Zone Maps; Debate About a Volcano Solution; Careers in Science & Engineering: Submersible Engineer
Lesson 3 People in Science & Engineering: Steven Chu; Careers in Science & Engineering: Sustainable Builders; What's Around You

MAKING SENSE OF PHENOMENA

This idea organizer is used to make sense of the following **anchoring phenomena**:
Lesson 1—Maps are models that can help us see patterns that may not be visible at Earth's surface.
Lesson 2—People who live in areas prone to natural hazards take special precautions to keep themselves safe.
Lesson 3—These two cars run off of batteries.

It also connects the investigative phenomena back to the anchoring phenomenon in each lesson.

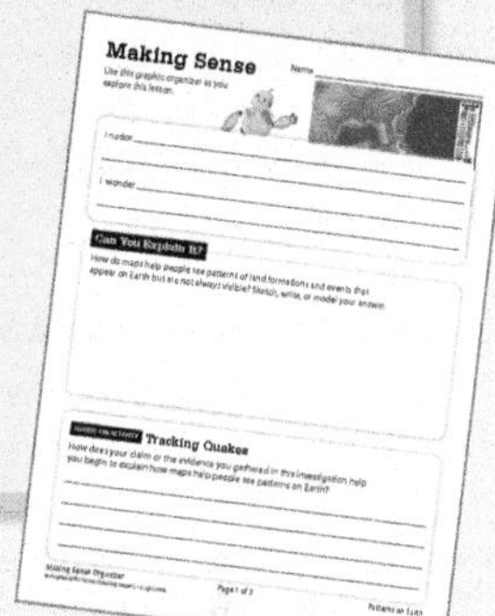
Making Sense
Name
Can You Explain It?
Tracking Quakes

Assessment

Unit Readiness Check: Are You Ready?
Lesson Quizzes: Can You Apply It?
Unit 5 Test
Performance-Based Assessment

Assessments are available in an editable, printable format or can be administered and auto-graded online.

LESSON

01 Patterns on Earth

ANCHORING PHENOMENON

Maps are models that can help us see patterns that may not be visible at Earth's surface.

ENGAGE **Can You Explain It?**

Students observe and ask questions about a map of the Caribbean Sea.

They answer the Can You Explain It? question to describe how maps help people see patterns of land formations on Earth.

EVALUATE **Lesson Check**

Students gauge their understanding of the anchoring phenomenon.

HANDS-ON ACTIVITY

EXPLORATION 1 **Tracking Quakes** 50 min

Investigative Phenomenon Maps are used to identify where earthquakes occur.

Students connect back to the **anchoring phenomenon** that people utilize maps to see patterns that appear on Earth.

HANDS-ON ACTIVITY

EXPLORATION 2 **Volcanic Eruptions** 30 min

Investigative Phenomenon Maps can be used to track where volcanoes erupt.

Students connect back to the **anchoring phenomenon** that people utilize maps to see patterns that appear on Earth.

EXPLORATION 3 **By Land or By Sea** 30 min

Investigative Phenomenon

Earthquakes, volcanoes, mountains, and trenches occur on Earth.

Students connect back to the **anchoring phenomenon** that land formations are not always visible.

EXPLORATION 4 **Finding Patterns**

Investigative Phenomenon Maps can be used to find patterns on Earth.

Students connect back to the **anchoring phenomenon** that maps help people see patterns that appear on Earth.

Making 3D Connections

The **anchoring phenomenon** in this lesson supports students' understanding of and application of these Next Generation Science Standards.

Building to the Performance Expectations

4-ESS2-2 Analyze and interpret data from maps to describe patterns of Earth's features.

SEP

Analyzing and Interpreting Data Analyze and interpret data to make sense of phenomena using logical reasoning. *(Explorations 1, 2, 4)*

Asking Questions and Defining Problems Ask questions that can be investigated and predict reasonable outcomes based on patterns such as cause and effect relationships. *(Explorations 1, 2, 3, 4)*

DCI

ESS2.B Plate Tectonics and Large-Scale System Interactions The locations of mountain ranges, deep ocean trenches, ocean floor structures, earthquakes, and volcanoes occur in patterns. Most earthquakes and volcanoes occur in bands that are often along the boundaries between continents and oceans. Major mountain chains form inside the continents or near their edges. Maps can help locate the different land and water features of Earth. *(Explorations 1, 2, 3, 4)*

CCC

Patterns Patterns can be used as evidence to support an explanation. *(Explorations 1, 2, 3, 4)*

Vocabulary

Word Wall

A word wall, anchor chart, or Language Development chart can be used to support vocabulary.

ocean trench a long, deep, narrow valley found on the ocean floor

You may want to include additional academic terms such as *constructive, detect, indicate, intersection, magnitude* and *occur* and any other terms students might struggle with.

Language Development Prompt students to complete the chart when they come to these highlighted terms within the lesson and to add their own terms as they come across unknown science terms.

Anchor Chart As you progress through the unit, you may want to use the Language Development chart as a guide to make a vocabulary-based anchor chart that can be displayed and filled out as a whole group during each lesson.

LESSON

01 Patterns on Earth

Activity Guide, pages 222–223

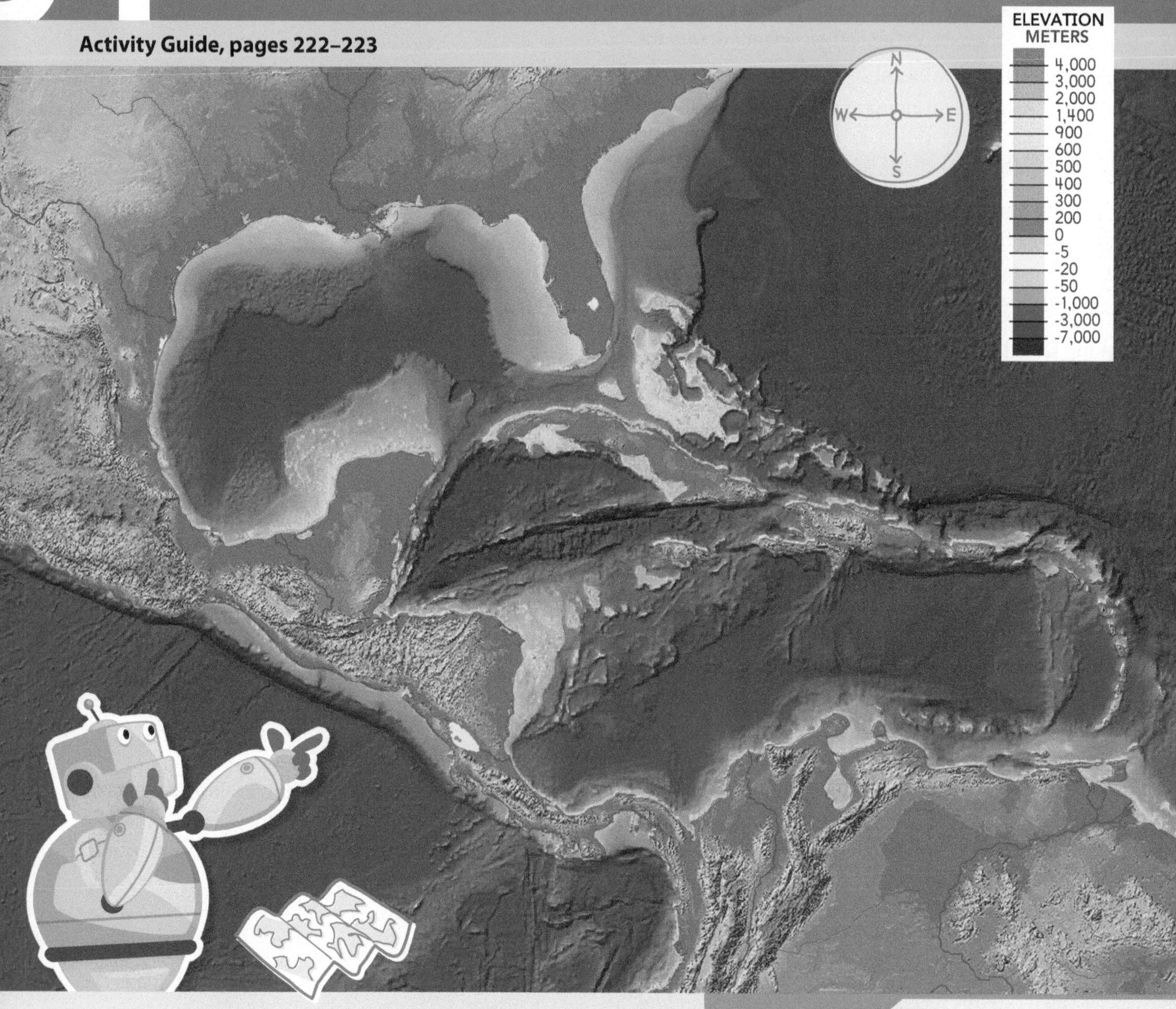

Students can engage in the Can You Explain It? content by observing the map or by exploring the corresponding video online.

ONLINE 

View a fly-over video of a coastline to observe formations on Earth.

ANCHORING PHENOMENON

Maps are models that can help us see patterns that may not be visible at Earth's surface.

PHENOMENON EXPLAINED

Maps can be used to see patterns in the locations of Earth's features. This map shows the underwater trenches and mountain ranges that form the islands in the Caribbean Sea.

Lesson Objective

Students will be able to analyze and interpret data from maps to describe patterns of Earth's features such as the location of mountain ranges, ocean trenches, earthquakes and volcanoes. They will be able to ask questions and investigate what causes earthquakes and volcanoes to occur in similar places.

Support Discovery

The following prompts can be used to guide student-led discovery.

I notice . . .

After observing the map or watching the video, students should record what they noticed about the map. If students struggle to record observations, ask them to analyze what the different colors on the map mean.

Sample answer: I notice there is a dark ridge along the islands and there are mountains near the edge of the continents.

I wonder . . .

After observing the map or watching the video, students should record what they want to find out more about in relation to what the map shows. If students struggle to record what they wonder about the map or video, have them ask a question about what they don't understand about the map.

Sample answer: What is the dark ridge?

Can You Explain It?

In Can You Explain It?, students make an initial claim that explains the **Anchoring Phenomenon.**

Sample answer: Maps can show information about land formation patterns and patterns about events on Earth's surface that aren't easy to see.

In the lesson, students gather evidence about how maps can be used as models to see patterns on Earth. This will enable students to give a more complete explanation of the **Anchoring Phenomenon** at the end of the lesson.

Alternative Phenomenon

If students are unfamiliar with maps, discuss apps they may be familiar with that give directions. It could be a public transportation app for buses, or a cell phone app for drivers. If possible, present a globe to the students. Discuss how it models land formations and water features on Earth. Leave the globe out for students to explore.

SOCIAL EMOTIONAL LEARNING

Guide students to reflect on their goals from previous lessons and on any feedback they received. Then have each student set a personal goal for this lesson and make a plan for how to achieve the goal. Throughout the lesson, take daily breaks for students to track their progress in meeting their goals. As students move from lesson to lesson, they can continue to work towards their initial goals or set new ones. If students struggle setting goals for this lesson, share with them some of the following ideas: identifying what maps show, analyzing and interpreting data, participating more during activity/group work or ensuring everyone in the group has a chance to share an idea, or persevering when an activity or topic is difficult.

LESSON 01

FUNomenal READER

Modeling Maps

WHEN TO USE

SCIENCE 

- Anchoring Phenomenon / Alternative Phenomenon
- Options for ELA Instruction
- Build on Prior Knowledge
- Preview the Phenomenon
- Read to Learn
- Support Sense Making
- Science Stretch
- Check for Comprehension

Option 1 Use before students begin the lesson in the Activity Guide to provide an engaging model to introduce the lesson's phenomenon.

Option 2 Use after students have completed the Activity Guide to reinforce students' understanding of the lesson phenomenon by exploring a related phenomenon.

ELA 20 min

- Options for ELA Instruction
- Build on Prior Knowledge
- Read to Learn

Option 3 To use during designated ELA Reading time for independent reading, whole-class instruction, or small-group instruction, look for this icon: 

Plan

ANCHORING PHENOMENON / ALTERNATIVE PHENOMENON

The anchoring phenomenon in the Activity Guide is *Maps are models that can help us see patterns that may not be visible at Earth's surface.* The main example is a map of the underwater trenches and mountain ranges that form the islands in the Caribbean Sea. The FUNomenal Reader presents a similar phenomenon (*Patterns on Earth's surface can be modeled using maps*), and the example is a classroom assignment to build a 3D model from a flat map. Both present the same science concepts and cover the same standards but with different phenomena. Guide students to draw connections between the two situations and to understand the underlying principle: maps can be used to show patterns on Earth's surface.

Options for ELA Instruction 

Choose one of the following anchor chart options and project it or print copies. Then display and introduce the chart before reading the text. Revisit the chart after reading the text and encourage students to discuss how the skill connects to the text.

Text Features Have students refer to the *Text Features Anchor Chart* to help them identify the various text features in this story. As they page through the story, students should notice photos, lists, and different kinds of maps. Guide them to understand that these visual features help explain ideas in the text.

Ask and Answer Questions Use the *Ask and Answer Questions Anchor Chart* when introducing, developing, or reviewing those skills in the context of this story. Discuss how Scott's class develops a "Questions to Investigate" list in their classroom.

Argument Have students consult the online *Science and Engineering Practices Handbook* for more information on the claim-evidence-reasoning format used by the students in the story. You can also use the *Identify Claim Anchor Chart.*

Preview

ELA **Build on Prior Knowledge** Ask volunteers to share what they know about maps, where they have seen them, and if they have ever used a map. Draw a large figure on the board that approximates the shape of the classroom. Guide students in imagining the room from a bird's-eye view, as on maps they have seen. Ask students to name objects in the classroom. List the things they name, and invite volunteers to show those things on the classroom map.

Preview the Phenomenon Have students study the photo on page 3 of the story, which shows a teacher pointing to a variety of maps. Encourage students to record any questions they have, reminding them that this story is related to Earth science. Point out that their questions might change as they read through the story. Have them keep their questions handy and periodically check to see if any can be answered.

STANDARDS SUPPORTED

SEP

Analyzing and Interpreting Data

Asking Questions and Defining Problems

DCI

ESS2.B Plate Tectonics and Large-Scale System Interactions

CCC

Patterns

Modeling Maps (continued)

Discover

Read to Learn 

The **Read to Learn** suggestions inside the book's front cover encourage students to interact with the book multiple times for different purposes.

Preview Students look for unfamiliar words and share them with a partner. New terms may include *fascinating, symbol,* and *compass rose.* Have students look up words they aren't sure about and notice how they are used in the context of the story.

Skim Students skim the photos in the story. Have them turn to a partner and share their predictions of what the story will be about.

Read As students read the story, ask them to look for connections to one of the following anchor chart skills. **Text Features, Ask and Answer Questions, Argument**

Support Sense Making

Choose one or more of the following:

- Have small groups of students carry out the activity in the story. Hand out unlabeled state maps and have students work together to figure out what state it is based on the map symbols. If time allows, they can make a 3D model of the state using clay or other materials.
- Ask students if the claims the kids in the story make about map symbols are supported by evidence and reasoning. How is recognizing patterns part of their reasoning?
- Invite students to plan a local hike—or a walk around the school's neighborhood, if feasible. They can find a map of local topographic features and use it to plot their route. Have them explain their choices.
- Scott says about art, "It's my favorite subject. I never thought about how I could use it in other subjects, though." Guide students to discuss how art can be used to convey ideas in science, social studies, reading, and math.

Extend

Science Stretch

The **Science Stretch** suggestions inside the book's back cover help students think about what they read. Students can complete one or more as time allows.

Determine what kind of model would be best to show the patterns of a weather event, earthquake, or volcano. Provide different types of maps or links to online sites for students to use as resources.

Develop a handbook for using a specific type of map. Have students work in small groups to plan and develop their handbook.

Analyze patterns on a map and define problems that could affect travel by car, train, or airplane in that region. Help students understand the need to have up-to-the-minute information when making travel plans.

SOCIAL EMOTIONAL LEARNING

How could you help a friend enjoy studying a topic they don't think they are good at? **Sample answer:** I would give them lots of help, encouragement, and positive feedback.

Check for Comprehension Have students pause to think of the concepts presented in this story. Have them respond to the following prompts: *I became more aware of . . ., I didn't realize that . . ., I still don't understand . . .* Have volunteers share their responses with the class.

EXPLORATION 1 HANDS-ON ACTIVITY

Tracking Quakes

Activity Guide, pages 224–227

TIME ESTIMATE

day 1 day 2

SHORT ON TIME?

This activity can be done as a whole class to save the time individual pairs of students would take to plan and conduct the investigation.

POSSIBLE MATERIALS

- ☐ world map with country boundaries
- ☐ data on earthquakes from the USGS

PREPARATION

You might distribute world maps to students or help them use a search engine to find and print large, clear online maps of the world. Clarify that the USGS, or United States Geological Survey, is a government science agency that tracks earthquakes all over the world.

INVESTIGATIVE PHENOMENON
Maps are used to identify where earthquakes occur.

Phenomenon Explained Students explore the **investigative phenomenon** by planning and conducting an investigation to identify where recent earthquakes have occurred. They state a claim about where most quakes occur and use evidence to support it.

Form a Question After reading the introductory paragraph about earthquakes, students should form a question about where earthquakes occur. If they have trouble forming a question, ask them to think about different areas on Earth and ask a question about one of those areas. **Sample answer:** Do earthquakes occur under water?

STEPS 1 and 2 Students pairs find and record data on 20 earthquakes that occurred in the past week. Prompt students to prepare a data table with three columns to show each earthquake's date, location, and magnitude. If necessary, guide an online search of the latest USGS earthquake activity. **Search:** latest earthquakes USGS

STEP 3 Students plot the locations of the 20 earthquakes on a world map and analyze the data to identify the type of area where most earthquakes occurred. **Sample answers:** The quakes have occurred mainly near coasts. Some quakes have occurred under water.

Doing research if necessary, students explain what an earthquake's magnitude indicates. **Sample answer:** the strength of the earthquake

- **Make a Claim** Claims should indicate where earthquakes most often happened.
- **Evidence** Students should cite evidence from their data and the mapped locations of earthquakes.
- **Reasoning** Students should explain their reasoning based on the evidence of the mapped locations; they can observe a pattern that earthquakes most often occur along the edges of continents, or near coasts.

FORMATIVE ASSESSMENT

MAKING SENSE OF PHENOMENA

Students gain understanding that maps can help keep track of where earthquakes occur as they explore the **investigative phenomenon.** They should connect this to the **anchoring phenomenon** that people utilize maps to see patterns that appear on Earth. Students should recognize that while earthquakes are not visible, mapping where they occur on Earth's surface reveals a pattern.

REMEDIATION If students struggle to connect the **investigative phenomenon** back to the **anchoring phenomenon,** have them think about how using a map to track earthquakes can show if earthquakes happen in a specific pattern, or near certain places.

MAKING SENSE OF PHENOMENA IDEA ORGANIZER

After completing Exploration 1, students can fill in the **Idea Organizer** to summarize the connection between how maps can be used to identify where earthquakes occur and the anchoring phenomenon that people utilize maps to see patterns that appear on Earth.

Activity Outcome

Students should design and follow the steps of an investigation to determine where earthquakes occur and what pattern they follow.

Performance Indicators	
	observe and record data about the date, location, and magnitude of earthquakes
	analyze data about the date, location, and magnitude of earthquakes to identify patterns
	make a claim about where earthquakes often happen
	support the claim using collected data as evidence

SOCIAL EMOTIONAL LEARNING

Have students think about how communication skills and teamwork helped them and their partner complete the hands-on activity. Encourage them to discuss how they communicated ideas, such as what their data tables should look like, and how they divided up tasks, such as finding and recording information.

EXPLORATION 2 | HANDS-ON ACTIVITY

Volcanic Eruptions

Activity Guide, pages 228–229

TIME ESTIMATE

SHORT ON TIME?

Have a small group of students conduct the investigation, while the rest of the class records the data.

POSSIBLE MATERIALS

- ☐ world map with country boundaries
- ☐ data on volcanoes from the Smithsonian Institution

PREPARATION

Point out that students should plot the volcanoes on the same map they used to track the earthquakes. They should use a different symbol to identify volcanoes. Clarify that the Smithsonian Institution's National Museum of Natural History has a Global Volcanism Program that gathers data on volcanoes all over the world.

INVESTIGATIVE PHENOMENON
Maps can be used to track where volcanoes erupt.

Phenomenon Explained Students explore the **investigative phenomenon** by planning and conducting an investigation to track recent volcanic eruptions.

Form a Question If students have trouble forming a question, ask them to think about different areas on Earth and ask a question about one of those areas. **Sample answer:** Do volcanoes erupt in the middle of continents?

Investigate Your Question Student pairs find and record data on 10 volcanoes that erupted in the past week and then plot the locations on the same map used to locate earthquakes. Prompt students to prepare a data table with three columns to show each volcano's name, location, and whether the eruption is new or ongoing. If necessary, guide an online search of the Global Volcanism Program at the Smithsonian Institution National Museum of Natural History webpage to find data on the latest volcanoes. **Search:** current eruptions Smithsonian Institution

Remind students to analyze the data and the maps to look for patterns. Students identify the type of area where most volcanoes erupted. **Sample answer:** near coastlines

- **Make a Claim** Student claims should indicate where volcanoes are erupting.
- **Evidence** Students should cite evidence from their data and the mapped locations of volcanoes.
- **Reasoning** Students should explain their reasoning based on the evidence of the mapped locations; they can observe a pattern that volcanoes most often occur in a particular area, such as near coastlines.

FORMATIVE ASSESSMENT

MAKING SENSE OF PHENOMENA

Students gain understanding that maps can be used to track volcanic eruptions as they explore the **investigative phenomenon.** They should connect this to the **anchoring phenomenon** that people utilize maps to see patterns that appear on Earth. Students should recognize that the pattern volcanoes form is not visible to someone observing a volcanic eruption on Earth's surface but becomes clear when many volcanoes are shown on a map.

REMEDIATION If students struggle to connect the **investigative phenomenon** back to the **anchoring phenomenon,** have them think about how the same map that tracks volcanic eruptions can reveal a pattern that shows where volcanoes tend to occur.

MAKING SENSE OF PHENOMENA IDEA ORGANIZER

After completing Exploration 2, students can fill in the **Idea Organizer** to summarize the connection between how maps can be used to identify where active volcanic eruptions occur and the anchoring phenomenon that people utilize maps to see patterns that appear on Earth.

Activity Outcome

Students should design and follow the steps of an investigation to determine where volcanoes occur and what pattern they follow.

Performance Indicators	
	observe and record data about the locations of erupting volcanoes
	plot the locations of recent volcanic eruptions
	analyze the data about the locations of erupting volcanoes
	make a claim about where erupting volcanoes tend to occur
	support the claim using collected data and patterns observed as evidence

EXPLORATION 3

By Land or By Sea

Activity Guide, pages 230–231

TIME ESTIMATE

INVESTIGATIVE PHENOMENON
Earthquakes, volcanoes, mountains, and trenches occur on Earth.

Phenomenon Explained Students explore the **investigative phenomenon** by learning about land formations under water and on land and by finding out how they are mapped.

Shaking and Melting

Direct students' attention to the two photos and captions. Clarify that energy builds up when large blocks of underground rock (plates) strain against each other; earthquakes happen when this energy is suddenly released. In volcanoes, high underground temperatures and pressure melt rock; the accompanying gases may push the molten rock out in a surface explosion. When molten rock comes to the surface, it is called lava.

Up and Down

Refer students to the illustration and point out the additional features of mountains and ocean trenches. Have volunteers read about each feature next to its icon. Stress that ocean trenches and underwater mountains are mostly not easily visible from Earth's surface.

Mapping the Ocean Floor

Everyday Phenomenon **When sound waves moving through the air hit an object like a wall, they bounce back, causing an echo.**

Students should understand that sound waves can create echoes that bounce back when they hit objects. Clarify that sonar uses sound waves that move under the water and that the waves bounce back when they hit underwater objects. Using sonar, experts are able to map what lies under the ocean's surface.

Before students evaluate the likely advantages and disadvantages of sonar mapping of the ocean floor, discuss how using sound waves allows mapping of underwater landforms without having to go under water to explore them. Then ask students if mapping landforms without seeing them could result in any inaccuracies, or mistakes.

SOCIAL EMOTIONAL LEARNING

Before students discuss the answer with their group, clarify what it means to give constructive feedback. Elicit or explain that the feedback should include positive aspects of student efforts and should try to improve those efforts without being mean or disrespectful. Offer this model for positive feedback: "You did a really good job/That's an interesting idea/etc. (something positive), but I think you can improve it by___."

FORMATIVE ASSESSMENT

MAKING SENSE OF PHENOMENA

Students gain understanding of Earth's landforms and natural events as they explore the **investigative phenomenon.** They should connect this to the **anchoring phenomenon** that land formations are not always visible. Students should recognize that maps can show the locations of underwater mountains and ocean trenches and the patterns in which they occur.

REMEDIATION If students struggle to connect the **investigative phenomenon** back to the **anchoring phenomenon,** have them consider how using a map to pinpoint underwater mountains could help show whether those mountains happen near certain kinds of places, or in a specific pattern.

MAKING SENSE OF PHENOMENA IDEA ORGANIZER

After completing Exploration 3, students can fill in the **Idea Organizer** to summarize the connection between how earthquakes, volcanoes, mountains, and trenches occur on Earth and the anchoring phenomenon that land formations are not always visible.

EXPLORATION 4

Finding Patterns

Activity Guide, pages 232–234

TIME ESTIMATE

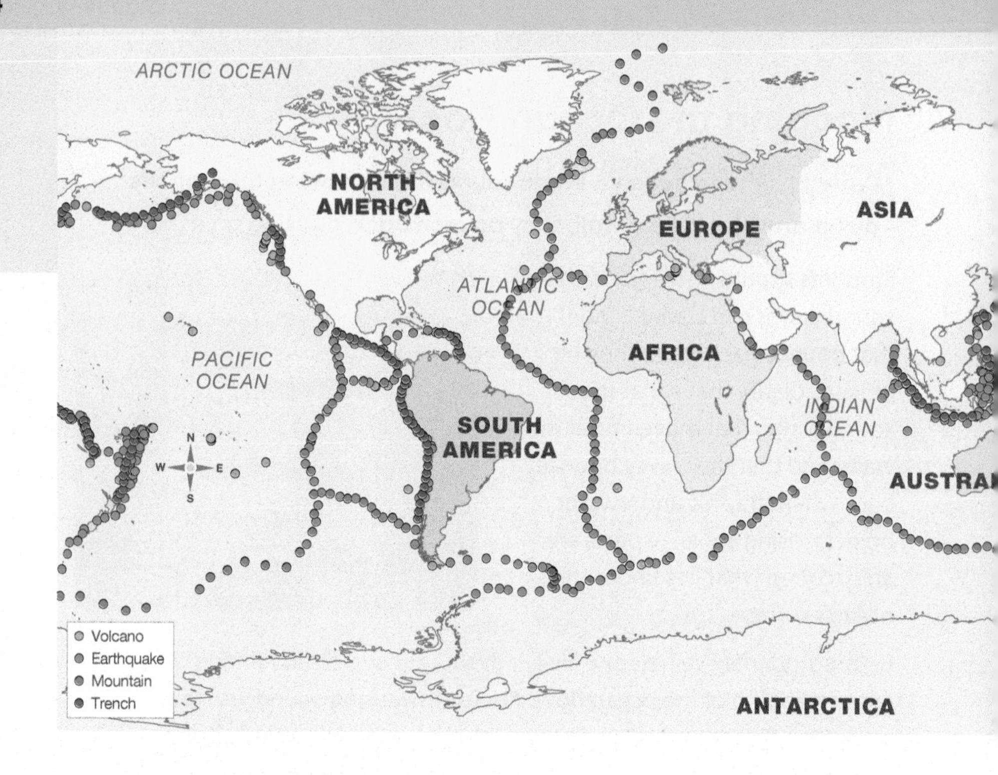

INVESTIGATIVE PHENOMENON

Maps can be used to find patterns on Earth.

Phenomenon Explained Students explore the **investigative phenomenon** by studying maps to recognize and identify the locations of Earth's structures and where volcanoes and earthquakes have occurred

Finding Patterns on the Ocean Floor

Work with students to use the map on page 232 to identify locations of underwater earthquakes and volcanoes and determine the patterns of where these events occur. Help them recognize that underwater earthquakes and volcanoes occur both in the middle and on the edge of oceans and that most underwater mountains are in the middle of oceans.

Patterns on Land

Ask students to work with a partner as you read aloud the final caption on page 233. Have partners take turns pointing to the maps on the page to show each other what the caption says about the locations of mountains, volcanoes, and earthquakes.

California Quake Plot

Everyday Phenomenon **A grid system can be used to pinpoint a location.**

Students should connect the **everyday phenomenon** about using a grid system to the **anchoring phenomenon** that maps help people see patterns that appear on Earth.

Help students understand that latitude and longitude work like a city street grid, or like the grid of columns and rows on a chart or graph. Have partners use the information about longitude and latitude on the chart on page 234 to pinpoint the five earthquake epicenters on the map of California and then describe any pattern they form.

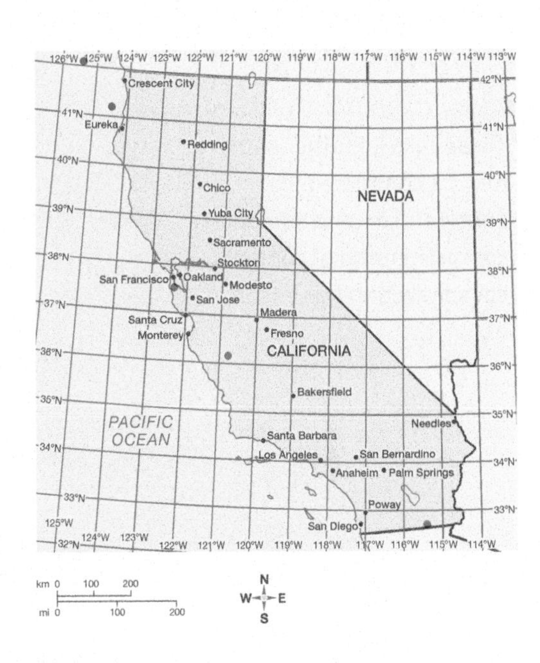

FORMATIVE ASSESSMENT

MAKING SENSE OF PHENOMENA

Students gain understanding of the patterns maps show as they explore the **investigative phenomenon.** They should connect this to the **anchoring phenomenon** that maps help people see patterns that appear on Earth. Students should recognize that maps can be used to show the locations of underwater features, land features, and where volcanoes and earthquakes occur.

REMEDIATION If students struggle to connect the **investigative phenomenon** back to the **anchoring phenomenon,** have them consider the patterns they observe on the maps on these pages and how maps allow them to see those patterns.

MAKING SENSE OF PHENOMENA IDEA ORGANIZER

After completing Exploration 4, students can fill in the **Idea Organizer** to summarize the connection between how maps show patterns of Earth's features and the anchoring phenomenon that maps help people see patterns that appear on Earth.

LESSON 01

ONLINE-ONLY RESOURCE

Take It Further

Engage • Explore/Explain • **Elaborate** • Evaluate

TIME ESTIMATE

These Take It Further paths may be completed to enrich and extend students' comprehension of content covered within this lesson.

ONLINE

People in Science & Engineering: Lewis, Clark, and Sacagawea

In this feature, students learn about how Lewis, Clark, and Sacagawea worked to map the terrain of the United States.

Volcano Formation

Students explore how different types of volcanoes occur.

Volcanic Islands

Students learn about underwater volcanoes that rise from the ocean floor.

People in Science & Engineering: Carol Reiss

Students learn about Carol Reiss, PhD, who studies California's coasts to better understand earthquakes, tsunamis, and volcanoes.

FORMATIVE ASSESSMENT

Lesson Check

Activity Guide, pages 235–237

Engage • Explore/Explain • Elaborate • Evaluate

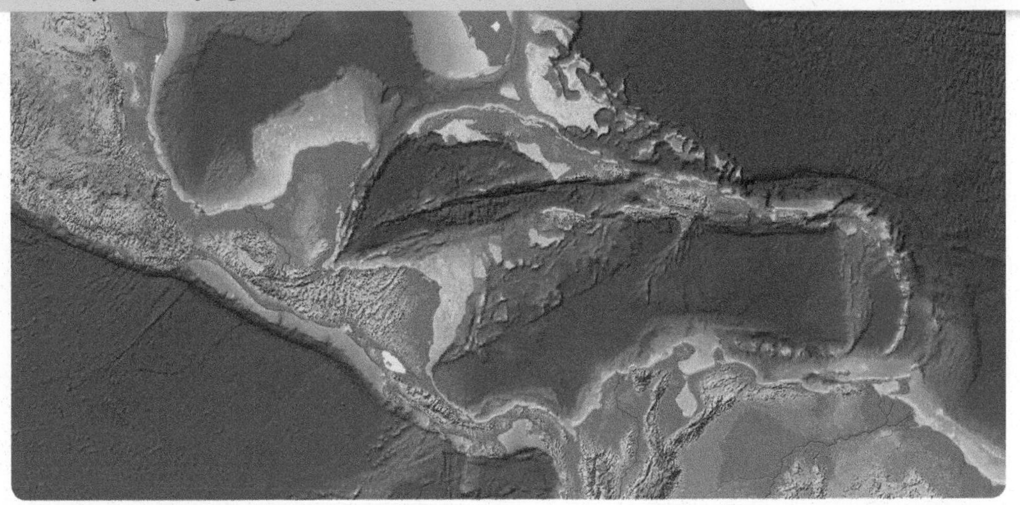

Can You Explain It?

Now I know or think that . . .

Sample answer: This map identifies features near and around the Caribbean Sea. You can see an ocean trench along the islands and where mountains form on land.

After completing the lesson, use the **Making Sense Idea Organizer** to summarize the connections between the **investigative phenomena** and **anchoring phenomenon.**

MAKING CONNECTIONS

After students complete the lesson, they should be able to answer a question about an alternative phenomenon to explain how a map could show patterns on Earth that are otherwise not visible.

Sample answer: A map could show where the San Andreas Fault is located, how large it is, and what earthquakes occurred near it. If you tracked the earthquakes, you could see the pattern of where earthquakes occurred along the fault.

Checkpoints

1. a—mountains; b—ocean trenches; c—volcanoes; d—earthquakes
2. b—edges of the Pacific Ocean
3. b—It shows a pattern in the locations of volcanoes; d—It shows a pattern in the locations of past earthquakes.
4. c—an ocean trench
5. **Sample answer:** The coastlines at the edges of the Pacific Ocean have many volcanoes. Because the volcanoes erupt red-hot lava, this ring along the coastlines is known as the Ring of Fire.
6. **Sample answer:** Most underwater earthquakes occur near underwater mountains. Most underwater volcanoes are near the centers of oceans. Most ocean trenches are near coastlines.

SOCIAL EMOTIONAL LEARNING

Have students write journal entries reflecting on their experiences of working with partners. Ask them to consider what went well and what didn't. How effectively did they communicate? What different skills did each partner bring to the partnership? What new insights about science did they gain from discussions with their partner? Have students address these questions in their journal entries.

LESSON

02 Reducing the Impacts of Natural Hazards

ANCHORING PHENOMENON

People who live in areas prone to natural hazards take special precautions to keep themselves safe.

ENGAGE **Can You Explain It?**
Students observe and ask questions about preparing for a storm. They answer the Can You Explain It? question to consider how scientists and engineers might reduce the impacts of natural hazards.

EVALUATE **Lesson Check**
Students gauge their understanding of the anchoring phenomenon.

HANDS-ON ACTIVITY

EXPLORATION 1 Strong, Stable Structures

Investigative Phenomenon Buildings are constructed in certain ways to withstand earthquakes.

Students connect back to the **anchoring phenomenon** that engineers design and test solutions to reduce the impacts of natural hazards.

HANDS-ON ACTIVITY

EXPLORATION 2 Make Your Own Seismograph

Investigative Phenomenon Engineers and scientists use seismographs to detect and measure ground movement.

Students connect back to the **anchoring phenomenon** that scientists use solutions to reduce the impacts of natural hazards.

EXPLORATION 3 Natural Hazards

Investigative Phenomenon Natural Hazards result from Earth processes, and threaten people and property.

Students connect back to the **anchoring phenomenon** that natural hazards can have very destructive impacts on people and their property.

EXPLORATION 4 Natural Hazard Solutions

Investigative Phenomenon Patterns in natural hazards can be used to design solutions.

Students connect back to the **anchoring phenomenon** that solutions can be used to reduce the impacts of natural hazards.

Making 3D Connections

The **anchoring phenomenon** in this lesson supports students' understanding of and application of these Next Generation Science Standards.

Building to the Performance Expectations

4-ESS3-2 Generate and compare multiple solutions to reduce the impacts of natural Earth processes on humans.

3-5-ETS1-2 Generate and compare multiple possible solutions to a problem based on how well each is likely to meet the criteria and constraints of the problem.

SEP

Constructing Explanations and Designing Solutions Generate and compare multiple solutions to a problem based on how well they meet the criteria and constraints of the design solution.
(Explorations 1, 2, 4)

DCI

ESS3.B Natural Hazards A variety of hazards result from natural processes (e.g., earthquakes, tsunamis, volcanic eruptions). Humans cannot eliminate the hazards but can take steps to reduce their impacts.
(Explorations 1, 2, 3, 4)

ETS1.B Designing Solutions to Engineering Problems Testing a solution involves investigating how well it performs under a range of likely conditions.
(Explorations 1, 2, 4)

CCC

Cause and Effect Cause and effect relationships are routinely identified, tested, and used to explain change. *(Explorations 3, 4)*

Influence of Science, Engineering, and Technology, on Society and the Natural World Engineers improve existing technologies or develop new ones to increase their benefits, to decrease known risks, and to meet societal demands.
(Explorations 1, 2, 4)

Vocabulary

Word Wall A word wall, anchor chart, or Language Development chart can be used to support vocabulary.

natural hazard an Earth process that threatens people and property

You may want to include additional academic terms such as *simulates, resistant, determine, processes,* and *properties* and any other terms students might struggle with.

Language Development Prompt students to complete the chart when they come to these highlighted terms within the lesson.

Anchor Chart As you progress through the unit, you may want to use the Language Development chart as a guide to make a vocabulary-based anchor chart that can be displayed and filled out as a whole group during each lesson.

LESSON

02 Reducing the Impacts of Natural Hazards

Activity Guide, pages 238–239

© Houghton Mifflin Harcourt Publishing Company • Image Credits: ©Mpi10/Media Punch Inc/Alamy

Students can engage in the Can You Explain It? content by observing the photograph or by exploring the corresponding video online.

ONLINE 

View a video about preparing for a natural hazard.

ANCHORING PHENOMENON
People who live in areas prone to natural hazards take special precautions to keep themselves safe.

PHENOMENON EXPLAINED
People who live in areas where natural hazards occur can reduce the impact of such hazards by preparing for them to protect their homes and property and, most importantly, their lives.

Lesson Objective

Students describe a variety of Earth processes that can be hazardous to humans and cause damage to property. They also design solutions to show how the impact and effects of natural hazards can be lessened. They learn about how scientists and engineers work with various tools and systems to reduce the impacts of natural hazards.

Support Discovery

The following prompts can be used to guide student-led discovery.

I notice . . .

After observing the photograph or watching the video, students should record what they noticed about what the people were doing. If students struggle to record observations, ask them to think about the high winds and rain of a hurricane, and what people might to do protect their house.

Sample answers: I notice the men are covering the windows with metal shutters.

I wonder . . .

After observing the photograph or watching the video, students should record what they want to find out about how to reduce the impact of a natural hazard, such as a hurricane. If students struggle to record what they want to know about, ask them to think of questions about what else people can do to protect themselves from hurricanes.

Sample answers: Why are they are covering the windows? Do some materials offer better protection than others?

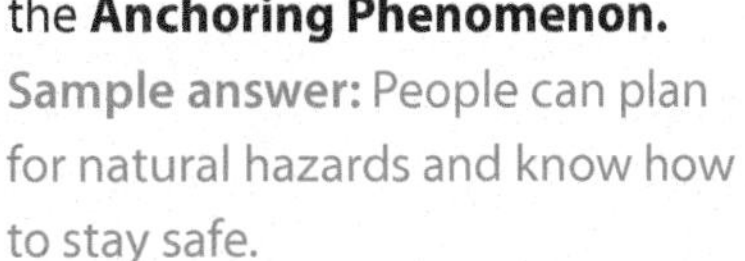

Can You Explain It?

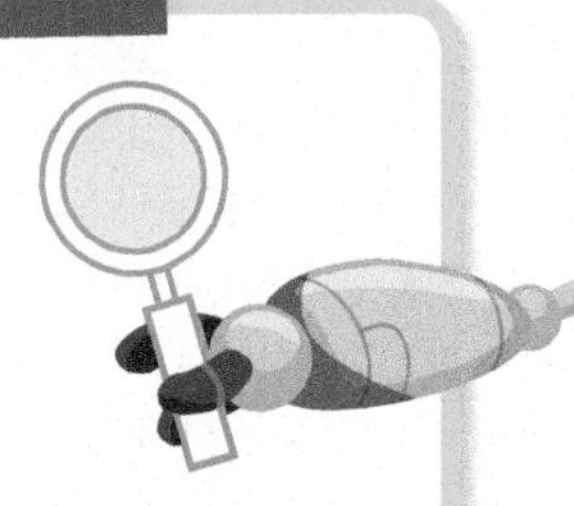

In Can You Explain It?, students make an initial claim that explains the **Anchoring Phenomenon.**

Sample answer: People can plan for natural hazards and know how to stay safe.

Students will gather evidence about how to reduce the impacts of natural hazards. This will enable them to give a more complete explanation of the **Anchoring Phenomenon** at the end of the lesson.

Alternative Phenomenon

If students are unfamiliar with hurricanes and their effects, discuss other kinds of storms they've experienced and the aftereffects those storms. On the board, generate a list of natural hazards: blizzards, earthquakes, floods, tornadoes, etc. Point out that, whether a natural hazard happens unexpectedly (earthquake) or if it's predicted, they can be prepared.

SOCIAL EMOTIONAL LEARNING

Guide students to reflect on their goals from previous lessons and on any feedback they received from their teachers or peers. Then have each student set a personal goal for this lesson and make a plan for how to achieve the goal. Throughout the lesson, take daily breaks for students to track their progress in meeting their goals. As students move from lesson to lesson, they can continue to work towards their initial goals or set new ones. If students struggle setting goals for this lesson, share with them some of the following ideas: identifying how to prepare for natural hazards, constructing explanations and designing solutions, participating more during activity/group work or ensuring everyone in the group has a chance to share an idea, or persevering when an activity or topic is difficult.

LESSON

02

FUNomenal READER

Hotshots!

WHEN TO USE

SCIENCE 

- Anchoring Phenomenon / Alternative Phenomenon
- Options for ELA Instruction
- Build on Prior Knowledge
- Preview the Phenomenon
- Read to Learn
- Support Sense Making
- Science Stretch
- Check for Comprehension

Option 1 Use before students begin the lesson in the Activity Guide to provide an engaging model to introduce the lesson's phenomenon.

Option 2 Use after students have completed the Activity Guide to reinforce students' understanding of the lesson phenomenon by exploring a related phenomenon.

ELA 

- Options for ELA Instruction
- Build on Prior Knowledge
- Read to Learn

Option 3 To use during designated ELA Reading time for independent reading, whole-class instruction, or small-group instruction, look for this icon: ELA

Plan

ANCHORING PHENOMENON / ALTERNATIVE PHENOMENON

The anchoring phenomenon in the Activity Guide is *People who live in areas prone to natural hazards take special precautions to keep themselves safe.* The main example is adding storm shutters to protect windows from wind damage. The FUNomenal Reader presents a similar phenomenon (*People can minimize the impact of wildfires*), and the example is a hotshot firefighter sharing tips for reducing the impact of wildfires on homes and communities. Both present the same science concepts and cover the same standards but with different phenomena. Guide students to draw connections between the two situations and to understand the underlying principle: people can reduce the impacts of natural hazards.

Options for ELA Instruction 

Choose one of the following anchor chart options and project it or print copies. Then display and introduce the chart before reading the text. Revisit the chart after reading the text and encourage students to discuss how the skill connects to the text.

Text Features Have students refer to the *Text Features Anchor Chart* to help them identify the various text features in this story. As they page through the story, students should notice diagrams, a map, illustrations, and photos. Guide them to understand that these visual features help explain ideas in the text.

Author's Purpose Use the *Author's Purpose Anchor Chart* to discuss why the author wrote this story. Was it mainly to persuade, to inform, or to entertain?

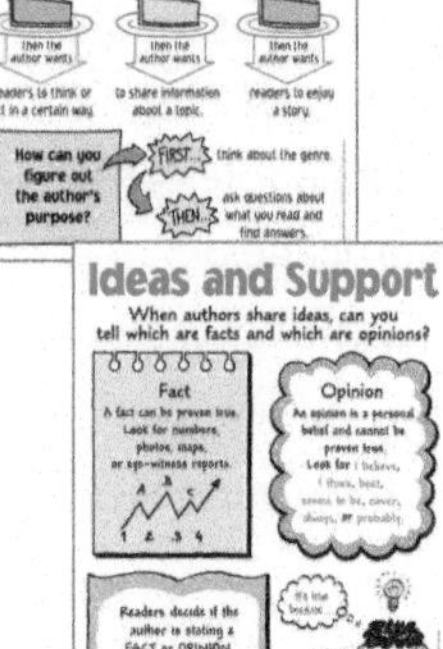

Ideas and Support Use the *Ideas and Support Anchor Chart* to discuss the difference between fact and opinion. Have students determine if these and other statements are fact or opinion: *Fire plays an important role in many ecosystems.* (fact) *Hotshot firefighters are better than regular firefighters.* (opinion) *Brush on the forest floor provides a home for many forest animals.* (fact)

Preview

ELA **Build on Prior Knowledge** Students already know that natural hazards exist, but they may not know that there are things scientists and engineers can do to prepare for these events and make communities safer and able to withstand them. Gauge students' knowledge of the topic by asking what they know about natural hazards. If any students have experienced a natural hazard firsthand, invite them to share their experiences—but be aware that this may be a difficult topic for some students.

Preview the Phenomenon Ask students to study the illustration on page 4 of the story, which shows a person in front of an image of a wildfire. Encourage students to record any questions they have about the presenter and what he might be talking about. Point out that their questions might change as they read through the story. Have them keep their questions handy and periodically check to see if any can be answered.

STANDARDS SUPPORTED

SEP

Constructing Explanations and Designing Solutions

DCI

ESS3.B Natural Hazards

ETS1.B Designing Solutions to Engineering Problems

CCC

Cause and Effect

Influence of Science, Engineering, and Technology on Society and the Natural World

Hotshots! (continued)

Discover

Read to Learn 

The **Read to Learn** suggestions inside the book's front cover encourage students to interact with the book multiple times for different purposes.

Preview Students look for unfamiliar words and share them with a partner. New terms may include *natural hazard, wildfire,* and *hotshot.* Have students look up words they aren't sure about and notice how they are used in the context of the story.

Skim Students skim the illustrations, photos, and diagrams in the story. Have them turn to a partner and share their predictions of what the story will be about.

Read As students read the story, ask them to look for connections to one of the following anchor chart skills. **Text Features, Author's Purpose, Ideas and Support**

Support Sense Making

Choose one or more of the following:

- Have students make a T-chart to show how fire can both help and hurt an ecosystem. They should refer to the details of Mr. Delgado's interview in the story. Discuss why firefighters sometimes use "prescribed burns."
- Students can work in pairs to write a job description for a hotshot firefighter, based on details in the story. They should include duties, required training, and the equipment a hotshot must be able to use. Post the job descriptions on a bulletin board in the classroom, along with drawings or magazine cutouts of hotshot firefighters.
- Explain that Earth's processes can cause natural hazards, but natural hazards can also be the result of human behaviors. Have students come up with a list of human behaviors they think could cause natural hazards and share them with the class. The list could be in the form of a cause-effect organizer.
- Have students find out more about the work being done at the Missoula Fire Lab in Montana and report their findings to the class. Discuss why it is important for scientists there to control wind speed, humidity, and temperature.

Extend

Science Stretch

The **Science Stretch** suggestions inside the book's back cover help students think about what they read. Students can complete one or more as time allows.

Prepare an emergency preparedness plan for your family. Provide books about natural hazards in your area or links to online sites for students to use as resources.

Write a blog post about how scientists use technology to reduce the impacts of forest fires. Have students work with a partner to conduct research and discuss their thinking.

Make a poster about how engineers have developed fire-resistant materials. Students might want to focus on the hotshot uniform or the fire shelter Mr. Delgado mentions during his interview.

SOCIAL EMOTIONAL LEARNING

How did the students in this story exhibit good communication skills?
Sample answer: The students raised their hand before speaking in class and didn't interrupt each other.

Check for Comprehension Have students write a short paragraph in response to this statement: *People can minimize the impact of wildfires.* They should use details from the story in their response.

EXPLORATION 1 HANDS-ON ACTIVITY

Engineer It • Strong, Stable Structures

Activity Guide, pages 240–242

TIME ESTIMATE

day 1 day 2

SHORT ON TIME?

This activity can be done as a whole class to save the amount of time individual groups would take to plan and conduct the investigation.

POSSIBLE MATERIALS

- ☐ cardboard rolls
- ☐ building blocks or sticks
- ☐ paper
- ☐ chenille sticks
- ☐ yarn or string
- ☐ tape or glue

PREPARATION

Provide space for students to conduct their experiments. Distribute paper for groups who plan to draw their test or results. You may want to allow time for yourself to review students' plans before they conduct their tests.

Make sure students understand the meaning of *flexibility*.

INVESTIGATIVE PHENOMENON

Buildings are constructed in certain ways to withstand earthquakes.

Phenomenon Explained Students explore the **investigative phenomenon** by planning and conducting a fair test to show that sturdier, more flexible materials and systems will better withstand movement in an earthquake. Students record data to serve as evidence.

Form a Question After observing the photographs, students should form a question about testing the ability of structures to withstand earthquakes. If students struggle to form a question, ask them to think about what kinds of things might go into planning and constructing a building. **Sample answer:** What are the properties of materials used to build structures that can withstand earthquakes?

STEPS 1 & 2 Students plan and test the materials and evaluate how different materials and constructions withstand motions during an earthquake. Students should design a test to determine the properties of buildings and building materials that withstand earthquake-force shaking. Students should identify materials they will use, how they will build their structures, and how they will test their structures. They should also identify the data they will gather. Students may collect any data they wish to explain how people can reduce the impacts of natural hazards.

- **Make a Claim** Claims should indicate that stronger, flexible materials arranged with greater stability will withstand earthquakes better.
- **Evidence** Students should cite as evidence their observations about materials and construction.
- **Reasoning** Students should explain their reasoning. Stronger, sturdier, more flexible materials and constructions with greater stability and flexibility likely withstood shaking better.

FORMATIVE ASSESSMENT

MAKING SENSE OF PHENOMENA

Students gain understanding that different materials and forms of construction enable buildings to withstand earthquakes as they explore the **investigative phenomenon**. They should connect this to the **anchoring phenomenon** that engineers use strong materials such as metal, to protect weaker areas, such as windows in areas prone to natural hazards.

REMEDIATION If students struggle to connect the **investigative phenomenon** back to the **anchoring phenomenon,** have them discuss and describe the types of materials that protect windows from the high winds caused by a hurricane, and why the type of material matters when it comes to reducing the storm's impact.

MAKING SENSE OF PHENOMENA IDEA ORGANIZER

After completing Exploration 1, students can fill in the **Idea Organizer** to summarize the connection between how buildings are constructed in certain ways to withstand earthquakes and the anchoring phenomenon that engineers design and test solutions to reduce the impacts of natural hazards.

Activity Outcome

Students should design and follow the steps of the test in order to observe that materials and forms of construction can create strong, stable structures.

Performance Indicators	
	make a plan to use the given materials and record observations in an organized way
	design a solution and test how well it meets the criteria and constraints
	test the solution to investigate how well it performs under different conditions
	make a claim that different materials or construction arrangements will withstand shaking better
	support the claim using recorded observations as evidence

EXPLORATION 2 HANDS-ON ACTIVITY

Make Your Own Seismograph

Activity Guide, pages 243–245

TIME ESTIMATE

day 1 day 2

SHORT ON TIME?

You may wish to complete Step 1, Step 2, or both steps ahead of time. Students would begin the activity by attaching the marker to the box.

POSSIBLE MATERIALS

- ☐ shoebox without lid
- ☐ ruler
- ☐ pointed tip scissors
- ☐ construction paper
- ☐ clear adhesive tape
- ☐ 2 rubber bands
- ☐ fine line marker
- ☐ yarn or string

PREPARATION

Collect enough shoeboxes for the number of groups you'll have for this activity. Markers must be taller than the height of the boxes for this activity to work. Consider constructing a seismograph yourself beforehand so that you have a sample seismograph for them to model. If students struggle to make the marker hang straight down, they can roll up a small piece of clay and wrap it around the tip of the marker.

INVESTIGATIVE PHENOMENON
Engineers and scientists use seismographs to detect and measure ground movement.

Phenomenon Explained Students explore the **investigative phenomenon** by observing how a seismograph records movement such as seismic waves. The marker is suspended in such a way that it doesn't move when the box does so it can capture the movement of the box.

Form a Question After observing the photograph, students should form a question about how a seismograph works. If students struggle to form a question, have them look more closely at the rolls in the picture and guess what the drawings represent. **Sample answer:** How does a seismograph record seismic waves?

STEPS 1, 2, 3, and 4 Students assemble the seismograph by taping together a long piece of paper and feeding it through the two slits in the center of the long sides of the box. Students attach the marker so it is suspended with its tip just touching the paper.

STEP 5 Have students conduct their investigation with light shakes to represent a weak earthquake and more vigorous shaking to mimic a stronger one. **Sample answer:** The seismogram shows smaller waves during the weaker shaking and shows larger waves during the stronger earthquake.

Have pairs think about how their seismograph worked well and what could have worked better. **Sample answer:** Our seismometer could be improved by attaching the pen more securely to our box.

- **Make a Claim** Claims should indicate that the pen records data; stronger earthquakes have larger waves on a seismogram.
- **Evidence** Students should compare their two seismograms as evidence of how seismographs record seismic waves.
- **Reasoning** Students should cite evidence to explain their reasoning; for example, stronger shaking produced bigger waves on seismogram.

FORMATIVE ASSESSMENT

MAKING SENSE OF PHENOMENA

Students gain understanding of how seismographs measure and record ground movement as they explore the **investigative phenomenon**. They should connect this to the **anchoring phenomenon** that scientists use solutions to reduce the impacts of natural hazards.

REMEDIATION If students struggle to connect the **investigative phenomenon** back to the **anchoring phenomenon,** have them think about ways that we record and predict the weather, and then use that information to be prepared.

MAKING SENSE OF PHENOMENA IDEA ORGANIZER

After completing Exploration 2, students can fill in the **Idea Organizer** to summarize the connection between using seismographs to detect and measure ground movement and the anchoring phenomenon that scientists develop solutions to reduce the impacts of natural hazards.

Activity Outcome

Students should follow the steps of the experiment in order to construct a seismograph that produces seismograms by recording movements.

Performance Indicators	
	follow instructions to build a seismograph
	test the seismograph under a range of conditions
	identify the cause and effect relationship between the strength of an earthquake and what its seismogram looks like
	make a claim about how seismographs record data about seismic waves
	support the claim using observations as evidence

SOCIAL EMOTIONAL LEARNING

Have students discuss why taking turns is important when working with a partner and what they would do next time to improve the process. Have them consider these strategies for working collaboratively:

- Read the instructions together and make sure both partners understand.
- Divide responsibilities and assign equal roles in the activity.
- Share ideas respectfully.

EXPLORATION 3

Natural Hazards

Activity Guide, pages 246–248

TIME ESTIMATE

day 1 day 2

Materials Alert For this exploration you may want to provide writing or drawing paper and allow students to choose and elaborate on one of the natural hazards shown.

INVESTIGATIVE PHENOMENON
Natural hazards result from Earth processes and threaten people and property.

Phenomenon Explained Students explore the **investigative phenomenon** by examining the causes and effects of a range of natural hazards. Understanding the processes that cause these hazards can help us prepare for them.

Nature's Dangers

Everyday Phenomenon **Hurricanes can destroy large and small buildings.**

Have students brainstorm different kinds of weather. Remind them that weather is the result of natural processes as heat circulates around the globe, and we see it every day. Students should understand that the planet is always changing and that natural hazards are the natural effects of Earth's processes.

Cause and Effect

Help students recognize that understanding the causes and effects of natural hazards helps us prepare for them. Scientists and engineers make devices to detect natural hazards, and develop tools and materials that can better withstand their effects. Being informed about natural hazards helps people protect themselves and their property and minimize the danger.

FORMATIVE ASSESSMENT

MAKING SENSE OF PHENOMENA

Students gain understanding that natural hazards are a result of Earth's natural processes as they explore the **investigative phenomenon**. They should connect this to the **anchoring phenomenon** that natural hazards can have very destructive impacts on people and their property.

REMEDIATION If students struggle to connect the investigative phenomenon back to the anchoring phenomenon, have them describe the hurricane photo on Activity Guide page 247: Strong winds and rain are pushing against the trees and will hit windows and structures with just as much force.

MAKING SENSE OF PHENOMENA IDEA ORGANIZER

After completing Exploration 3, students can fill in the **Idea Organizer** to summarize the connection between how natural hazards result from Earth processes and the anchoring phenomenon that natural hazards can have very destructive impacts on people and their property.

EXPLORATION 4

Natural Hazard Solutions

Activity Guide, pages 249–252

TIME ESTIMATE

day 1 day 2

Materials Alert For this exploration, have markers and large paper for students to create and present ideas for their disaster supply kits.

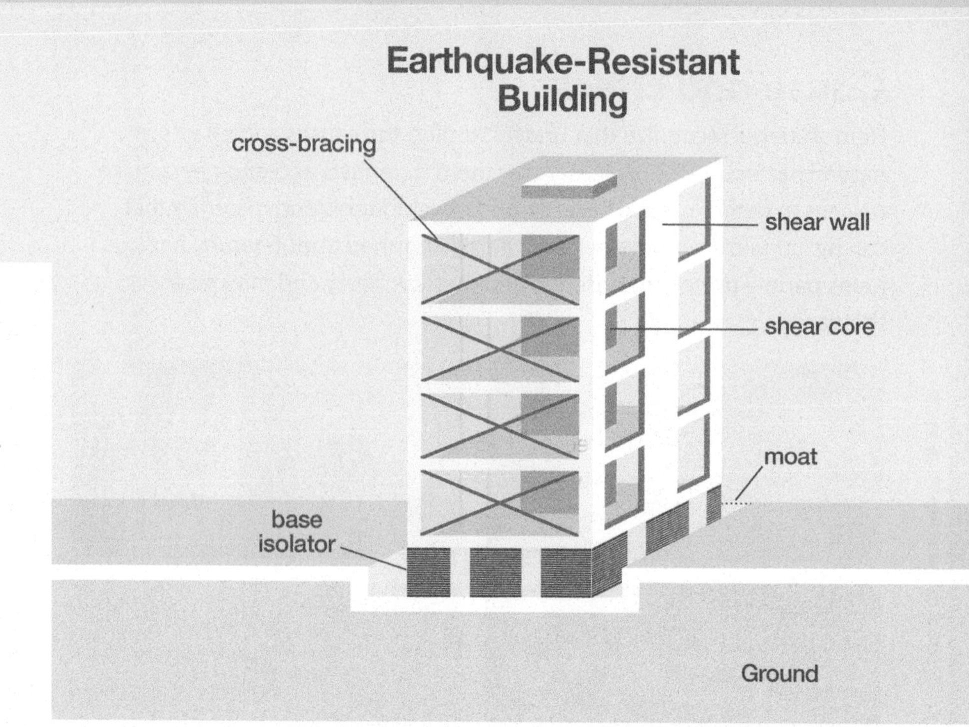

INVESTIGATIVE PHENOMENON
Patterns in natural hazards can be used to design solutions.

Phenomenon Explained Students explore the **investigative phenomenon** by understanding patterns common to natural hazards. Scientists, engineers, and everyday citizens can use this knowledge to prepare for natural hazards and minimize the damage they cause.

Expect the Unexpected

Engineers and scientists use their knowledge about how earthquake movements affect buildings to build safer, stronger buildings. Reinforced walls and base isolators reduce the impact of ground movement beneath the building to minimize shaking and to keep people safer. Have students connect back to the beginning of the lesson where the two men were putting metal over the windows. Allow students time to discuss why the men chose metal over other materials. Brainstorm other materials people use to prevent damage from natural hazards.

What's the Pattern?

Everyday Phenomenon **Weather forecasts help us prepare and know what to wear.**

Students should connect the everyday phenomenon that weather forecasts help us prepare for storms to the anchoring phenomenon that solutions can be used to reduce the impacts of natural hazards.

Studying the patterns of natural hazards helps scientists understand their typical warning signs so we can prepare ourselves. This is similar to checking the weather forecast. By understanding weather patterns, meteorologists can predict when there will be rain; in turn, we know to wear a raincoat or carry an umbrella.

SOCIAL EMOTIONAL LEARNING

Help students understand that being prepared for a natural hazard can help them stay calm and feel safer. They should become familiar with natural hazards common to the region and discuss preparedness with their families. Tell students that government agencies have helpful online resources for information.

Disaster Supply Kit

Students may feel better when knowing they have a plan for a natural disaster that may occur. Help students identify which sort of natural disaster could occur in your region and provide materials so students can plan their disaster supply kits.

Reducing Impacts with Technology

Technology allows scientists to measure and detect changes that can indicate a coming natural hazard. For instance, buoys use sensors that analyze how much the buoys move to detect tsunamis.

FORMATIVE ASSESSMENT

MAKING SENSE OF PHENOMENA

Students gain understanding that recognizing the patterns in natural hazards helps scientists to design solutions as they explore the **investigative phenomenon**. They should connect this to the **anchoring phenomenon** that solutions can be used to reduce the impacts of natural hazards.

REMEDIATION If students struggle to connect the **investigative phenomenon** back to the **anchoring phenomenon,** have them think about the kinds of patterns that would help people prepare for a hurricane. For example, understanding wind speed and direction helps predict a storm's impact.

MAKING SENSE OF PHENOMENA IDEA ORGANIZER

After completing Exploration 4, students can fill in the **Idea Organizer** to summarize the connection between recognizing the patterns of natural hazards and the anchoring phenomenon that scientists and engineers work on various tools and systems to reduce the impacts of natural hazards.

LESSON 02

ONLINE-ONLY RESOURCE

Take It Further

Engage • Explore/Explain • **Elaborate** • Evaluate

TIME ESTIMATE

These Take It Further paths may be completed to enrich and extend students' comprehension of content covered within this lesson.

ONLINE

People in Science & Engineering: Waverly Person

In this feature, students read about Waverly Person, PhD, a seismologist and geophysicist.

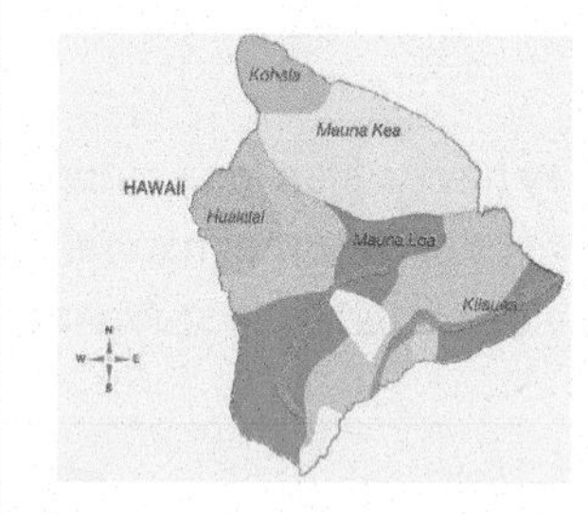

Hawaii Island Lava Hazard Zone Maps

Students interpret a lava hazard zone map of Hawaii to assess the risk of areas near an active volcano.

Debate about a Volcano Solution

Students research two proposed methods of reducing the impact of volcanic eruptions.

Careers in Science & Engineering: Submersible Engineer

Students explore the role of submersible engineers and vehicles that can be used underwater.

FORMATIVE ASSESSMENT

Lesson Check

Activity Guide, pages 253–255

Engage • Explore/Explain • Elaborate • Evaluate

Can You Explain It?

Now I know or think that . . .

Sample answer: Students should list and describe each hazard they choose. People can lessen the impacts of natural hazards by watching for patterns that can predict an upcoming natural hazard and by engineering solutions to decrease the impact of the hazard. Engineering processes allow people to find out what parts of the solutions don't work so they can fix them.

After completing the lesson, use the **Making Sense Idea Organizer** to summarize the connections between the **investigative phenomena** and **anchoring phenomenon.**

MAKING CONNECTIONS

After students complete the lesson, they should be able to compare different methods of preparing for natural hazards. These methods are based on observation of patterns of previous natural hazards and the effects they have had in the past. **Sample answer:** This house is on stilts to reduce the chances of flood damage, much like the shutters are used to minimize hurricane damage. The difference is that they are solutions for different natural hazards.

Checkpoints

1. t. left: volcanic eruption; b. left: earthquake; t. right: landslide; b. right: tsunami
2. a–both; b–earthquake; c–earthquake; d–volcano
3. b—volcano and d—lightning strike
4. a—drought and d—wildfire
5. Tsunami; **Sample answer:** If a tsunami passes under a buoy, data sent is to a warning center. Volcano; **Sample answer:** measures ground tilt when molten rock moves under it. Earthquake; **Sample answer:** shows size and location of an earthquake's source.
6. **Sample answer:** Knowing the causes and effects of natural hazards can help people plan which solutions would be most useful to stay safe.
7. **Sample answer:** An earthquake can cause a landslide when it shakes Earth's surface. Materials on hillsides and slopes might get shaken free of their positions, starting a landslide.
8. **Sample answer:** Earthquake magnitude must be greater than 3.

SOCIAL EMOTIONAL LEARNING

Have students reflect on the concepts they have explored. Groups or partners should come up with a list of questions they want to investigate. Each group or pair should choose one question. Have students set goals to help them go about finding answers to the question. Help students identify the number of goals and how much time is needed to complete each goal.

LESSON

03 Resources

ANCHORING PHENOMENON

These two cars run off of batteries.

ENGAGE **Can You Explain It?**
Students observe and ask questions about battery-powered cars.

They answer the Can You Explain It? question to explore what they know about how new technologies allow for new sources of fuel.

EVALUATE **Lesson Check**
Students gauge their understanding of the anchoring phenomenon.

HANDS-ON ACTIVITY

EXPLORATION 1 **Modeling Energy Resource Use** 80 min

Investigative Phenomenon
Nonrenewable resources run out over time.

Students connect back to the **anchoring phenomenon** that new technologies allow for new energy sources.

HANDS-ON ACTIVITY

Exploration 2 Running on Sunshine 90 min

Investigative Phenomenon
Energy from the sun is a renewable resource that can be captured.

Students connect back to the **anchoring phenomenon** that new technologies allow for people to more efficiently capture energy from different sources.

EXPLORATION 3 **Materials We Use** 60 min

Investigative Phenomenon
Humans use resources from nonrenewable sources for energy.

Students connect back to the **anchoring phenomenon** that new technologies affect how people use resources.

EXPLORATION 4 **Exploring Renewable Resources** 30 min

Investigative Phenomenon Humans use resources from renewable sources for energy.

Students connect back to the **anchoring phenomenon** that new technologies affect how people use resources.

EXPLORATION 5 **Pros and Cons** 

Investigative Phenomenon
Nonrenewable and renewable energy sources have benefits and drawbacks.

Students connect back to the **anchoring phenomenon** that new technologies affect how people use resources.

Making 3D Connections

The anchoring phenomenon in this lesson supports students' understanding of and application of these Next Generation Science Standards.

Building to the Performance Expectations

4-ESS3-1 Obtain and combine information to describe that energy and fuels are derived from natural resources and their uses affect the environment.

4-PS3-4 Apply scientific ideas to design, test and refine a device that converts energy.

3-5-ETS1-2 Generate and compare multiple possible solutions to a problem based on how well each is likely to meet the criteria and constraints of the problem.

SEP

Obtaining, Evaluating, and Communicating Information Obtain and combine information to explain phenomena. *(Exploration 1, 2, 5)*

DCI

ESS3.A Natural Resources Energy and fuels that humans use affect the environment. Some resources are renewable over time, and others are not. *(Explorations 1, 2, 3, 4, 5)*

PS3.D Energy in Chemical Processes and Everyday Life The expression "produce energy" typically refers to the conversion of stored energy into a desired form for practical use. *(Explorations 2, 3, 4)*

ETS1.B Developing Possible Solutions Testing solutions involves investigating performance. *(Explorations 2, 5)*

CCC

Cause and Effect Cause and effect are used to explain change. *(Explorations 1, 2, 4, 5)*

Interdependence of Science, Engineering, and Technology Knowledge of relevant scientific concepts and research findings is important in engineering. *(Explorations 1, 4, 5)*

Influence of Science, Engineering, and Technology, on Society and the Natural World People's needs and wants change, as do their demands. Engineers improve technologies. *(Explorations 4, 5)*

Vocabulary

Word Wall A word wall, anchor chart, or Language Development chart can be used to support vocabulary.

resource anything that you use to live

natural resource a material from nature that people can use

nonrenewable resource a resource that, once used, cannot be replaced in a reasonable amount of time

pollution waste products that damage an ecosystem

renewable resources resources that can be replenished within a reasonable amount of time

You may want to include additional academic terms such as *conserve, converted, extract, generate, processed,* and *replenish* and any other terms students might struggle with.

Language Development Prompt students to complete the chart when they come to these highlighted terms within the lesson and to add their own terms as they come across unknown science terms.

Anchor Chart As you progress through the unit, you may want to use the Language Development chart as a guide to make a vocabulary-based anchor chart that can be displayed and filled out as a whole group during each lesson.

LESSON

03 Resources

Activity Guide, pages 256–257

© Houghton Mifflin Harcourt Publishing Company • Image Credits: (t) ©UrosPoteko/Alamy; (b) ©Houghton Mifflin Harcourt

Students can engage in the Can You Explain It? content by observing the photograph or by exploring the corresponding video online.

ONLINE

View a video to see cars powered by electricity in action.

ANCHORING PHENOMENON

These two cars run off of batteries.

PHENOMENON EXPLAINED

Over time, energy sources used to power cars have changed. While cars used to be powered primarily by fuel from non-renewable resources, changes in technology now allow cars to use alternative sources. This electric car runs off of energy stored in a battery, much like the remote-controlled toy car.

Lesson Objective

Students understand that humans use energy and fuels derived from natural resources. They also evaluate cause and effect relationships about renewable and nonrenewable resources to draw conclusions about the benefits and drawbacks of using each resource type.

Support Discovery

The following prompts can be used to guide student-led discovery.

I notice . . .

After observing the photograph or watching the video, students should record what they noticed about the two cars. If students struggle to record observations, ask them to compare the two vehicles.

Sample answer: I notice that one car is a regular car while the other car is a toy car.

I wonder . . .

After observing the photograph or watching the video, students should record what they want to find out about how these cars are powered. If students struggle to record what else they want to know, have them identify a similarity or difference between the two cars and ask a comparison question related to consumption.

Sample answers: I wonder which car has a longer lasting battery.

Can You Explain It?

In Can You Explain It?, students make an initial claim that explains the **Anchoring Phenomenon.**

Sample answer: Cars used to run on nonrenewable resources, but new technology means that cars can run on batteries.

Students will gather evidence about how new technologies allow for new fuel sources. This will enable them to give a more complete explanation of the **Anchoring Phenomenon** at the end of the lesson.

Alternative Phenomenon

If students are unfamiliar with electric cars or remote-controlled toy cars, show them a remote control car and its power source (a battery). Discuss the various devices they use every day that are powered by the energy stored in batteries—cell phones, laptops, etc.—and how batteries make life more convenient.

SOCIAL EMOTIONAL LEARNING

Guide students to reflect on their goals from previous lessons. Then have each student set a personal goal for this lesson and make a plan for how to achieve the goal. Throughout the lesson, take breaks for students to track their progress in meeting their goals. If students struggle setting goals for this lesson, share with them some of the following ideas: understanding that humans use natural resources, evaluating cause and effect relationships, participating more during activity/group work or ensuring everyone in the group has a chance to share an idea, or persevering when an activity or topic is difficult.

LESSON 03

FUNomenal READER

Energy Savers

WHEN TO USE

SCIENCE 

- Anchoring Phenomenon / Alternative Phenomenon
- Options for ELA Instruction
- Build on Prior Knowledge
- Preview the Phenomenon
- Read to Learn
- Support Sense Making
- Science Stretch
- Check for Comprehension

Option 1 Use before students begin the lesson in the Activity Guide to provide an engaging model to introduce the lesson's phenomenon.

Option 2 Use after students have completed the Activity Guide to reinforce students' understanding of the lesson phenomenon by exploring a related phenomenon.

ELA 20 min

- Options for ELA Instruction
- Build on Prior Knowledge
- Read to Learn

Option 3 To use during designated ELA Reading time for independent reading, whole-class instruction, or small-group instruction, look for this icon: ELA

Plan

ANCHORING PHENOMENON / ALTERNATIVE PHENOMENON

The anchoring phenomenon in the Activity Guide is *These two cars run off of batteries*, and the main examples are an electric car and a battery-operated toy car. The FUNomenal Reader presents a similar phenomenon (*Most household appliances use energy*), and the example is a family who wants to decrease their energy use. Both present the same science concepts and cover the same standards but with different phenomena. Guide students to draw connections between the two situations and to understand the underlying principle: energy resources can be conserved.

Options for ELA Instruction 

Choose one of the following anchor chart options and project it or print copies. Then display and introduce the chart before reading the text. Revisit the chart after reading the text and encourage students to discuss how the skill connects to the text.

Context Clues Use the *Context Clues Anchor Chart* if students struggle to understand the meaning of some words or terms. Remind them to break each one down into its basic components. For example, *nonrenewable* can be broken down into *non-*, *renew,* and *-able*. Have students define each part and infer the meaning of the term from its parts.

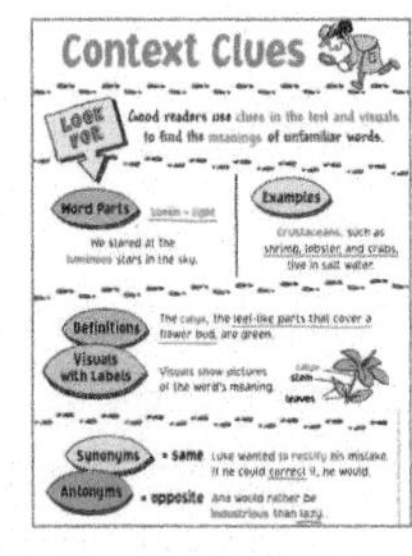

Respond to Text Display the *Respond to Text Anchor Chart* before reading. Tell students they will use one of these methods to respond to the story after they have finished reading: think, connect, remember, create. After reading, have individuals choose the method they prefer and take five to ten minutes to craft a response.

Informational Text Use the *Informational Text Anchor Chart* to discuss the difference between literary and informational text. Help students understand that this story has fictional characters (Maya and her parents) presenting factual information about energy use at home.

Preview

ELA **Build on Prior Knowledge** Many students will know that most appliances run on electricity, but they likely won't know how or why. Remind them that when they turn something on, it is running on some kind of energy source. Ask students to explain what makes a stove or oven run (gas or electricity). Ask what makes a bus or tractor run (gas or fuel). Then have students identify other objects and tell what makes them run.

Preview the Phenomenon Ask students to study the illustration on pages 4–5 of the story, which shows a family standing in their kitchen. Encourage students to record any questions they have about what might be going on. Guide them to think in terms of energy usage in the home. Point out that their questions might change as they read through the story. Have them keep their questions close by and periodically check to see if any can be answered.

STANDARDS SUPPORTED

SEP

Obtaining, Evaluating, and Communicating Information

DCI

ESS3.A Natural Resources

PS3.D Energy in Chemical Processes and Everyday Life

CCC

Cause and Effect

Interdependence of Science, Engineering, and Technology

Influence of Engineering, Technology, and Science on Society and the Natural World

Energy Savers (continued)

Discover

Read to Learn 

The **Read to Learn** suggestions inside the book's front cover encourage students to interact with the book multiple times for different purposes.

Preview Students look for unfamiliar words and share them with a partner. New terms may include *fossil fuel, nonrenewable resource,* and *energy efficient.* Have students look up words they aren't sure about and notice how they are used in the context of the story.

Skim Students skim the illustrations in the story. Have them turn to a partner and share their predictions of what the story will be about.

Read As students read the story, ask them to look for connections to one of the following anchor chart skills. **Context Clues, Respond to Text, Informational Text**

Support Sense Making

Choose one or more of the following:

- Be sure students can identify the phenomenon presented on the opening pages of the story: most household appliances use energy. The story is about Maya and her parents' efforts to find ways to save energy and thereby reduce their energy bills.
- Maya says that electricity in most of her state is made by natural gas–powered plants. Have small groups of students do research to find out what type of energy powers most of your community or most of your state. Have groups combine their findings and make a classroom bulletin board about local energy sources.
- If feasible, invite a member of your local government or another expert to visit your classroom and talk about energy use.
- Maya says that natural gas is considered to be a "cleaner" fuel source but is responsible for emitting harmful gases into the atmosphere. Have students do research and then hold a classroom debate over the pros and cons of natural gas or another fuel source. Have students refer to the online *Science and Engineering Practices Handbook* for information on presenting an argument.

Extend

Science Stretch

The **Science Stretch** suggestions inside the book's back cover help students think about what they read. Students can complete one or more as time allows.

Make a plan to conserve energy in your school or classroom. Have students create their own checklist similar to the one in the story.

Write a blog post about where your community's electricity comes from. Provide books, websites, and other resources for students to use when doing research.

Test the energy efficiency of light bulbs. Have students make a plan for their investigation. If time allows, students can conduct their investigations.

SOCIAL EMOTIONAL LEARNING

What did you learn from this story? Share your ideas with a classmate.
Sample answer: I learned that there are lots of ways my family can use less energy at home.

Check for Comprehension Have students choose three scenes from the story (kitchen, living room, etc.) and write a one-sentence summary for each that explains how energy can be saved there.

EXPLORATION 1 HANDS-ON ACTIVITY

Modeling Energy Resource Use

Activity Guide, pages 258–261

TIME ESTIMATE

day 1 day 2 day 3

20 min 30 min 30 min

SHORT ON TIME?

Choose an investigation question and a modeling method in advance. Explain the model to the class, then have each group gather and analyze data to write a claim about nonrenewable resource use. Have volunteers compare claims and evidence in class discussion.

POSSIBLE MATERIALS

- ☐ small paper cups
- ☐ counting chips
- ☐ posterboard
- ☐ drawing and writing tools
- ☐ other objects students need to complete their plan

PREPARATION

Decide how many groups you will have for the activity. Make sure each group has ten paper cups and at least 30 counting chips to use in their models. Each group will need a table or small circle of desks for a work space. You may wish to have students revisit this activity upon completing Exploration 3.

INVESTIGATIVE PHENOMENON
Nonrenewable resources run out over time.

Phenomenon Explained Students explore the **investigative phenomenon** by modeling how matter and energy flow is related to nonrenewable resource use.

Form a Question After observing the photograph, students should form a question about the costs and benefits of nonrenewable energy resource use. If students struggle to form a question, ask them to think about the effects of nonrenewable resource use. **Sample answer:** How do time and use affect the availability of nonrenewable resources?

STEPS 1, 2 and 3 Students make a plan for how they will use a model to investigate their question. They then organize and analyze their data. Students should identify additional materials, describe how they will test their model, and determine the data to be collected. Possible model: Counting chips = coal resources; cups=coal reserves, various uses for coal products in society, and locations where coal waste products enter the environment. Students transfer chips among cups to model how coal reserves replenish too slowly to meet the demand for coal use. Students may choose to "utilize" chips to show that energy is used to mine coal. Student data should reflect the results of their investigation.

STEP 4 Students should compare and contrast their findings with another group. Remind students to look for patterns as they identify similarities and differences in the data. Students' plans may vary greatly, but they should all come to the conclusion that nonrenewable resources can run out.

- **Make a Claim** Students should make a claim about nonrenewable energy resource use based on their data.
- **Evidence** Students' evidence should support their claim.
- **Reasoning** Students should relate their claim and evidence to what they observe about the availability and use of nonrenewable energy resources.

FORMATIVE ASSESSMENT

MAKING SENSE OF PHENOMENA

Students gain understanding that nonrenewable energy resources run out as they explore the **investigative phenomenon.** As students model how matter and energy flow as related to nonrenewable resource use, they should connect the idea back to the **anchoring phenomenon** that new technologies allow for new energy sources. Students should understand that nonrenewable resources run out over time, so replacements need to be found.

REMEDIATION If students struggle to connect the **investigative phenomenon** back to the **anchoring phenomenon,** have them discuss why switching cars from gasoline use to battery use might be needed or beneficial.

Activity Outcome

Students should design a model to investigate the use of nonrenewable energy resources.

Performance Indicators	
	develop a model that shows the costs and benefits of using nonrenewable energy resources
	gather data related to an investigation question
	identify the cause and effect relationship of nonrenewable resource use
	Support a claim using collected data as evidence

MAKING SENSE OF PHENOMENA IDEA ORGANIZER

After completing Exploration 1, students can fill in the **Idea Organizer** to summarize the connection between nonrenewable energy resources running out over time and the anchoring phenomenon that new technologies allow for new energy sources.

SOCIAL EMOTIONAL LEARNING

Students should identify ways to handle disagreements with a partner. **Sample answer:** We took turns speaking and even when we might disagree with each other's idea, we still tested it.

Discuss the importance of actively listening to everyone in a group and having a judgement-free zone. For example, explain that recording all ideas before work begins leads to better solutions in the end, and it helps everyone feel that their ideas are valued.

EXPLORATION 2 **HANDS-ON ACTIVITY**

Engineer It • Running on Sunshine

Activity Guide, pages 262–265

TIME ESTIMATE

day 1 day 2 day 3

SHORT ON TIME?

Provide a materials reference sheet rather than having students conduct research.

You might also prepare design kits for each group in advance.

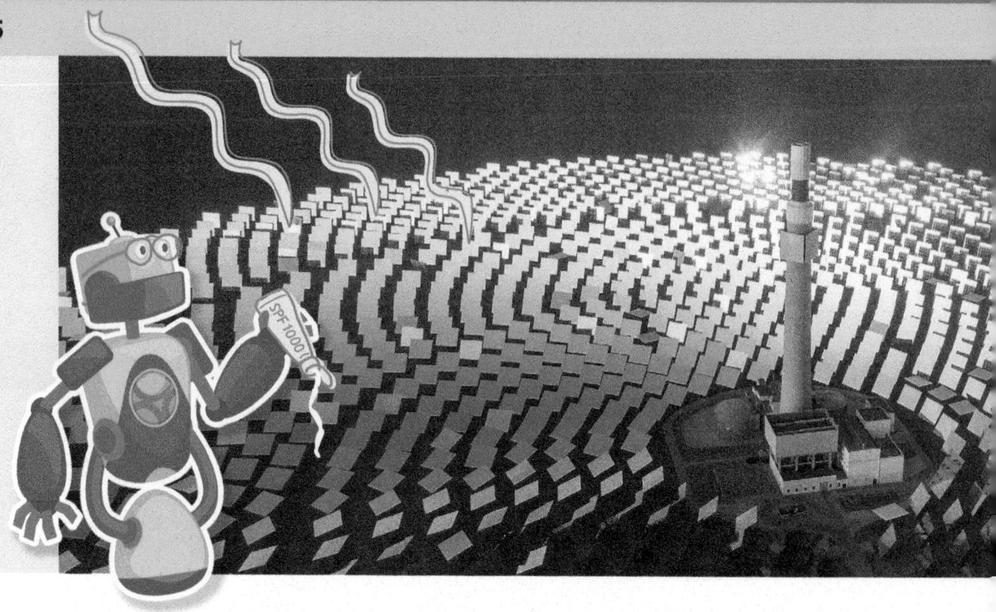

POSSIBLE MATERIALS

- ☐ sand container and sand
- ☐ scissors and tape
- ☐ thermometers
- ☐ timer or watch
- ☐ measuring cup
- ☐ 2 cups
- ☐ cardboard box
- ☐ black paint
- ☐ black construction paper
- ☐ plastic wrap and wax paper
- ☐ packing peanuts
- ☐ newspaper
- ☐ cotton balls
- ☐ aluminum foil
- ☐ paper plates
- ☐ plastic shopping bags
- ☐ paper towels

Materials Alert Remind students that many of the materials used in the activity might be used again.

INVESTIGATIVE PHENOMENON
Energy from the sun is a renewable resource that can be captured.

Phenomenon Explained Students explore the **investigative phenomenon** by designing a method to collect energy from the sun.

Form a Question After observing the photograph, students should form a question about how energy from the sun can be used to heat sand. If students struggle to form a question, have them think about the materials listed for the activity and which ones might be used to heat sand. **Sample answer:** Can we use energy from the sun to warm sand?

STEPS 1–4 Students research materials, identify criteria and constraints, brainstorm design solutions and select one to test, submit a diagram, and build their device. **Sample answer:** Criteria–heater uses sunlight to heat sand; Constraints–limited materials, staying within the time limit. Students test their device and record the temperatures of sand inside each cup. **Sample answers:** communicate; repeat experiment; **Sample answer:** highest temperature occurred after 20 minutes and was higher than initial temperature

STEPS 5 and 6 Students evaluate their data, then develop and test a new device. Students compare the temperatures from both cups and explain if the materials used worked. If they didn't work, students should identify replacements. After testing a new design, students should identify the improvements and how they met the criteria and constraints.

STEP 7 Students compare their results with the other groups.
Sample answer: Some heaters worked better than others. Those had better designs and trapped more sunlight and heat inside the device.

- **Make a Claim** Claim should state whether the device heated the sand.
- **Evidence** Students should provide temperature data that compares the cups of sand inside and outside the device.
- **Reasoning** Students should explain that maximizing energy trapped inside the device will result in higher sand temperatures.

FORMATIVE ASSESSMENT

MAKING SENSE OF PHENOMENA

Students gain understanding that energy from the sun is a renewable resource that can be captured as they explore the **investigative phenomenon.** As students design a method to collect energy from the sun, they should connect the idea back to the **anchoring phenomenon** that new technologies allow for people to more efficiently capture energy from different sources. Students should recognize that the more efficient solar heaters were able to capture more energy from the sun.

REMEDIATION If students struggle to connect the **investigative phenomenon** back to the **anchoring phenomenon,** have them discuss how sunlight might be used to run cars.

Activity Outcome

Students should design a device that uses sunlight energy to heat sand.

Performance Indicators	
	design a solar heater that heats sand to a maximum temperature in 20 minutes
	evaluate the design against criteria, constraints, and the designs of other groups
	improve the design and retest
	make a claim about the solar heater design
	support the claim using evidence and reasoning

PREPARATION

Begin gathering materials for the activity several days in advance. Ask students to bring in used cereal boxes, packing boxes, and newspaper. Materials are also available at grocery stores or discount stores. Stores may be willing to give you empty boxes and packing peanuts without charge.

MAKING SENSE OF PHENOMENA IDEA ORGANIZER

After completing Exploration 2, students can fill in the **Idea Organizer** to summarize the connection between how energy from the sun is a renewable resource and the anchoring phenomenon that new technologies allow for people to more efficiently capture energy from different sources.

EXPLORATION 3

Materials We Use

Activity Guide, pages 266–268

TIME ESTIMATE

day 1 day 2

Materials Alert Use the internet to locate a list of energy providers in your local area that you can share with your students. You might find this information on your local Chamber of Commerce webpage.

INVESTIGATIVE PHENOMENON
Humans use resources from nonrenewable sources for energy.

Phenomenon Explained Students explore the **investigative phenomenon** by comparing different nonrenewable energy resources. They explore where different resources may found, as well as how they are collected and processed. You may choose to have students revisit their models from Exploration 1 after finishing this Exploration.

Resources Around You

To relate nonrenewable resources to the time needed to form them, have students identify the biological, chemical, and physical processes that form each nonrenewable resource shown on page 266.

Where Are They Found?

Remind students of how maps can be used to identify patterns on Earth. Students should circle uranium as the rarest natural resource on the map. Discuss any patterns they observe on the map. Have students identify the resources produced closest to where they live on the map. You might also show students a list of energy providers listed by your local Chamber of Commerce. Have groups of three to four students generate a list of how they might have used each of the resources in the last day or week.

Collecting and Processing

Explain to students that collecting and processing energy resources depends on various technologies. Have students work with a partner to identify a technology needed to obtain each energy resource described on page 266. Encourage students to research technologies, as needed.

FORMATIVE ASSESSMENT

MAKING SENSE OF PHENOMENA

Students gain the understanding that humans use resources from nonrenewable sources for energy as they explore the **investigative phenomenon**. They should connect the idea back to the **anchoring phenomenon** that new technologies affect how people use resources. Students should understand that people use natural resources for many things and that nonrenewable resources are often used as fuel sources, but need to be removed from Earth's crust in order to be used.

REMEDIATION If students struggle to connect the **investigative phenomenon** back to the **anchoring phenomenon,** ask students to think about how the invention of systems that could drill deep into Earth's crust allowed humans to use fossil fuels and natural gas for energy.

MAKING SENSE OF PHENOMENA IDEA ORGANIZER

After completing Exploration 3, students can fill in the **Idea Organizer** to summarize the connection between humans using nonrenewable resources for energy and the anchoring phenomenon that new technologies affect how people use resources.

EXPLORATION 4

Exploring Renewable Resources

Activity Guide, pages 269–270

TIME ESTIMATE

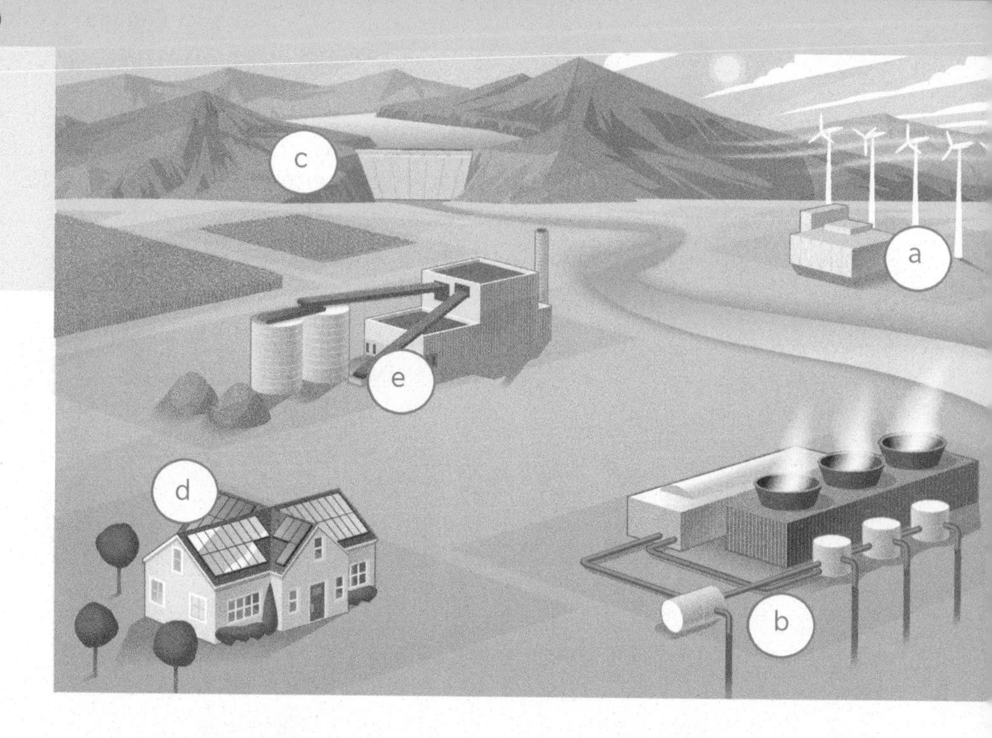

INVESTIGATIVE PHENOMENON
Humans use resources from renewable sources for energy.

Phenomenon Explained Students explore the **investigative phenomenon** by comparing renewable energy resources. They learn about the different energy stations needed to provide each type of resource.

Use It Again

Show students a photograph of a solar cell that powers street lamps or a calculator. Discuss how the solar cell can provide energy in a very short period of time and that it may be used over and over. Discuss how even though the solar cell is collecting energy during the day, it stores power to be used to light the lamp at night.

Everyday Phenomenon **Solar energy can be stored in batteries.**

Students should connect the **everyday phenomenon** that portable solar devices store energy in a battery for later use to the **anchoring phenomenon** that cars can run using batteries. Discuss how development of technologies that capture energy from renewable sources also includes those that store the energy for an extended period of time.

Energy Stations

Ask students to identify the energy source for each energy station shown on page 270 (wind, sunshine, heat from the Earth, moving water). Have students work with a partner to list where each type of energy station might be built, then ask volunteers to share their ideas. Discuss how each energy station must be placed where the energy resource required is plentiful. Make a connection between where each energy station is positioned to the importance of understanding the types of natural hazards that occur in different places. Discuss why it is important to understand how natural hazards are predicted and ways people stay safe when it comes to the placement of energy stations.

FORMATIVE ASSESSMENT

MAKING SENSE OF PHENOMENA

Students gain an understanding that renewable energy sources replenish rapidly as they explore the **investigative phenomenon**. As students explore renewable energy sources, they should connect the idea back to the **anchoring phenomenon** that new technologies affect how people use resources. Students should understand that renewable resources are also available for energy, and that new and more efficient technologies are emerging, allowing us to capture energy from these sources.

REMEDIATION If students struggle to connect the **investigative phenomenon** back to the **anchoring phenomenon,** ask them to think about how cars that run on batteries charged by solar power reduce the use of a nonrenewable energy source.

MAKING SENSE OF PHENOMENA IDEA ORGANIZER

After completing Exploration 4, students can fill in the **Idea Organizer** to summarize the connection between humans using renewable resources for energy and the anchoring phenomenon that new technologies affect how people use resources.

EXPLORATION 5

Pros and Cons

Activity Guide, pages 271–274

TIME ESTIMATE

day 1 day 2

Materials Alert Gather large pieces of white paper and colored markers for student groups to use when they are evaluating the relative efficiency of different energy resources.

INVESTIGATIVE PHENOMENON
Nonrenewable and renewable energy sources have benefits and drawbacks.

Phenomenon Explained Students explore the **investigative phenomenon** by identifying the benefits and drawbacks of nonrenewable and renewable resources.

How We Use Resources

Students use information about nonrenewable resources to match cause and effect statements related to their use. Discuss how cons related to a resource may be connected to the collection, transportation, or storage of an energy resource, not only to byproducts of its use. Answers: b, a, c

Benefits and Drawbacks & Hybrid Cars

Students match renewable energy stations to their benefits and drawbacks. They also explore a diagram about the technologies that make hybrid cars work. Answers for table (top to bottom): biomass station, hydroelectric dam, wind turbines, solar panels, geothermal stations; Explain: Cause 1 matches to Effect 2, Cause 2 matches with Effect 1.

Going Green Debate

Have students work in a group to review and compare the different nonrenewable and renewable energy sources they learned about during the lesson. You may choose to give each group a large piece of drawing paper and colored markers to record their ideas. Students should gather information related to how the resources are collected and processed, as well as relative energy costs associated with each resource's pros and cons. Students should use their work to help them choose which energy source they think is most efficient.

- **Make a Claim** Claims should identify which energy resource the student thinks is most efficient; for example, solar energy.
- **Evidence** Students should cite three facts about energy sources to support their claim. If they select solar energy, they can say that it is renewable, so it will last, that it produces little waste, and that it doesn't need to be transported.

SOCIAL EMOTIONAL LEARNING

Have students share examples of how nonrenewable resource use can affect organisms and their environment.

Sample answer: Oil spills can damage environments and harm animals and their habitats.

Discuss how evaluating the pros and cons of energy resource use is important to developing safe solutions. If scientists and engineers ignore drawbacks, it can lead to societal conflicts and long-term damage to ecosystems.

FORMATIVE ASSESSMENT

MAKING SENSE OF PHENOMENA

Students gain the understanding that all energy resources have pros and cons as they explore the **investigative phenomenon**. As students explore the benefits and drawbacks of nonrenewable and renewable resources, they should connect the idea back to the **anchoring phenomenon** that new technologies affect how people use resources. Students should understand that both renewable and nonrenewable resources have benefits and drawbacks, but that new technologies are providing new sources of fuel. More efficient technologies can decrease the drawbacks of both sources of energy.

REMEDIATION If students struggle to connect the **investigative phenomenon** back to the **anchoring phenomenon,** have them identify how the development of solar panels might have changed how people use energy resources.

MAKING SENSE OF PHENOMENA IDEA ORGANIZER

After completing Exploration 5, students can fill in the **Idea Organizer** to summarize the connection between nonrenewable and renewable energy resources having benefits and drawbacks and the anchoring phenomenon that new technologies affect how people use resources.

LESSON

ONLINE-ONLY RESOURCE

03 Take It Further

Engage • Explore/Explain • **Elaborate** • Evaluate

TIME ESTIMATE

These Take It Further paths may be completed to enrich and extend students' comprehension of content covered within this lesson.

ONLINE

People in Science & Engineering: Steven Chu

In this feature, students learn about Asian American physicist, Steven Chu, PhD, and his projects related to energy.

Careers in Science & Engineering: Sustainable Builders

Students find out about engineers who build energy-efficient, green buildings and consider sustainable features in homes.

What's Around You

Students research nonrenewable resources in their state or town.

FORMATIVE ASSESSMENT

Lesson Check

Activity Guide, pages 275–277

Engage • Explore/Explain • Elaborate • Evaluate

Can You Explain It?

Now I know or think that . . .

Sample answer: New technologies help us minimize the effects of using nonrenewable resources. We currently use nonrenewable resources, such as oil, coal, and gas, but engineers are improving renewable resource technology, such as solar panels and wind turbines.

After completing the lesson, use the **Making Sense Idea Organizer** to summarize the connections between the **investigative phenomena** and **anchoring phenomenon.**

MAKING CONNECTIONS

After students complete the lesson, they should be able to answer a question about an alternative phenomenon to explain how a solar panel in a backpack allows campers to use a new source of energy.

Sample answer: Campers used to be able to only use energy sources they found or brought with them on their trips. New technologies mean that they can use solar power to charge a battery that they can use for different things while hiking or camping.

Checkpoints

1. (clockwise from top left) c, d, b, a
2. inexpensive; decreasing quickly; hundreds of millions
3. **a.** Air is polluted with harmful gases; **c.** Ecosystems can be harmed.
4. **c.** natural gas
5. it will never run out; it produces little or no pollution
6. Dams are built—Valuable land can be flooded. Some processes...—Geothermal stations can cause pollution
7. **d.** It can produce air pollution.
8. **Sample Answer:** solar—benefits: renewable, clean energy; drawbacks: panels need sunshine, expensive; wind—benefits: renewable, clean energy; drawbacks: blades can hurt birds, loud

SOCIAL EMOTIONAL LEARNING

Have students reflect on the concepts they have explored about energy resources, then ask groups or partners to come up with a list of additional questions they would like to investigate. Have each group or pair choose one. Students should set short-term goals to help them go about finding answers to the question. Help students identify the number of goals and the amount of time needed to complete each one.

UNIT

05 Review

Activity Guide, pages 278–280

The Unit review items enable you to assess student comprehension of core ideas, as well as cross cutting concepts and science and engineering practices.

1. **DOK 1** **b.** coal

If students chose **a** or **d**, they may have been thinking "once live organisms," instead of "once live plants."

2. **DOK 2** **a.** It is a natural resource.
b. Its use causes pollution.
d. It is a nonrenewable resource.

If students choose **c,** guide them to study the image and describe what they see (a gas station).

3. **DOK 1** A **fossil fuel** is a useful, concentrated source of energy, but is **nonrenewable energy.** Tidal, **solar,** and **wind** energy are **renewable energy**. This is because they can be replaced naturally in a reasonable time.

If students select incorrect terms from the word bank, they should review Lesson 3, Exploration 3, Materials We Use, *and* Exploring Renewable Resources.

4. **DOK 3** **Sample answer:** I would need to know the typical wind and sunlight patterns for a year. I would also need to know about nearby streams or oceans. I need this information so I can plan how to collect enough energy every day.

Have students think about the renewable resources they learned about in Lesson 3. They should imagine the environments where each type of renewable resource would work best.

5. **DOK 2** Energy from this source [picture of bright sun] can be **stored,** the effect of which allows energy to be used when it is not being produced.

If students selected an incorrect term from the word bank, ask them to identify the energy source in the picture (the sun).

6. **DOK 3** **Sample answer:** The criteria for the vehicle would be that it needs to travel more miles on one charge than current vehicles and would need less time to charge. The constraint would be that it must use only renewable sources to generate the energy for the vehicle's battery.

If students struggle review the terms criteria and constraints as well as review the different ways energy is stored.

7. **DOK 3** **Sample answer:** A hurricane forms as the energy in warm ocean water fuels strong winds and heavy rains.

If students struggle to explain the cause and effect relationship between water, wind, and hurricane formation, have them review Lesson 2, Exploration 3, Natural Hazards.

8. **DOK 2** **a.** along a fault line

If students chose **b** or **c**, have them to review the maps they made in Lesson 1, Exploration 1, Tracking Quakes. If they chose **d**, they may think that big cities are more earthquake prone. Have them locate on the map where large, earthquake-prone cities are located.

9. **DOK 2** **a.** near coasts

If students struggle to answer the question, have them review the maps they made in Lesson 1, Exploration 2, Volcanic Eruptions.

10. **DOK 2** **b.** Most of them are found on land.

If students struggle to recognize the correct answer, guide them to consider each answer choice based on their analysis of data from the maps and activities in Lesson 1, Exploration 4, Finding Patterns.

3D Item Analysis	1	2	3	4	5	6	7	8	9	10
SEP Analyzing and Interpreting Data		•	•					•		•
SEP Constructing Explanations and Designing Solutions				•			•			
SEP Obtaining, Evaluating, and Communicating Information		•			•	•				
DCI ESS2.B Plate Tectonics and Large-Scale System Interactions								•	•	•
DCI ESS3.A Natural Resources	•	•	•	•	•	•				
DCI ESS3.B Natural Hazards							•	•	•	•
DCI PS3.D Energy In Chemical Processes and Everyday Life	•	•	•		•	•				
ETS1.B Developing Possible Solutions						•				
CCC Cause and Effect	•			•	•	•	•	•		
CCC Patterns								•	•	•
CCC Influence of Engineering, Technology, and Science on Society and the Natural World		•				•				
CCC Interdependence of Science, Engineering, and Technology				•		•				

Notes:

Index

Index

D

E

Index

F

Index

Index

Index

Index

Index